Henry E. Sigerist: Autobiographical Writings

HENRY E. SIGERIST: AUTOBIOGRAPHICAL WRITINGS

Selected and translated
by
Nora Sigerist Beeson

Montreal
McGILL UNIVERSITY PRESS
1966

to Christopher Sigerist Beeson

EDITOR'S PREFACE

The ideas of Henry E. Sigerist, his wide interests in medical history and scholarship, are easily accessible to anyone who takes the trouble to read his many published books and articles. The personality behind these ideas is not as readily visible, and yet it was precisely his spirit and warmth, his aliveness, his interest in people that inspired the many with whom he came into contact.

The written word is a poor substitute for the person; but perhaps the man's own words come as close to revealing the intangibles of his character as anything. And perhaps the random jottings of a devoted journal-keeper are in their own way a better record than a systematic autobiography which, at best, is always a personal distortion with an eye on the public.

Fortunately for Sigerist, everything had some possible value as a scrap of history, as an explanation of some detail which at the moment was impossible to fathom, but might in time to come provide some interesting and useful information. As a result, everything—old bank books, bills, student microscopes, swords, pictures, letters, magazines, and books —was not only carefully preserved, but moved twice across the Atlantic Ocean at great expense and trouble.

It was natural that this type of person would also keep a record of the events in his life. The pleasure of reliving memories, trips, and encounters with people was added to the simple recording of happenings. Sigerist's love of orderliness also contributed to his need for keeping photo albums, scrap books, travel journals, and diaries. Even as a boy, and later as a student, he noted down the impressions of his trips to Italy, illustrated with his own photographs. It was also a way of studying something new, a more systematic method of crystallizing random thoughts.

This record-keeping, whatever form it took, was a personal affair with no thought given to the use or publication of this material. It fulfilled a need, gave pleasure, and became a hobby. The deliberate writing of wise thoughts, philosophical comments, or profound remarks was not at all the intention of the author. Sigerist's ideas on civilization and particularly medicine as it fitted into the scheme of our culture were shaped and

vii

expressed in his published works. The diaries and journals were for himself—a storehouse of happenings, a way of expressing moods and feelings, a space to speculate, sometimes wrongly, a place to size up accomplishments and make plans for future work.

For us who wish to piece together a whole from the parts, this type of personal record has advantages and disadvantages. Much of importance is omitted. Gaps leave tantalizing hiatuses. And yet a portrait does appear, an unconscious self-portrait, a picture of a person—his likes and dislikes, his depressions, his sense of frustration and failure, his driving self-discipline for work, his joys and pleasures, and finally his preoccupation with death.

Thus, in choosing the entries for this book from a vast amount of material, I have been guided first of all by the necessity to present as good a self-portrait as possible. Perhaps what most distinguished him were the many varying facets of his character: renowned for his thought and scholarship, he was as much a "doer" as a "thinker." Some of his colleagues felt that the more activist phase of his career in America was somewhat of a "betrayal" of his earlier, more "learned" interests. Yet his greatest field of influence was precisely in the United States where he served to widen the purely scholarly field of medical history into one which included contemporary social reform movements of all kinds. As a historian he was primarily interested in the past, but history, according to him, was lived and made every day. The past was used to interpret the present and to look into the future. At first he was more interested in revivifying the "great doctors" of past ages, but he was happiest when he felt that he had contributed to the shaping of present and future medical generations with his infectious enthusiasm for an historical outlook toward medicine. He was always an advocate of a notion that is only now being seriously examined—that better physicians, scientists, and statesmen result not just from more specialized knowledge, but from a richer comprehension of the historical, cultural, and humanitarian values of our civilization.

Though his profession, that of medical historian, is usually considered narrow and limited, Sigerist's concept of history like that of Jakob Burckhardt included all facets of culture as well. Sigerist considered the arts and politics sister fields to medicine and science, and these were constantly drawn into his field of vision. The arts were as much part of his life as of his study. He was a phenomenal reader in world literature, ancient and modern, and one day amused his friends, who were checking off their familiarity with the "great books" on the St. John's list, by having read most of them and in their original language. He loved music; not a bad cellist in his younger days, he later "rationed" his time by attending all the concerts he could. Many musicians were close friends and were often invited to his constantly open house.

Painting was sought not only in museums all over the world, but in the lowliest of wayside chapels in the Swiss countryside, or in illuminated manuscripts, or inside a particularly fine *palazzo*. Here again a highly developed aesthetic sense gave him pleasure and satisfaction; but the arts were part and parcel of the history of a period, illuminating segments that added to the comprehension of the whole.

His fascination with politics was probably his least objective interest. Often misunderstood and maligned for his interest in the workings of Soviet society, his study of Soviet medical planning and of Marxism was but a result of his passionate hatred of Fascism and of his search for a social Utopia which promised justice and equality to all. The imperfections in the only socialist state were dismissed as necessary stages on a road which led to a goal that Sigerist also was working for—improved living for everyone. This same search led him eventually further away from Soviet practices to a study of India in the hope that the East might offer a more workable method of obtaining essentially the same end. Never did he put aside his faith in the underdog. If the exploitations of capitalism became at times almost an abstraction, applied to all kinds of situations, this came from his abiding belief in the dignity of man, *all* men, and from his desire to advance actively and personally any benefits that might enhance mankind.

Sigerist loved people. He needed the stimulus of students and colleagues, and missed the interchange of ideas after he gave up his university career. He was equally at ease with the most prominent minds as with the carpenters and gardeners who worked in his house and garden. He was interested in them as individuals as well as members of a society, and his conversations with them gave him clues to the reality of social problems. For example, the difficulties of wine growers in southern Switzerland, where he lived during the last ten years of his life, were as much a personal problem to him as to the villagers. To Sigerist, the social scientist, their troubles became a symptom of increasing urbanization, raised land values, poor prices, the young people's lack of interest in tending the vines, or simply the loss of skill in a trade that had been passed on for ages from one generation to another.

His interest in human beings also explained his staggering correspondence which he was never willing to curtail, however great the demands made on his time. It was important to him to answer every query personally and to involve himself in any problem presented to him. His love of good friends and good company went hand in hand with his fondness for good food, cooking, and wine—all delights that must be shared with others to be fully enjoyed. No visitor was ever turned away.

His zest for living made him impatient with those who frittered away their time aimlessly, who were not alive to the beauties surrounding them, who vegetated without being consciously aware of each moment. He was able to sustain the tempo of his living by a careful scheduling of his time. Work plans were made for the year, for each week, for every day and hour. His work rooms in Baltimore were set up so that with a minimum of effort and time he could move from one table to another, each piled high, neatly, with a different project. For years his lunch was eaten at the table with his medieval manuscript work. Tea was brewed carefully and consumed in great quantities during the day. The quiet evening hours were often his most productive time, and entering his study to say good-night, I would gasp for air in the thick cigarette smoke.

My sister and I had little contact with my father until we began to share his interests. After that, a trip with him to the Louvre in Paris was a special delight even if we could not understand everything he said. I suppose the importance he gave to interesting work communicated itself to us, for we have both taken up professions.

If my first concern was to attempt to present Sigerist as a living person, my second main consideration in compiling the present book was to try as much as possible to place him in the larger context of the period in which he lived. The pattern of his life was shared by many others of his generation. Not exactly a "refugee" from Hitler's Germany, since he left before the dictator's take-over, he nevertheless undertook the great move to America because he was astute enough to realize that a fascist Germany was imminent. More than that, he had no delusions as to the direction such a government would take, although no one could foresee the horrors that were to come.

Always a citizen of the world, widely traveled and linguistically fluent in many languages, he nevertheless experienced many of the acclima-tization problems that beset so many European intellectuals in America. Although he embraced American life whole-heartedly, and never shared the usual refugee's niggling criticism of the country which was giving him shelter, he still retained some of his European ways of life. Until the War the four summer months—one-third of the year—were regularly spent abroad. My sister and I usually left school early, taking our exami-nations in the principal's office in May, and came back several weeks late in fall.

From the 1930's on Sigerist shared the liberal views of many intel-lectuals of his generation. During the War he worked so zealously for the maintenance of spiritual values in the midst of a military holocaust that he developed early symptoms of failing health. As did many other European—and American—thinkers he felt personally responsible for the failures of his generation, a generation that had unwittingly reared Nazism and brought on the ensuing War. And he felt that no sacrifice was great enough to alleviate those evils.

The post-war wave of loyalty oaths and McCarthy hearings, with their ensuing hysteria, was to him, as to many European-Americans, a re-enact-ment of the fascist tactics that had caused him to flee Europe years before. Though personal considerations prompted him to return to Swit-zerland in 1947, the atmosphere surrounding the investigations and the curtailment of personal freedom, so odious to any intellectual, played their part in his decision. Again, many others in similar circumstances re-turned to the countries of their birth.

Toward the end of his life Henry Sigerist used to speculate somewhat philosophically about the permanence of his influence. Some of his books, he felt, might continue to be read; others would gather dust on library shelves. More important were the people he had touched—the family he had left, the two grandchildren, and his many students who, he hoped, would carry on his concepts. It is only fitting to let one of them, Milton I. Roemer, speak of him here.

The impact of Henry Sigerist on a whole generation of young physicians in America was quite unique. Renowned clinicians like Osler or Cushing, of course, had influenced thousands, but medical history and sociology were, after all, not in the central stream of medical education. Yet he made these subjects exciting and extremely important for medical students, and through these subjects helped to shape the whole philosophy of medicine's place in the world for a substantial number of medical men and women. He inculcated in them the concept of medicine as a servant of society, as a task for the betterment of the life of people.

Why and how did Sigerist exert this influence? His great effectiveness and charm as a teacher and lecturer were part of the explanation. The bleak years of depression and its impetus for social reform, during which he worked in America, were doubtless also relevant. But most of all, it was his amazing combination of scholarship and action that accounted for his profound influence — both inside and outside the medical profession. Unlike most learned men, especially in the universities, he identified himself with the movements for social reform in the world around him. His view ahead was nearly always optimistic. "History spirals toward socialism," he said, and man would solve his problems. He sought to promote international good will, especially between the two giants, America and Soviet Russia. And because his views were grounded in knowledge, wide and deep, they were persuasive.

For thousands of thoughtful professional people in America and elsewhere, the social concerns of Sigerist represented the fruition of his life work. They were one of the goals to which his vast historical scholarship became eventually directed, a goal in which the physician would be a "social worker" and the whole structure of medicine would be reorganized to serve equitably the human needs of all people.

Perhaps the separate sections of this book seem at first glance somewhat disjointed. Yet from the material available I have made every effort to present Sigerist's life in chronological order, while keeping the narrative in his own words. Section I is the beginning of the autobiography which he started but never finished. This fragment actually gave me the idea of continuing his life story. Section II, the bridge between his student days and his American sojourn, is pieced together from published sources, and is the only part of this work that has appeared in print before. Section III is drawn from the extensive diaries that he kept year by year, day by day. The editor's task was to take from an embarrassment of riches those nuggets that might be meaningful to a reader, while communicating the personality of the writer.

Throughout my years of planning and working on this book I have received unending encouragement from the Henry E. Sigerist Research Fund Committee. Originally established in 1955 by his many friends and admirers to aid Sigerist's work on the *History of Medicine*, this Committee after his death continued to function until 1963 in order to oversee the completion of the unfinished Sigerist manuscripts and to find appropriate ways, with its modest resources, of memorializing his name. The present book would never have materialized without the selfless interest of all the members of the Committee. Among them I would like to mention especially the deceased John F. Fulton, the Committee's first president and Sigerist's literary executor, and Milton I. Roemer, the Secretary-Treasurer, who assumed most of the burdens of arranging meetings, agenda, and minutes and who gave so generously of his time and loyal friendship. Genevieve Miller helped with professional advice every inch of the way. Robert Leslie kept up my spirits when the task seemed impossible. Other members of the Committee included: Alan Gregg, Gregory Zilboorg, Iago Galdston, Erwin H. Ackerknecht, Esther Lucille Brown, Leslie Falk, George Rosen, George Silver, and Ilza Veith. Elizabeth H. Thomson of the Department of the History of Medicine, Yale University, administered the Fund and in all ways extended help and advice.

NORA BEESON
1965

CONTENTS

I

Autobiography

The Story of
a Non-conformist

In 1953, while working in Switzerland on the second volume of his History, the idea of writing an autobiography took shape, at the urging of a friend. It was a diversion—nothing more. Modesty prevented Sigerist from giving very serious attention to such a frivolous undertaking. Time could be snatched only sparingly from his big project. But it was fun.
In a letter of November 1953 he wrote:*

The other day, late at night, I did not feel like writing ancient history, and so I took some paper and all of a sudden I had an introduction to the autobiography. I have seen and experienced a lot, in Paris, Zurich, Leipzig, America, the Soviet Union, etc., but I never knew how to begin. Most autobiographies of physicians are frightfully boring. Of course it is "Dichtung und Wahrheit" but what I wrote is basically true. Many chapters, of course, will be very serious but I thought it was better to begin in a light vein so as not to discourage the reader. I shall not follow a strictly chronological order. Thus the first chapter will be on my early childhood in Paris in the nineties, but I shall also bring in whatever experiences I had in Paris.

And a few months later:

I was glad to hear that you liked the idea of the memoirs. I am still working on the Paris chapter and am progressing very slowly as I can devote time to it only late at night. But it is fun and you relive your whole life. A lot that you had forgotten comes back. It will show you what my technique is—not to write chronologically but as you recollect things.

How this literary stream-of-consciousness technique was to be continued is hard to predict. Only the Prelude and the first two chapters

* All chapter notes are by the Editor.

were ever written. Contrary to what Sigerist wrote a little later—"Should I ever be disabled so that I could not write my other books, I always could dictate the story of my life"—he did not continue the autobiography after his first cerebral accident.

His outline of the book shows the projected continuation of the two chapters which are presented here:

ORIGINAL OUTLINE OF THE AUTOBIOGRAPHY

Chapter	1	Prelude, Paris
	2	Zurich 1901-11, Beust School, Gymnasium
	3	London
	4	Munich
	5-6	Zurich, World War I, Russian Revolution
	7-10	Leipzig
	10-12	USA
	13-14	USSR
	15	Social Medicine
	16	Saskatchewan, India
	17	World War II
	18	Pura (Switzerland)
	19-20	Reserve

PRELUDE

She was sitting in my office staring at me and I felt extremely uncomfortable, not knowing why.

"I shall wait for you," she had said, on a Maryland farm, in that enchanting rolling landscape where rattlesnakes are scarce but poison ivy is plentiful. It was a warm summer night, with a moon and stars and mint juleps. "I shall wait for you. Do give me a ring when you are back."

A few days before, in a restaurant at the New York World's Fair, Ralph Ingersoll had asked me what plans I had for the summer. The war was on and I could no longer go abroad every year. I had just bought a new Chevrolet and I told Ingersoll that I intended to spend two months driving through the country from coast to coast, making a study of the various types of medical service plans in operation at the time. Ingersoll, who was just launching the liberal New York newspaper PM, jumped at that:

"This is just what I am looking for. Do send me a report every day!"

Every day seemed rather much, but I did send him a series of articles about the plans I studied, interviewing physicians, patients, administrators, visiting doctors' offices and hospitals, studying programmes and records. He published them in his paper without changing a comma. It was a marvelous tour in that summer of 1940. The news from Europe was appalling. One country after another was breaking down, conquered by the ruthless Hitler gang. They were butchering women and children from Stukas. Mussolini was shooting the French in the back, and here was the United States, peaceful, fertile, with people working, working again after the hard years of the depression. Here was New England in all its glory, the Great Lakes, the prairies, California, Indian reservations, and the South where people sing when they talk. I had seen this all before, more than once, but travelling through the vast expanse of the United States was an overwhelming experience every time.

And now I was back in Baltimore and she was sitting in my office staring at me and I felt extremely uncomfortable, not knowing why.

I had not telephoned after my return as I was supposed to. Instead. I had attended the bicentennial celebrations of the University of Pennsylvania as the delegate of the University of the Witwatersrand in Johannesburg. I am not a South African, neither British nor Boer, but I am an honorary graduate of the University of the Witwatersrand and when it was invited to send a delegate to Philadelphia the University asked me to represent it, which I was delighted to do. And I must say, I

5

played my part nobly. I had a beautiful red gown which looked decidedly foreign in America, a cap à la Henry VIII, and the black and yellow hood of my *doctor litterarum*. Many people came and thanked me for having travelled all the way from South Africa to Philadelphia. Of course I did not disappoint them but spoke of the traditional friendship between Pennsylvania and South Africa. It was a brilliant celebration which lasted a whole week with banquets, speeches, symposia. President Roosevelt came in person and delivered a splendid address. The Philadelphia Orchestra gave a superb performance of the Brahms *Symphony No. 2*, but I must say that I was rather startled when the concert began with the Russian Tsarist national anthem. If anybody had ever told me that I would have to get up to listen to "God protect our Tsar" I would have protested violently but my neighbor explained that this was also the Pennsylvania state anthem, of course with different words. In the academic procession we were lined up according to the age of our universities and my very young university happened to be just as young as the Curtis Institute so that I had the pleasure of marching with Mrs. Curtis and of discussing the rising star of Menotti with her.

September is the most beautiful month in America. It is warm but no longer hot. Nature is still in full glory, just beginning to change color. The week in Philadelphia was incredibly beautiful. I gave a paper in one of the symposia, listened to some of my colleagues, ate chickens and steaks, but I spent most of the time alone in one of the quadrangles of the campus reading Boethius, *De consolatione philosophiae*, and making plans for the coming academic year.

And now I was back in Baltimore and she was sitting in my office, staring at me and I felt extremely uncomfortable, not knowing why. In order to do something I showed her our Institute of the History of Medicine. We had a great deal that was of interest to non-specialists—Chinese sculptures, Singhalese books written on palm leaves, beautiful pharmacy jars, and hair from the tail of the first cow from which Edward Jenner had taken the lymph of cowpox. But then we were back at the office and suddenly I knew what was wrong: *malocchio*, the evil eye. That woman had the evil eye with which certain people can cast a spell upon you. Nonsense, there is no such thing. The evil eye is an old superstition in Mediterranean countries and people used to wear a great variety of amulets to ward off the effects of the *malocchio*. I remembered Italian fishing boats with huge eyes painted on them and I suddenly also remembered my old friend Arturo Castiglioni telling me that he had once met an individual in Rome who had the evil eye. Of course it was nonsense, a mere superstition, yet an hour later he was run over by a motor car. So you never can tell.

Two days later I entered the Johns Hopkins Hospital to have my tonsils removed. This was a serious matter, because we Europeans cherish our tonsils and keep them as long as we possibly can. But I was having trouble with my nose, a chronic rhinitis which plagued me a great deal,

6

and my doctor thought that the condition could not be improved as long as I had those filthy tonsils. Filthy, he said, and it is true that they were not particularly handsome. They had been cauterized with an electric needle when I was a small child in Paris. Then slices had been taken off them, in Paris and later again in Zurich, a most unpleasant procedure in spite of the ice-cream which used to follow the operation. Still, they were my tonsils, whatever was left of them, and I disliked the idea of losing an organ. But then I thought that my doctor, a very good doctor, as all Hopkins men are, was perhaps right and, besides, this was my chance to be like other people. I had lived in America long enough to know that it is not polite to be different from your neighbors. They had all sacrificed their tonsils on the altar of science, and so would I. I consented to have the operation performed.

The great day came. The evening before instead of supper I was given a thorough enema. In the morning instead of breakfast I was given an injection of something. Being a physician myself, I was familiar with the ritual that precedes an operation. "Don't worry, they'll fix you up," my orderly kept repeating. I did not worry a bit, was interested in what was going on and as a result of the injection I soon did not care a damn about what was happening. I was bundled up, was driven to the operating room. I intended to tell the anesthetist a joke but I was gone before I could utter one word. It was the first time I had an inhalation anesthesia and I must say it was most pleasant. America has perfected the technique of anesthesia, has made it a real art.

I woke up in my room as one does in such a case, slowly. I had the customary ice bag around my neck which felt pleasantly cool. The nurse had painted finger nails, I liked that. I regained consciousness gradually and as I did, it dawned upon me that my throat was sore, to be sure, but not sore enough. I had seen plenty of patients after tonsilectomies and knew what they felt. What had happened? The doctor came, looked rather embarrassed and finally told me that I still had my tonsils. The doctors had done their very best but whenever they opened my mouth and got ready to peel out the tonsils I stopped breathing and turned blue, completely blue, so that they had to flush my system with oxygen. They tried over and over again, in every conceivable position, for more than an hour, but always with the same result and since it would have been most unpleasant to have a professor of the medical school die on the operating table of the hospital attached to his school, they finally gave up.

Then suddenly I became aware of what had actually happened. "Doctor," I cried, "look here, I'll tell you. Two days ago a woman was in my office who had the evil eye. She cast a spell upon me and that is why the operation miscarried."

"Oh shut up," he said, "don't be a fool. I'll tell you what is wrong with you. You are a non-conformist even in deep anesthesia."

Maybe he was right. Yet I had tried so hard to be like other people.

7

PARIS AS I REMEMBER IT

To me Paris is the most wonderful city on earth. It is beautiful all through the year. In March you sense the advent of spring. You find it not in the countryside where nature is still asleep, but in the city where all of a sudden flowers are being sold at every street corner, carnations from the Côte d'Azur, Parma violets, tulips, daffodils, anemones. There is a scent in the air, a blend of perfumes with a touch of amber, of rubber, of fresh vegetables and sea food, undefinable yet unmistakable. Every city smells differently, and transported to any one of them blindfolded you would immediately know where you are. In London the sweet smell of Virginia tobacco dominates, in Baltimore it is mostly garbage, stirred up by rats.

Then in April all of a sudden the parks are green. The chestnut trees of the Champs Elysées have young leaves of tender green. Children are riding wooden horses on carrousels, catching rings with short lances as we did years ago. And when you caught a ring at every turn, you were entitled to a candy stick that you kept licking for an hour. It was sheer delight.

To sit in the Luxembourg Gardens with a book in the spring is one of the great joys that life has to offer. You look at the water basin where boys are sailing their boats. Little girls with flying skirts are skipping or trundling their hoops. You feel the presence of the Sorbonne, the wisdom and accumulated experience of centuries. You read, you meditate, and in front of you is a new young generation growing up, playing in a carefree way, but ready to carry on when the time comes, as you once did.

In the summer the Parisians flee the city, at least all who can afford to or have relatives in the country or at the seaside. Every Parisian has a deep longing for the country, but after spending a few days there he wishes he were back in town. Paris is supposed to be unbearably hot at that time. Of course it is not, at least not to us who have lived in America. What a pleasure it is to sit in the streets sipping coffee until late at night or to dance in the streets on July 14 remembering the French Revolution, the storming of the Bastille. It is a really popular holiday, everybody dances and drinks wine with everybody else without asking who you are. The Bastille was stormed; let us rejoice and forget for a moment that there are still many Bastilles that should be stormed, the stock exchange, the Bank of France, the headquarters of the Cagoulards —the hooded French fascists. Let us forget that Hitler is at the door, that the Spaniards are fighting a heroic fight against a fascist conspiracy. It is a warm summer night and we dance, sing, and drink wine.

Autumn of 1946. The war is over, the second in our lifetime. The first was bad enough but this second war was fought with the savagery of primitive people, with the difference however that modern science provides means for the mass destruction of men, women, children, and animals such as no savage has ever possessed. The Germans had rehearsed totalitarian war at Guernica in Spain, and Picasso's great mural will be a permanent record of this first step in our return to primitive barbarism. The Germans applied the teachings of Guernica to the whole of Western Europe, to England and Russia, and in the end experienced mass destruction in their own country. Their example was followed by whoever could afford to do it. Hiroshima and Nagasaki were still heaps of rubble.

I shall never forget the evening when the destruction of Hiroshima was announced. I was working on the campus of a great American university. A colleague who had been listening to the radio came running: "Have you heard? An atom bomb was dropped on a Japanese city." A group of us came together. We knew it meant the end of the war but there was no rejoicing only deep gloom. What had we done? To what was the world coming? Guernica, Lidice, now Hiroshima. It was no longer a fight between Homeric heroes, no longer a war between professional soldiers or national armies but savage mass destruction by all means available. The incitement to treachery was called psychological warfare, and a few years later a great power at war was to advertize for traitors and thieves, promising $100,000 and asylum to anyone on the other side who would betray his country and steal an airplane.

Autumn of 1946. The war is over and Paris is still Paris, has escaped destruction and is more radiant than ever. The weather is glorious, the city full of flowers and in the morning a veil of silvery mist is spread over it. We had not intended to be in Paris, but we were stranded there. We had been to Switzerland to see relatives, back in Europe for the first time in seven years. Switzerland was almost shocking, so untouched by the war, so prosperous, so clean, with buildings all redecorated, with geraniums on the window sills. But now we had to go home. The academic year was beginning soon at the Johns Hopkins University and Erica's* leave of absence from the Army Medical Library was expiring. We had reservations to fly home from Geneva but all the schedules were upset. There had been a few accidents with a new model of airplane that looked like a shark and apparently behaved like one. The government had stopped them for the time being and hundreds of passengers were stranded. We had to go home and went to our travel agent every day. Finally he said: "Look here, there is only one way for you to get home soon. Go to Paris, ask for the traffic officer of your airline. Put

*Sigerist's eldest daughter.

9

a bank note on the table and if it is large enough you will fly on the same day." I declared that I would rather stay in Europe the whole winter than do such a thing and kept telephoning to people and agencies I thought might be helpful.

At last I hit on a man who had been with the Swiss Legation in Washington, was with the airline now, knew me and on a Saturday got me two seats on the Monday plane from Paris to New York. Monday morning we arrived at Paris, went to the airline office, showed our reservations and I told the man that we were scheduled to fly the same day at six o'clock in the evening. He smiled and I smiled. Every spring I looked forward to going to Europe and every autumn I rejoiced at the idea of being back in America soon. After having travelled in central and eastern European countries it was always an infinite pleasure to see Pennsylvania Station in New York again and to enjoy the excellent service it gave you. Now I was thinking that tomorrow at noon I would be in New York, that for lunch I would eat a dozen cherrystone clams, one of America's great specialties, a thick steak broiled on hickory wood, and a piece of pumpkin pie. French cuisine is good as everybody knows, but America has great specialties also.

The man smiled and then quietly said: "Yes Sir, you are flying on today's plane, but today's plane is delayed, perhaps for two days, perhaps for four days, perhaps for eight days, we do not know. Just call up every morning and we'll tell you what the situation is." There we were, stranded, for a whole week, and a most delightful week it was, a gift from heaven, unexpected and the more deeply appreciated. Paris in all its glory. Art exhibits everywhere. A superb exhibition of Khmer art at the Musée Guimet. The theatres all active and flourishing. Times were by no means easy. There were serious shortages of food and even wine was scarce and expensive. But the people were full of good humor. One day I had to visit a friend who lived very close to the Luxembourg where a peace conference was being held. I took a taxi and a few blocks from the spot the police stopped the car, the chauffeur turned round and said: "Sir, I am awfully sorry that I cannot take you to the house. You know, it is on account of that bunch of crooks at the Luxembourg." I walked on but was soon stopped by another policeman who very politely requested me to walk on the other side of the street. Pointing to the Luxembourg he said: "It is on account of the imbeciles assembled there," whereupon another policeman added: "And to think that this will cost us one milliard francs."

And finally we flew off. At that time it was very difficult to get on a plane but once you were in the air the best possible care was taken of you. The stewardesses were charming and if you had felt uncomfortable their smile would have been enough to compensate for it richly. In the airplane we all discussed how we had managed to get on it. Next to me was a big fellow from Texas who said: "I intended to fly two months from now but I got tired of these old ruins and decided to go home.

10

After all there is only one country where a human being can live and that is Texas. So I took the boys of the airline office through the night clubs of Paris for three nights, whereupon I got a ticket now instead of two months later."

It was a heavenly week in autumnal Paris, but the winter is beautiful too. When I first came to Baltimore in 1931 Gilbert Chinard, Professor of French Literature, said to me that the winter in Baltimore was very similar to that in Paris, and it was true. The winter on the whole is mild, you may have snow flurries and frost, and you may hit an exceptionally cold winter, but this rarely happens.

And how delightful the people of Paris are! I do not mean the members of the Académie Française who undoubtedly are honorable gentlemen but rather stuffy, at least most of them. No, I mean the common people, the fishmonger who yells at you, the taxi driver who will drive carefully only if you whisper to him that the lady who is with you is pregnant, the craftsmen, and shopkeepers. I had written a book on medicine in the Soviet Union and wished to have it bound nicely. So I went to a bookbinder on the left bank and explained to him that the book obviously should be bound in red morocco leather and that it would be appropriate to have a hammer and sickle designed in the right upper corner. He seemed to agree but two months later he had not begun the work, nor had he six months later. As a matter of fact he never touched the book and I suspect that he was a royalist.

Another day I was walking in the neighborhood of the School of Medicine when a book in the window of a bookshop caught my attention. It was a new edition of Claude Bernard's *Introduction à l'étude de la médecine expérimentale,* first published in 1865 and after seventy years still the bible of the new experimental medical science. Claude Bernard came to Paris in 1834 hoping to make a career as a man of letters and dramatist. Instead he became the leading physiologist of the period whose work exerted a profound influence on the young naturalist school of literature. I had lost my copy of this classical book, entered the shop to buy a new one, and much to my surprise found a large stock of old medical books. I browsed for hours, bought about twenty volumes for the Leipzig Institute of the History of Medicine of which I was in charge at the time, and, ready to leave, asked the bookdealer to send me his catalogues in the future. "I do not publish catalogues," was his answer. "You have no idea how much the printing of a catalogue costs nowadays. And, moreover, if you print catalogues you must keep files of addresses of all the people who wish to receive them. This is much too much trouble." I tried to explain to him that he would sell many more books and would earn much more money if he had catalogues, but his immediate answer was: "My dear Monsieur. My daughter is married, my son is doing well. I own a shack in the country on the banks of the Seine where I go fishing on Sundays. Why on earth should I make more money?"

11

I shook hands with him and told him that he was a wise man. And he certainly was. So often the French are accused of being decadent because they have a different concept of progress from Americans, and because they do not get excited when their Cabinet is overthrown. Why should they get excited? The administrative work goes on with or without a Cabinet and besides sooner or later the same people come back in a somewhat different combination. Bigger is not better to the average Frenchman. A higher standard of living does not mean more mechanical gadgets but better food and better wine, more leisure, and also better poetry. Some remarkable anthologies of poetry were prepared at the height of the last World War.

While I was a professor at Leipzig I read French newspapers and books every day and always looked forward to spending the spring in Paris. Two such springs are particularly unforgettable to me, those of 1930 and 1931. The winter semester closed at the end of February and I was able to spend March and April in Paris. I stayed in a small hotel near the Odéon which had once been a Palais of the Grand Condé and had been a girls' college before it became a hotel. It was quiet and comfortable and I spent months working there. One year I was writing large sections of an *Introduction to Medicine* which was later translated into six languages including Chinese. The next year I was working on a biographical history of medicine, *The Great Doctors*, which had three German, two English, and a Spanish edition. I had the books I needed most with me and good libraries were easily accessible. I wrote ten pages every day, ten folio pages in longhand, in the blue, bound copy books that I had especially made. And when I had reached the bottom of page ten I stopped, sometimes in the middle of a sentence, made a few notes for the following day and was a free man. My day's work was done. Sometimes, when the subject was easy, I was through with my task in five to six hours, sometimes I needed ten to twelve hours when much additional research and reading were required. But I stuck to my ten pages every day.

I had worked this way all my life and am still doing it today. Friends used to tease me about my method and called it pedantic, but when I left Paris after two months I had at least five hundred pages ready for the press and I could tell my friends that Emile Zola, for whom I always had a profound veneration, had worked in exactly the same way. And even Guy de Maupassant, whose light novels seem to have been written on the spur of the moment, used to slave writing a set number of pages every day. Those who wait for inspiration for writing usually do not get it. When one has studied a subject and is full of it, then the empty white paper exerts an irresistible fascination and the words just drop out of your fountain pen.

When page ten was written I was free and the whole of Paris was mine. In such a city you can have complete privacy or meet as many people as you like. I used to have lunch with Swiss and American friends at the

Restaurant Medici where you had the Luxembourg on one side and the Church of the Sorbonne on the other and where the food was very good. My old classmate and friend Hans R. Schinz, Professor of Roentgenology at the University of Zurich and one of the most distinguished radiologists of Europe, was working at the Institut du Radium in Paris at that time. We met every day for lunch, and frequently went to the Luxembourg Gardens where we discussed everything under the sun.

In the evening I used to go to a delightful small restaurant which had the picturesque name Auberge de la Comète de 1812. A few years later it disappeared but in those years it was extremely pleasant. The only waiter was a white-haired gentleman. He always had the right suggestion for you. One evening he would say: "Monsieur looks tired today. Maybe some stuffed mushrooms, then a sweetbread Rossini with a Pontet Canet would be what you need." And it was. Another day when you came with a lady his suggestion was: "Madame, I am sure, would like some oysters and then perhaps a *poulet sauté à l'Estragon* with our good Chablis." She did and so did I. We have to eat in order to live, so why not eat well, why not make eating an art. The French succeed in doing it and so do the Chinese. They both have imagination and sauces, and both are needed for good cuisine.

When the ten pages were written I was free, free not only to meet friends but to visit art exhibitions of which there was such a profusion in Paris, free to go to the theatres. The Comédie Française and Opéra Comique were great delights of course, but what attracted us most were the small avant-garde theatres, the Montparnasse of Gaston Baty, l'Atelier of Dullin, the Vieux-Colombier of Copeau, where experiments in excellent theatre were made.

But then I was also free to roam in the city, to walk on boulevards and small streets, aimlessly. All of a sudden you found yourself on the Place des Vosges where Victor Hugo had lived, or in the Cité with temple on one side and castrum on the other, Notre-Dame today and the Palais de Justice. Two thousand years of history are inscribed in stone in Paris and it makes fascinating reading. And more than once, quite unconsciously I walked from the Place de l'Opéra down the Grands Boulevards towards Porte Saint-Martin, towards the spot where I was born, 42 rue d'Hauteville, on April 7, 1891.

My mother almost died of puerperal fever when she gave birth to me. There was little asepsis in the Paris of those days. The midwife used sponges that had not been boiled and if my mother had not had a very strong constitution she would not have survived the fever. She did however and lived in the best of health to the ripe old age of 88. It seemed advisable, however, to go to Switzerland for further childbirths. Still, I lost a young brother from typhoid fever a few years later. Every year we used to spend the summer months in the country, in Montmorency. Edmond, my little brother, came down with a high fever. The local

13

doctor was called. He did not own a fever thermometer, put his hand on the child's forehead, found that he had no abnormal temperature and attributed his condition to his molars. My mother who did own a thermometer told the doctor that the child had a temperature of 40° C. or 104° F., whereupon he remarked that with children you never could tell. A week later the child was dead. France produced outstanding medical scientists and clinicians, but the rank and file doctor remained poor for a very long time. Years later, remembering my little brother, I often thought how much time it takes for medical discoveries to penetrate, to be accepted, and to be applied by the mass of the general practitioners.

On one of my roaming expeditions in the neighborhood of my birthplace in the early nineteen thirties, walking aimlessly through the streets, thinking about my work, and making plans for the future I suddenly felt thunderstruck. My heart almost stopped beating and I did not know what was happening. I looked around and noticed that I was staring into the window of a pharmacy. On one side there was a glass jar with a blue fluid, on the other one with a red fluid, and in the middle a tube, and in the tube a tape worm preserved in alcohol. And this same tape worm had been there forty years before. The pharmacy was on my way to school and Mélanie, our maid who brought us to school every morning, used to say: "If you eat too much chocolate you will have such a worm in your tummy." The thought was simply terrifying and poisoned whatever gift of chocolate we received from Switzerland. And now looking at this miserable worm I suddenly relived my childhood years in Paris.

I was back at school, at the Cours Delarbre, a small private school in the neighborhood where children from the age of six to ten were instructed in one room by Madame Delarbre and her daughter Jeanne. I remembered my first days in school when I sat next to the teacher who taught me to read in a few days. The first words I read were, "Au feu ! au feu ! Fire ! Fire !" It was the story of a house on fire and ever since I have been afraid of fire. Many years later I studied Chinese and at King's College in London we read the Chinese childrens' primer, the *San Dze Ching,* which begins not with a description of a fire but with the words, "Man in the beginning is by nature good. People are naturally close to one another but the environment separates them."

It was a good school and in four years we learned not only the three R's but also the elements of physics, history, the geography of France with the *départements,* their *préfectures* and *sous-préfectures,* the rights and duties of the citizen, the moral obligations of man. Entering school in the morning we all put on black smocks which we loved because we had the advantage of cleaning our pens on our smocks. We did not receive medals for good performance and behavior as children in public schools did and we sometimes looked with envy on kids who walked around with ribbons and medals that looked like the *légion d'honneur.* But we got *bons points*, merit sheets, and for ten of them we received lozenges of sugar candy. We also got demerits for all kinds of sins and we knew that Gustave was whipped by his father whenever he came home thus branded. This made those of us who were never whipped shudder.

And then there was Gisèle in the school, the first girl I ever loved. We were six years old, both of us and of all classmates she was the one I loved most dearly. More than half a century has gone by, but I see her as if it had been yesterday. She was different from other girls, had a bush of very blond hair, had long bare arms and legs summer and winter, and her skirts were shorter than those of other girls. We were very shy in those days but if by accident I happened to touch her arms or legs while playing I had a strange feeling which scared and delighted me, made me feel elated and guilty at the same time. I left Paris at the age of ten and never saw her again, but I shall never forget her as long as I live, and all that is feminine in Paris will always be Gisèle to me. When I was in Paris in later years I often felt tempted to look her up, to put my head on her lap, and to tell her what she had meant to me. I never did because I knew well enough that never again would I find the blond little girl with long bare arms and legs. In the course of time her picture sometimes merged with that of Théophile Gautier and Adam's ballet *Giselle*. I never missed a performance of the ballet whenever I had a chance to see it in New York, London, Moscow, or Paris, and when Giselle emerged from the grave no longer a village girl but a light spirit I felt as if the Gisèle of my childhood had come to greet me.

Going to school was always exciting. We not only passed the tape worm but also the Folies Bergères where in the early morning the strangest decorations could be seen in front of the theatre. But most exciting were the days of the Dreyfus Affair. The Fort Chabrol was not far from our school. There was shooting, the street was closed and to us this was very thrilling. I have vivid recollections of the *affaire Dreyfus*. My parents were violently pro-Dreyfus and I shall never forget the evening when my father came home and enthusiastically told of having read Emile Zola's *J'accuse*. The French republic was in a deep crisis and when guests came to our home my mother asked them first of all not to talk about the *affaire*, otherwise there would immediately have been trouble. Years later we spent a summer holiday at Wengen in Switzerland and in the hotel, at the table next to ours, was Dreyfus with his wife and children who were about the same age as my sister and I, and his brother Léon who for many years had so valiantly fought to prove his brother's innocence.

The French Republic emerged victorious from this crisis and the *bloc républicain* was in power for many years. The French people never lost their sense of humor and were always ready to demonstrate for some cause or other. The parade of some foreign potentate through the boulevards was always an event for us. The King of Spain once came and all along the boulevards the people greeted him with the cry: "Assassin de

15

Ferrer!" the anarchist who had been executed in Barcelona. At the time of the Boer War President Kruger visited Paris. France was strongly anti-British, but Kruger looked so old and decrepit that the general comment was, "comme il est gaga!" The best parade I remember, however, was that of Tsar Nicolas II who came to Paris at the time of the World's Fair. It was a brilliant parade with the President of the French Republic, officers in great uniforms, *élite* troops. But the French populace was not impressed, and suddenly someone not far from where we stood began to sing a song that was very popular at that time: "Tout ça ne vaut pas l'amour, le bel amour, le vrai amour." The song spread like wild fire and wherever the Tsar went he was greeted with the words that true love was better. He must have thought that this was another version of the French national anthem.

I was born of Swiss parents. My father was from Schaffhausen which had been my family's city since 1545. Before that time we were farmers until one Sigerist moved to the city, and became a citizen and a craftsman. From then on my forebears were craftsmen for centuries, tanners mostly. They belonged to the tanners' guild which like all guilds took part in the administration of the city. A member of the family was once burgomaster. Then, in the nineteenth century, they gradually went into business. Tanning was now done in factories, no longer in the craftsmen's way, treading the hides in pits with feet which were drenched with gallic acid. Years later I saw this very method of tanning practiced in India and was most interested in it as it demonstrated graphically what my ancestors had done for many generations. It was not a healthy craft, as the operators breathed in the acid fumes from the pits; the average age of my forebears was well under sixty. One branch of the family remained in the leather goods trade to the present day. My grandfather became a wine dealer who supplied the restaurants and hotels of the canton with wine. He owned some vineyards on the hills overlooking the Rhine which are still in the family and produce a very pleasant light and slightly sparkling red wine.

My father left his home town at the age of eighteen, made a career in Paris, but always remained attached to Schaffhausen where we spent some time with our grandparents every summer. I made my first trip to Switzerland at the age of three months when I was baptized in the Church of St. John in Schaffhausen on July 19, 1891. We travelled to Switzerland every summer, always on the night train, and waking up in Basle, and having breakfast at the station with rolls that were so different in shape from the French ones, was most exciting.

My mother's forebears were goldsmiths who, until the end of the eighteenth century, lived in Kassel, Germany. During their years of apprenticeship, craftsmen in those days usually spent a few years abroad wandering from one country to another and working for different masters. In this way they acquired rich experience. One Wiskemann came to Zurich on his wanderings, fell in love with a local girl, and married her after he had become a citizen, which in Switzerland was a very difficult and costly affair. His son, my grandfather, became a goldsmith also, and had most of his training in Paris. But industrialization had begun, and instead of practicing his craft he opened a small factory for the plating of metal goods. Three of his four sons remained in the same branch, manufacturing or retailing metalware.

Thus I was born of good stock, from two lines of craftsmen, and on both my father's and mother's side I was the first to enter the halls of a university, and to devote his life to research and academic teaching.

It may be that my origins were responsible for the fact that I love the arts and crafts and am delighted whenever I see good craftsmanship. A well bound book, a glass vase from Murano, a Persian carpet, a Chinese carving of jade are sources of happiness as great as poetry, or music, or the contemplation of nature. We in the West are supposed to have a high standard of living probably because many of us have an infinity of mechanical gadgets for which we pay every month on the installment plan. But we are surrounded by ugliness, at least most of us are, because good craftsmanship has become exorbitantly expensive. Most objects of daily use, the many things we see and touch every day, are standardized factory-made horrors. The higher the standard of living has become the more we have developed a civilization of *ersatz*. Nylon and rayon are taking the place of silk, that noblest of all fabrics which used to be produced in such a wide range of variations. Plastics, horrible to see and touch, are replacing beautiful woods and metals. Instead of fresh fruit and vegetables, we have them canned or frozen. If you tell me that these are just as good as fresh ones, or that frozen meat is just as good as fresh meat, it simply means that you have forgotten what fresh food tastes like. The French are often blamed for lacking enthusiasm for refrigerators, but they know well enough that the icebox damages the taste of many foods, and that nothing ruins a sauce more rapidly than adding a shot of ice-cold cream or milk to it. I refuse to eat strawberries in the winter because this takes away one of the joys of spring. By no longer following the rhythm of the seasons we greatly impoverish our lives.

And the same thing has happened in other fields as well. When we were young we used to go to a concert every two weeks if not every week. And this was always a great event to which we looked forward every day, and for which we prepared by reading up on the music that we were going to hear or, if possible, by reading the piano score. Now you enter a room, people are standing around with cocktails in their hands, shouting at the top of their voices because the radio or the gramophone makes so much noise playing the Tchaikovsky *Symphony No. 4*. Movie and television have taken the place of the live theatre. Oh, I know what you are going to object to. Don't tell me! I am a physician and a socialist, and I have made these very objections many times myself. I know that it is better to have canned or frozen fruit and vegetables than none at all. I know the blessings of a refrigerator in a hot climate. I have a gramophone, and use it to study music. I know that the radio has brought music and entertainment to sick and lonely people who have no means of attending a concert. I am fully aware that we no longer live under feudalism or in the times of Huysmans and Oscar Wilde, that this is a democratic age. I have been fighting long enough for the common man, on four continents, fighting that he may have his share in the goods of this life instead of being promised paradise in the hereafter. We do not want the sweat of coolies, do not want beautiful objects made by starving craftsmen. Before we produce luxury goods we must see that everybody has the necessities—a decent home, plenty of wholesome food, and clothing, which obviously can be provided only through mass production in factories.

Yet I cannot help feeling sad that life has lost so much beauty in my own lifetime. The present European dress is probably the ugliest ever worn anywhere at any time. I remember an evening at the Hotel Taj Mahal in Bombay during the war. The dining-room was full of Indians and rich refugees from China, Indo-China, Siam, Burma, Indonesia. I have never seen such gorgeous and exquisitely beautiful dresses. In India, the poorest village woman looks like a Greek goddess. With industrialization Western dress is frequently adopted, and people who looked handsome and dignified in their native clothes now sometimes remind you of dressed-up monkeys. Industrialization, mass production, and standardization are unavoidable if people are to be liberated from the bonds of poverty; however it is to be hoped that the arts and crafts of the East will not perish but will be cultivated and passed on from one generation to the other until the day comes when the machine will satisfy the basic needs of all the people and they will be able to surround themselves not only with factory-made necessities, but also with beautiful handmade objects.

Switzerland is a very small country, covering an area of only 15,944 square miles. It is poorly endowed by nature. One-fourth of its territory is unfit for cultivation, unfit for human habitation. It has no mineral resources, no access to the sea, no colonies, and agriculture is not profitable. Its population of 4.7 million speaks four different languages and an infinity of dialects. And yet in spite of, or perhaps because of, these handicaps Switzerland has succeeded in becoming a very prosperous country and in many ways a very advanced country. Today, the average per capita income is high and wealth is more evenly distributed than in other countries. There are no slums in the cities, health conditions are good, educational standards high, and social legislation progressive.

Because the soil is poor, people have to work hard and be inventive in order to make a living. And love of their soil developed in the Swiss a fanatic sense of independence, and a readiness to fight for it that kept them free for six and a half centuries in the midst of all the vicissitudes of

Europe. Their common heritage created a bond between the Swiss which in the course of history proved to be stronger than those of race, language, or religion. Because the country has no raw materials, the people at all times were forced to deal and trade with foreign lands. The volume of foreign trade per capita of the population is greater in Switzerland than in any other country. Industries developed, not for mass production, but for the production of goods of high quality. Located in the center of Western Europe, at the source of the great rivers of the continent, Switzerland was by nature destined to be an open country, a bridge between north and south, between east and west, economically and culturally. But the country is small and the opportunities it offers to an enterprising young man are limited.

Hence, many Swiss have gone abroad and had good careers in foreign lands. In former centuries, entire Swiss regiments were in foreign service and their martial virtues were much appreciated. Poverty may have driven young mountain farmers to seek service as mercenaries but probably even more it was a spirit of adventure. When you grow up in a mountain valley the horizon is very close, and if you are curious the day comes sooner or later when you want to know what is on the other side of the mountain. You climb it, and see other valleys and other mountains. You go on until you reach the plain and ultimately the sea. And some then want to know what the world looks like on the other side of the sea.

Some Swiss went abroad as adventurers of genius like Paracelsus or Thurneisser zum Thurn, physician and alchemist, who promised to make gold for the Margrave of Brandenburg, failed, obviously, but built the first printing press in Berlin, probably murdered his wife, but ended his life peacefully in a monastery. Others were pioneer adventurers like "General" Sutter, the settler of Sacramento who developed agriculture in California. In the village in the Italian part of Switzerland where I am writing these lines lives a family, Pelli, whose history is characteristic of many Ticinese families. One of their forebears, born in 1656, was a military engineer and architect who built fortresses for the King of Denmark and was ennobled by him. One of his descendants was a painter who decorated the theatres of Venice, Padua, Udine, and other cities. He had a son who was also a painter and decorated churches in his homeland. Another member of the family was an engineer and architect in Russia, built palaces in Moscow, St. Petersburg, and Novgorod. Another was a painter who lived mostly in Venice, but also in Odessa; and still another, a painter too, died in Chile.

The list of Swiss scientists who had brilliant careers abroad is long, men like the great mathematician Leonard Euler who in the eighteenth century was a luminary of the Russian Academy of Science, or the anatomist, physiologist, botanist, poet, and theologian Albrecht von Haller, who was a pillar of the new University of Göttingen and founded its famous Academy. The country is small and for a man of talents it is all too easy to build up a local reputation which, however, rarely extends beyond the borders. Many Swiss, however, crave a larger field of action. An architect of genius like Le Corbusier would never have built a city in India if he had remained in his home town all his life, and a composer like Honegger had infinitely greater influence living in France and becoming a member of The Six.

Many Swiss went abroad as business people. They were liked because they were hard-working, enterprising, and honest. My father was one of them. If he had stayed at home he might have taken over his father's wine business as two of his brothers did. But he was ambitious and adventurous, went to Paris, which had a large Swiss colony, and worked at first in a bank. Just at that time the new aniline dyes came into use and he became the representative of one of the largest German chemical factories, the Badische Anilin- und Sodafabrik. Many others would have been satisfied with this job as it provided a good income without involving any risk. But my father was not, and soon along with a few others, he founded a shoe company called Chaussures Raoul. It was a stockholding company of which he was the first director. When he died at the age of forty-two the company had over one hundred stores in Paris, ten branches in the provinces, and several abroad.

To me it was a great blessing that I was born in France and spent my first ten years there. We were Swiss to be sure, and all of us felt much attached to the homeland, but growing up in a large foreign city, in one of the great cultural centers of Europe, broadened our horizon from the very start and prevented us from ever becoming provincially narrow. French was my first language. At home we spoke nothing but French although my mother taught us some Swiss German that we spoke very hesitantly—with our grandparents and cousins in Switzerland. To the present day I count only in French, I think in French whenever I am tired, and write diaries and other personal notes in French. Although most of my education was in the German-speaking part of Switzerland, the French classics were always and still are much closer to my heart than those of Germany.

On one of my aimless wanderings through Paris in the early 1930's I was once more walking down the Grands Boulevards when suddenly I felt frightfully weary. My legs were heavy and dragged. I looked around and saw on the other side of the boulevard a pastry shop, Brioches de la Lune. Yes, that was it. Every afternoon Mélanie, the maid, took my sister and me to one of the parks, as my parents insisted that we should have fresh air and exercise whenever the weather permitted it. We went to the Palais Royal Garden, played with our humming top or with marbles according to the season, for every game had its season. Or we went to the Tuileries Gardens where the water basins were our delight, although Mélanie tried to prevent us from getting too close to the water for fear that we might fall in. I had a boat, however, and was very proud of it. The shell was made of metal and you could rig it as a sailboat, a steamship, a merchant vessel, or a passenger ship. It was my favorite toy, for it made me dream of foreign lands as did the books of Jules Verne, dreams which still haunt me today although many of them have materialized. Returning from the parks we walked along the Boulevards and approaching the Porte St. Martin began to feel very tired. Then Mélanie would buy us a *brioche de la lune* which tasted very good. And it still did more than thirty years later.

My parents were always afraid that one of us might get lost in the large city. We had our name and address written on the inside of our belts, and were instructed in case we lost Mélanie to go to the next policeman, to ask him to take us home, and to tell him that father would give him a very good tip. We were told that policemen were the friends of children and that only bad people went to jail. Since then I have learned that French policemen are anything but lambs and that against all laws are allowed to beat the people they arrest to pulp, whether guilty or innocent, just for fun and to release nervous tension— a sport that is called *passer à tabac*. I have also learned that today in most countries people are put in prison not only for crimes, but also for political heresy. Few governments feel secure enough to be able to tolerate real opposition or even criticism.

Paris in the nineties was a large city to be sure, with much traffic, with an endless number of carriages and buses, and there were traffic accidents then as there are today, and traffic jams when a horse fell and could not get up. But Paris still had many of the traits of a small town. Every day a herd of goats passed our house led by a young goatherd who would milk his animals in front of the house. Goat milk was recommended for people suffering from consumption and other diseases of the chest. Another street vendor would come selling a lovely cream cheese which was made in the shape of a heart. Huge fellows from the Auvergne, who looked frightening to us, sold coal, others bought and sold rags and old clothes. They all had their cries which we knew and imitated and which must have been the same for centuries.

Sometimes I was allowed to accompany our cook when she went shopping for the household. She was a Swiss girl, but she soon learned the ways of Paris and became a very excellent French cook who stayed with my mother for over thirty years. The shopping was all done in the neighborhood and was a real art. Every item of food was bought in a different shop and politeness required that in every one you had a talk with the *patronne*. And you had to be skillful. Camembert was not bought wrapped in tinfoil and in boxes. The cheeses were lined up on a board and you touched at least a dozen of them in order to decide which one was just right. Butter came in blocks of many kilos, and when you wanted a pound it was sliced off with a wire. We disliked the smell of the fish store, but what it had for sale made us dream of the sea, a great variety of fish, lobsters, crayfish, shrimps, mussels, oysters. It was years before I was to see the ocean for the first time—since we spent all our summer holidays in the Swiss mountains—and it was not in France but in Belgium. I well remember the day. We had come to Ostend, were walking from the station toward the beach. Our lips felt salty and there was a smell of seaweed in the air. I walked against the wind, ahead of the others, in great excitement—and there it was, the sea, not blue but green, the door to Asia and Africa. I did not think of America at that time.

Our Paris butcher was a great friend too, chiefly because of his shop window. He liked to display his meats in a particularly picturesque way and when he had a nice pig's head he used to put it in the middle of the window with a Prussian soldier's pointed helmet on top. Twenty years after the Franco-Prussian War anti-German feeling was still very strong and the loss of Alsace-Lorraine was bitterly felt. The monument of the province on Place de la Concorde was always wrapped in black mourning crape.

As my mother had moved to a foreign city she wanted to live close to my father's office and we had an apartment in the same block. It was cozy and nicely furnished but primitive compared to present standards. Of course there was no electricity in such a house in 1890. We had kerosene lamps which gave a very pleasant light and did not smell if they were kept clean. We also had gas in some places, but this was a real hazard. My parents had an open gas light in the bedroom. One night they came home from the theatre and lit the gas flame. My mother went to bed and fell asleep. My father went to the bathroom and a draft blew out the light. When he came back he thought my mother had turned off the light, and he went to sleep also. Meanwhile the gas was streaming out. Fortunately the smell woke my father who jumped out of bed and tore open the windows, otherwise I would have lost my parents at a very young age. In those days everybody was sensitized to the smell of illuminating gas. Fires were frequent, and the fear of fire was very real. The fire engines were heard every day. Once we saw the top floors of a neighboring house burn out and my father used to tell how he was at the Opéra Comique when the theatre burned to the ground. *Mignon* was being performed; my father was sitting in one of the front rows when he noticed a flame spreading from the limelights to the stage. In an instant the whole scenery was on fire and the theatre was filled with smoke. A terrific panic ensued with everybody rushing to the main exit. As the doors of the boxes opened out and the corridors were packed full of people, nobody could escape from the boxes which were later found full of charred corpses. Horrible scenes developed with people fighting for their lives, trampling down women, shrieking. My father was saved through his presence of mind. Being in a front row stall he had little chance of ever reaching the main exit. So he looked for a side door, found one, and walked out unharmed while the theatre was a blazing furnace. He had to tell us the story many times. Maybe it was due to this miraculous escape that *Mignon* remained his favorite opera all his life.

Plumbing was practically non-existent in our apartment. We had running water, but that was about all. The toilet was a dark hole between the parlor and living room, a place we dreaded. We had no bathroom, but a huge bathtub stood in the entrance hall covered with boards and a Persian carpet. On Saturdays the tub was rolled into the bedroom, buckets and buckets of hot water were brought up from the street by two men, and we were thoroughly washed and scrubbed. On other days we were simply washed standing in a flat tub. It was primitive, but we kept clean.

Later, in 1898, we moved into another, much larger apartment, 16 rue d'Abbeville. It was a new structure and we were the first occupants of the flat. It had all the comforts available at that time—a lift, electricity, a bathroom with a gas stove, central heating, a chute for the garbage, a beautiful kitchen. Of course we liked it, but I have particularly warm feelings for our first apartment with all its primitiveness. It made me realize that plumbing and modern conveniences are useful to be sure, but not really important. Our childhood in Paris was at least as happy as that of my children. The luminaries of French science, learning, literature, and art of that time—Pasteur, Berthelot, Taine, Renan, Zola, Mallarmé, Verlaine, Cézanne, Monet, and so many others—were creating their immortal works in surroundings that were as primitive as ours, and electricity would not have improved them. Of course it would be foolish not to use electricity and other conveniences since we now have them and since they are cleaner, safer, and easier to handle at a time when domestic help is almost unavailable. But we should always keep in mind that basically such conveniences are not important, that plumbing is not culture, that the true standard of living is not material, not determined by technology, but by the people's emotional and spiritual demands and their means of satisfying them.

Being Swiss my parents believed in the value of fresh air more than the average Parisian did at that time, and every year in the late spring we moved to the country where we stayed until late autumn interrupting the period for a voyage to Switzerland at the height of the summer. We had rented a small country house in Montmorency, just north of Enghien-les-Bains, close enough to Paris so that my father could commute. Montmorency was famous for its forest, a favorite point of excursion for wedding parties who used to roam the woods riding on donkeys. There could not be a funnier sight than a bride all in white, with a veil and orange blossoms, riding sideways on a donkey, scared that she might be thrown off—which happened more than once to the great enjoyment of the party.

The region was a paradise, one huge garden which grew the finest vegetables and fruit not only for Paris but for export to many countries. The owner of our house, Monsieur Larcher, was an agriculturist and we used to go with him to his fields to cut asparagus, salad, artichokes, and whatever the season produced. He was a famous fruit grower. Every apple on his espaliers grew in a paper bag so that it would be spotless, and shortly before the apples ripened the bags were removed, the German or Russian eagle was applied, and thus marked with imperial insignia the apples were sent to the courts of Berlin and St. Petersburg. Next to our garden was a peach orchard and when the fruit was ripe we would shoot at it with slingshots and when we hit the peaches they would be blown to bits.

Our garden was a great source of happiness. It seemed enormous but was probably much smaller than I remember. Old horse chestnut trees grew in front of the house and I always think of them when I see certain paintings by Monet. At night the nightingales sang in the trees so loudly that they often prevented us from going to sleep. I always wanted to see and feed them—a bird that could make so much noise could not possibly be small—but I never succeeded. On the other side of the house the garden extended far into the fields and was full of flowers and fruit trees. I loved the country all my life, always wanted to live in the country to see the sun rise and set, to live in nature and with the seasons. This love was born in the French countryside and I had to wait almost half a century before I could settle in the country again.

I often wondered what one's earliest childhood reminiscences are. I remember the night when my sister was born. I was two years and nine months old. Mélanie woke me up to tell me that I had a little sister and I know that I woke up from a dream—I saw a muticolored spiral that was turning around very fast. But I think I have an earlier recollection, a great scare. It was in the country. I was squatting, playing at the sandpile. I was dressed like a girl, as very young boys were, in a blue and white checkered dress. Then suddenly a huge coal cart passed with black horses running, with black-faced men shouting. I was very scared.

I remember a fright of another kind which I experienced much later when I was about eight years old. Again it was in the country. The neighbors had a boy about my age. We used to play together frequently. He was a Roman Catholic and I a Protestant. One day he gave me a vivid description of how I would roast in hell for being a Protestant. He urged me to abandon my heresy and embrace the Catholic faith. I told him that my parents were Protestants, that we were all Protestants in our family. "Forget your parents," he said. "You have a soul to save, join our Church." We talked and talked, and when I came back to the house I felt utterly sick, vomited, and did not have the courage to tell my mother what had happened. I was put to bed on the assumption that I had an upset stomach. The next morning the nature of a healthy boy had overcome the scare. I woke up still a Protestant and merry as a lark.

My father came from a very religious family. His parents never had a meal without saying grace and this seemed very strange to us when we visited our grandparents. Aunt Mina was forever in touch with angels and urged me to read a chapter of the Bible every day—which I did not do. But she did every night, and when she had read that "the children of Israel turned again, and went a whoring after Baalim, and made Baal-berith their god" she went to sleep peacefully. She gradually became deaf and bore her infirmity with great resignation regretting only that she could no longer hear the birds sing. My mother, who was a confirmed rationalist, suggested that she should see a doctor, but Aunt Mina was very emphatic that her deafness was the will of God. My mother finally dragged her to a doctor who found that her ears were clogged with wax. When it had been removed she suddenly heard the birds sing again—another miracle of God. My mother never went to church. Her ideal of Christianity was that one should live a decent life following the principles of the Gospel and that this was much more important than prayers and the singing of hymns. My father also emancipated himself from the rigid religious rules of his family but I think that basically he remained religious. As a child I was sent to Sunday school in Paris. All I remember is that the minister had a blond beard and at the end of the sermon asked us not to forget *le petit nègre* at the exit. This little negro was a small statue with a slit into which you dropped a coin intended for the African mission. To me the statue exerted a great fascination for it meant foreign lands which I wanted to visit some day.

My sister and I were confirmed in Zurich with all the ritual that goes with it, and I had my children baptized because I did not want them to think that they were different from other children. As a matter of fact Buddhism always appealed to me more as a religion than Christianity. I like its iron logic. Life is what you make it. There is no need for an original sin, a saviour, or a personal god. Your Karma is the result of your actions, good and evil, and the ultimate goal is the nirvana. The word freedom is so much abused today, but I have come to believe more and more that freedom has nothing to do with the form of government. There are no free countries and slave countries. The early Christians were freer than the Roman emperors who put them in chains and threw them to the lions. You are free when you are free from material needs and from passions. The individual who thinks he must have a bigger and better car every few years and an infinity of mechanical gadgets is not a free man but a slave, and so is the senator who is filled with ambition and hatred of all those who do not conform to his views. India is the great hope of the world today and has a great lesson to teach.

What else does one remember from early childhood? Not only scares but praise. One Christmas Eve, when I was about six years old, we had a beautiful tree in the parlor with real candles. We sang carols, received gifts, then blew out the candles and went to have a festive dinner. I was always afraid of fire and suddenly remarked "Are we sure that all the candles have been blown out?" My father went to have a look and indeed one candle had been overlooked, had fallen down and the carpet was on fire. It was extinguished without much trouble but ten minutes later the room would have been ablaze. I was the hero of the day and felt very proud.

25

The World's Fair of 1900 was a great event and to us the Swiss Village with its cardboard mountains and waterfalls was the chief attraction. There was a shooting gallery where one shot at a target with crossbows like Wilhelm Tell. My father once asked jokingly if I would like to have a shot. Of course I did. I was nine years old, the crossbow was very heavy. I aimed very carefully and by God I hit the mark and received an ashtray with Wilhelm Tell on it that I still possess. Of course I was very proud and it was my good luck that I was not asked to make a second shot. I was always good at shooting. This is a national sport in Switzerland. When you travel through the country on Sundays you hear shots wherever you go because all people of military age are required to engage in target practice every year. I remember an amusing incident which happened in Munich when I was a medical student. I was with my friend Hans Schinz on the Oktober Wiese where there was some kind of fair although it was not October but spring. I was immediately attracted by a shooting gallery with clay pipes and all kinds of moving clay animals. I thought it would be great fun to wreck the place. I asked for two rifles, suggested to Schinz to start at the right while I would begin at the left. Every shot was a hit, the clay burst, and after a short while the owner of the gallery was in tears and implored us to stop as otherwise he would be completely ruined. Of course we complied with his request and when he heard that we were Swiss he said: "Ah, the Swiss, to us they are just terrible."

One also remembers injustice met with in childhood. The year 1900 was not only the end of a century but was to bring about the end of the world according to some tabloid sheets. On a given day a comet was to hit our planet. This was exciting news. Our parents explained that this was utter nonsense, but the maids seemed worried and we children did not quite know what to believe. The day came, nothing happened, and we were to go on a walk in the afternoon. I looked out of the window to see what the weather was like. From a Paris flat one does not see much sky and what I saw were heavy clouds so that I took an umbrella along expecting rain. Once in the street, however, we saw that the weather was very good and that the clouds I had seen were about the only ones in the sky. My mother and sister, seeing the umbrella, immediately began laughing at me, implying that I had taken it to protect myself against the comet or against the crumbling walls of houses. It was not true, and I resented the accusation, but to the present day I am being teased about that confounded umbrella.

The years went by. I lived in Switzerland, in Germany, and America, but Paris and France always remained close to my heart. I always considered French my real mother tongue. I was never able to count in any language but French and this was a handicap when I went to a German-speaking school. Seeing Paris again not as a child but as an adolescent or young student was sheer delight. These were voyages of discovery in the beloved city. To the child the Louvre was a garden or a department store, but now it was a palace and museum with all its treasures. And there was something feminine in the atmosphere of Paris that was captivating, I cannot describe it. It was not the Folies Bergères or Casino de Paris, not the cocottes of the Boulevards or the Bois de Boulogne. It was rather a scent in the air, the graceful way in which a girl student wore her simple beret, the song heard in a cabaret, the poor little girl who sold you a bunch of violets.

While I was a professor at Leipzig I always had a French daily newspaper, several weekly papers, and monthly magazines so that I always kept in very close touch with Paris. And when we lived in America we went to Europe every summer until the outbreak of World War II, and Paris was always the first and last stopping station on the Continent. What a joy it was to see the city again, to eat *coq au vin* instead of *à la* king, *truffes au champagne* instead of sweet potatoes.

Two such summers in Paris stand out particularly vividly in my memory, those of 1937 and 1938. In 1937 the Popular Front was in power with a socialist, Léon Blum, as premier. It was a great year with great hopes. It seemed that France had found her revolutionary tradition again, remembering 1793, 1830, 1848, and 1871. A wave of enthusiasm swept over the country—not unopposed obviously. In hundreds of communities communists and socialists were elected mayors and invariably they first of all improved the sanitary conditions, the water supply, and sewage system. They created Maisons de la Culture in the villages with libraries, radios, gramophones. Lectures were held and exhibits displayed. The four most progressive theatrical producers were appointed as advisors to the Comédie Française, the most conservative and tradition-bound theatre. There was even hope that the French university system, very progressive one hundred and fifty years ago, but a fossil now, might be reorganized.

In 1937 Paris had a brilliant World's Fair. I do not know if it was ever completed but it certainly was not when it was opened. Wooden boards were covered with hammers and sickles and with inscriptions "Down with Hitler!" The center of attraction was the Soviet Pavilion with its beautiful stainless steel statues of two industrial and agricultural workers, a man and a woman, and just opposite it the Nazi Pavilion. Large crowds queued up in front of them and you were pushed through by the mob so that you hardly had a chance to see the details. Not far away from them was the American Pavilion, a very good one, which illustrated the achievements of the New Deal, with excellent pictures of the Tennessee Valley Authority. It was empty most of the time but it had very comfortable armchairs and when people were tired and their feet were sore they sought armchairs there for a rest or even a nap. The issue was clear. Nobody was interested in liberalism at that moment. The polarization of society to the left and to the right was advancing with giant strides; communism, or at least some form of socialism, and fascism were the real issues.

27

Before delving into the political anxieties of those days I would like to stop for a moment and recall the figure of Viorica, a charming woman who today is probably rotting in a Rumanian prison if she is still alive. She was a surgeon, married to a much older surgeon, once her teacher, a man who played an important part in the International Society of the History of Medicine and who either was a member of the cabinet of his country or in jail. On a hot summer day after a long committee meeting, Viorica quite spontaneously invited some of us to dinner at the Rumanian restaurant at the World's Fair. She looked so young and sweet, was small and had something that reminded you of a cat, that most lovable of all creatures. The food and wines were delicious, the *tsiganis* came to your table and played melodies into your ear that almost made you weep. You forgot the world, the class struggle, the impending war, and the next morning I sent Viorica a bunch of violets.

But then I went back to the Fair, to the Spanish Pavilion where Picasso's mural depicted the horrors of Guernica. The Spanish Civil War was on and was fought with the cruelty inherent in a civil war. World War II had reached Europe. It had started long before, in 1931, when Japan had attacked China. It had spread west when Italy invaded Ethiopia. It was now being fought on European soil. The Germans were testing their new weapons and methods in Spain. When the air force of the Condor Legion made an experiment in total warfare at Guernica, an experiment that was analyzed and widely discussed in German military literature, most people refused to believe that this was merely a dress rehearsal and that one of the next cities to be bombed would be London. The British government pretended to have no information about German troops operating in Spain. And yet the Germans sang loudly enough for the world to hear: "We are German legionaries; we fly victorious over all frontiers."

At Geneva, Litvinov never tired of appealing to the peace-loving nations, urging them to join together to meet the growing menace through collective security action. Litvinov was one of the few statesmen in the world who could afford to reprint the speeches he made before the war without being ashamed of himself. But nobody listened to him and the impending war was accepted as inevitable.

For a while there was still hope that the working class would be strong enough to direct events in the democratic countries. The French sit-down strikes were extraordinarily successful. The workers not only took the best possible care of the machinery, but the mayors of the communities involved fed the strikers, and the nation's foremost singers and actors came to entertain them. There was a strong revolutionary movement in Europe which scared the reactionary circles and drove them into the fascist camp. Léon Blum was forced to betray Spain and to boycott the legal, democratically elected government of that country. British ships were sunk off the Spanish coast and nobody ever protested. British women were stripped to the skin by Japanese in China and no protest was heard. Fascism was on the march—triumphant in Europe and Asia. Economic pressure was brought to bear on the French government in order to wreck the Popular Front which fell apart under the onslaught. The spread of World War II seemed inevitable and it was just a question of whether the war could be postponed for another year or two.

Still more dramatic was the autumn of 1938. I was in Paris waiting for my family as we intended to sail back to America on the *Queen Mary*. French mobilization had begun. Regiments were marching in the streets singing the International, and the officers did not look happy. I had had an extraordinarily busy summer which had begun pleasantly enough with a week in London, the city I like best next to Paris and to which I feel deeply attached since my early student days. Then I had conducted a travel seminar through the Soviet Union where we had studied the organization of the country's health services. It had been a beautiful summer; the Caucasus and the Crimea were more glorious than ever, but one felt that war was imminent. It was not clear whether the Japanese or the Germans would attack first, but war was expected and the most popular song that summer had been: "If there is war tomorrow, if the enemy attacks, the Soviet people will rise like one man." From Kiev I had gone to Warsaw where a cousin of ours was First Secretary of the Swiss Legation. We heard a great deal. Conditions were far from satisfactory with food riots in some provinces. Then I had gone to Prague, and, as I was not anxious to travel through Nazi Germany, I had flown from Prague to Zurich over the Nazi land. My neighbor was a German *émigré* and as he looked out of the window he suddenly said: "I have never been air sick in my life, but today I wish I were."

Switzerland was an island of peace but the threat from the north was distinctly felt. The Nazis and the Italian fascists tried hard to create a fascist movement in the country—but unsuccessfully. The question of race could not be raised in a country where people of German, French, and Italian origin had lived peacefully side by side for centuries. The Jewish population was not large and played an important part in the economic life of the country. It was impossible to arouse open anti-semitism. Switzerland had no imperialist ambitions, had no lost empire to reconquer, and did not feel a mission to redeem the world. The *Führerprinzip* was abhorrent to a democratic country where the people were trained in self-administration, and the idea of a corporative state appealed to only a few youngsters. Still, the threat from the north and south was manifest and all the more dangerous as both dictators acted emotionally and not rationally.

Then I had to go to Yugoslavia to attend the Congress of the International Society of the History of Medicine of which I was a vice-president. It was a brilliant affair with receptions, banquets, a military parade on the birthday of the young King, and a court ball in old Viennese style. We traveled all over that beautiful country as guests

29

of the government. But the pressure was felt here also. The country was a fascist dictatorship, and as I had just been in Russia I was suspect and had the definite impression that I was being followed. I mentioned it to a friend who asked me what type of a gent was shadowing me as they had two types, the gangster and gigolo type. I think my man was a blend of both but he seemed perfectly harmless. The Congress was opened at Zagreb. Soon a delegation of medical students and young physicians came to see me. "You have just been in the Soviet Union," they said. "We are starved for news as we are not supposed to hear anything about that country. Would you be willing to tell us what you have seen and how their medical system functions?" Of course I was glad to do it. The lecture was arranged and to arouse less suspicion was held in the Physicians' Building, the very place where the historical Congress was held. While on the ground floor they were discussing Hippocrates and medical folklore, I on the top floor was talking of Soviet factories and farms and their medical services, the plains of the Ukraine, the mountain valleys of the Caucasus, the health resorts of the Black Sea coast. Attendance was strictly by invitation. People filing in had to present a card; when the last had entered, the door was locked, and the student chairman came to me. "You are among friends," he said. "Talk quite freely and as long as you possibly can." I spoke for two hours and never have I had a more attentive and more appreciative audience. The following day the papers reported that I had given a fascinating address on the development of social medicine in the United States. After the lecture I noticed a young student who walked with great difficulty with two canes. I inquired whether he had suffered an attack of polio but was told that he had been caught teaching the peasants to read and write, had been arrested and beaten up by the police until his bones were broken. I was also introduced to a young and very charming girl student who had been beaten to pulp for the same "crime." I am sure that most members of my audience later joined Tito's partisans and fought for the liberation of their country.

The Congress went on brilliantly but there was tremendous tension underneath. Germany and Italy had sent large and well-disciplined delegations, pure Aryan, of course, as Italy had just passed the anti-Jewish laws which excluded men like Arturo Castiglioni. When the time came to decide where the next conventions should be held, Berlin and Rome were chosen much against our will. But what could we do? The United States government did not subsidize international conventions. In Scandinavia and the other democratic countries one could count on very little financial help. The Spanish government in 1935 had contributed the equivalent of $30,000; Yugoslavia must have spent at least as much; and the fascist authorities of Germany and Italy were prepared to entertain in the most lavish way. Many of us decided that since our vote was not strong enough we would at least protest by staying away and leaving the fascists alone, congratulating one another in our absence.

30

The highlight of my Yugoslavian tour was Andrija Štampar. He is one of the greatest physicians, hygienists, public health officers, and medical educators of our time. In my long career I came to know two types of public health people: one well-trained, doing a good job, highly efficient, and knowing exactly what is possible and what is impossible. The other type is made up of people who have no specialized training but have imagination and a political philosophy. To them nothing is impossible. Štampar is one of them; another is Semashko, the first Commissar of Health of the USSR, who for many years practiced in a suburb of Paris, had no specialized training in public health but knew what must be done to protect the people's health and did it when the time came. And in England and America were the great pioneers of public health not often laymen—lawyers, such as Chadwick and Shattuck? This does not mean that a thorough course in a school of hygiene and public health is wasted. Technical knowledge is necessary but in addition one must have imagination, faith, courage, and a few other qualities.

Štampar has them all and this has made it possible for him to build up a great health system for his country. We first met in Moscow in 1936 when he was on his way home from China and joined a delegation of health workers of the League of Nations. Then in the spring of 1938 he once came to my office in Baltimore in utter despair. "Sigerist," he said, "do help me. I have been on a study tour through the United States—very interesting! I saw model water supplies, sewage systems, hospitals, laboratories, everything. A few days ago I was in a city in the South and they wanted to show me their new water supply, but then I blew up. Everybody in our profession knows what an ideal water supply should be like. It is just a question of money whether we can afford to build it or not. I wanted to see their unsolved problems and asked them to show me their slums. And by God, they had them. I saw homes where the water supply consisted of a bucket of rain water in front of the shack, and another bucket next to it that served as toilet. And on all my tour I met nobody but distinguished professors and great health administrators. I am sick and tired of them and would like to meet just plain ordinary people and young students. Can you arrange that for me?" Of course I could. The following evening I had my sociology seminar at my home. They sat all over the floor wherever there was space. Štampar came, a big husky man of two hundred pounds, sat in an armchair which crashed under his weight. Another was found. I introduced him and asked him to tell us what he had done in Yugoslavia. And then for several hours he told us a tale which sounded like an epic.

When he was a medical student Croatia was still Austrian and he studied in Vienna as a matter of course. Back home he started to practice in a small town, and his first experience was with a strange-looking man who came to his office, put some gold coins on the table, and declared that the same amount would be paid to him every month as had been done to his predecessor. Štampar was puzzled until he found

31

out that the man was the keeper of the local house of prostitution which he was to examine periodically, and the money was simply a bribe to prevent him from examining the girls. Needless to say he refused the money emphatically and antagonized his environment for the first, but by no means for the last, time.

After World War I, thirty years old, he was appointed Director of Public Health of his now independent country. Yugoslavia was in a wretched condition, destroyed by war and epidemics. The task of reconstruction seemed desperately difficult. He began his work in a health department that consisted of a table and a few chairs. But soon he attracted a group of young doctors whom he inspired and filled with enthusiasm for the great task. There were no office hours for these young men and women; they worked day and night. Instruments and apparatus were secured mostly from Germany as reparations. Increasing funds were appropriated by the government, and in ten years time three hundred health institutions were created from nothing, urban poli-clinics, rural health centers, hospitals, sanatoria, health resorts, labora-tories. And it was all done in a new spirit realizing that medicine was now to be social medicine, not a commodity to be sold on the open market to the few who could afford to buy it, but a service freely available to all.

Of course he made enemies, distributing quinine free of charge in malaria regions where doctors used to make profits by selling the drug. Several times he was shot at and pressure was brought on the government to discharge him. But as long as the country had a parliament the peasants backed him up. He knew that they were the backbone of the country, that they needed health more than anybody else. And they knew that he was one of them. Then came the year 1929. Parliament was dissolved, the Constitution scrapped. The peasants lost their voice in government and Štampar their support. The reactionary forces could now oppose him more strongly and one day he was driven out of office. He went to China where other peasants needed him.

In World War II the Germans arrested him and he was kept in jail, in Graz, for four years until the Russians liberated him. He likes to say that the Gestapo saved his life because the Ustachi of the traitor Pavelich would undoubtedly have killed him. His faith in the future of his country and the love of his wife kept his morale high during these long, trying years, and today he is the President of the Academy of Science and Art, Director of the School of Hygiene and Public Health, Dean of the School of Medicine of Zagreb, and is as full of ideas as he was as a youngster. He played a leading part in the foundation of the World Health Organization and was the Chairman of the Interim Commission in the beginning. In Geneva they like to call him *Le Père* Štampar, justly so as in many ways he is the father of the organization and is largely responsible for the superb and progressive preamble of its Constitution. We now meet almost every year in Geneva or Pura, and

I am happy to be able to count such a man among my friends.

The Congress of the History of Medicine of 1938 was over and Štampar drove me in his Ford to Croatian villages to show me some of his work. He was out of office at that time but the peasants worshipped him. Women kissed his hands and greeted him as the savior of their children. After a few days he dropped me at Ljubljana where I was to take the Orient Express on the following morning. I was now on my own, no longer a delegate of the American Association of the History of Medicine, no longer a guest of the government. Štampar was gone, and I was looking forward to seeing my family in Switzerland soon. The following morning I went to the station early. I had a reservation on the train and did not want to miss it. It was September 18. Czechoslovakia had just been put under martial law. Premier Daladier and Foreign Minister Bonnet of France had just flown to London to consult with the British government. War seemed imminent and everybody was nervous. When I came to the station and stood with my bags on the platform there was not a soul around, but a few minutes later a man in a trench coat came and placed himself close to my right. Two minutes later another fellow of the same type was on my left. I knew them to be thugs. More came, plain-clothes men and gendarmes in full regalia until I was completely surrounded by them and all the exits of the station were guarded. I cannot deny that I felt very uneasy. I had not committed any crime, was not a member of any political party, but of course there was that clandestine "subversive" lecture about public health in the USSR, and in those days everything was crazy and you never could tell what might happen.

After what seemed an eternity the train appeared, slowed down, stopped and all the police people rushed at one of the cars arresting a man whom they had been expecting and who apparently was trying to leave the country. Two minutes later I felt most comfortable in my first-class sleeping compartment. I shared it with a Czech who was extremely nervous—no wonder as his country was just being sold to the Nazis. I tried to say a few appropriate words, what a tragedy it would be for the country to lose its independence that it had won only twenty years ago. At this he jumped up and yelled: "This is not all, the worst is my collection of Bohemian glass. I have the finest collection of glass in the country. My grandfather started it, my father continued it and I invested all my savings in it. Do you realize how breakable glass is, do you? If the Nazi beasts come they'll drink from these glasses, they'll smash them on the wall! Oh, I'd rather be dead than live to see such a thing happen." In the meantime he was fleeing to Switzerland where, he said, he had a handsome bank account.

Soon after Ljubljana one crosses into Italy and at the border the train was literally stormed by police troops—*carabinieri*. They pulled all the blinds down, locked the cars, kept us for many hours and examined every compartment from top to bottom, looking under the

33

seats and under cushions, knocking at the partitions to see if they sounded hollow. I had a pile of books and pamphlets mostly about maternal health and child welfare. A *carabiniere* spent a whole hour going through this literature page by page. He smoked my cigarettes but did not skip one page. What was going on? We could not buy a paper and the policemen refused to answer any questions. Two days later, in Switzerland, I heard what had happened. Mussolini was visiting Trieste that day and an attempt was to be made on his life. Hence all the fuss.

Hours late our train moved on. Riding through the fertile plains of the Veneto and Lombardia at this beautiful season was always sheer delight which was only spoiled by the fact that on every empty wall letters stared at you: *IL DUCE HA SEMPRE RAGIONE*—the Duce is always right. I am sure I was not the only one who asked himself how long he would be right. Or you read: *CREDERE — OBBEDIRE — COMBATTERE* — to believe, to obey, to fight. Surely everybody believes in something; but the Italians are not anxious to obey orders and they are ready to fight (have done it for centuries) for what they believe in, which may not be what the government wants them to believe. It was late at night when we reached the entrance of the Simplon tunnel at Domodossola. Again we were kept waiting for hours, again people were arrested on the train. At long last we entered the tunnel and knew that on the other side was Switzerland, but with another border, one more customs inspection. When we arrived in Brig the Swiss customs man came, spick and span, with a broad smile, saluted, and said: "Gentlemen, I assume you have nothing but your personal effects. Thank you!" The train was so late that he was probably anxious to go home, but what a relief not to be treated as a criminal.

I had another meeting to attend, in Holland, the two hundredth anniversary of the death of the great Dutch physician Hermann Boerhaave. The University of Leyden and the Netherlands Society of the History of Medicine had invited their members to academic functions and a two-day pilgrimage to all the places where Boerhaave had ever been. They had in addition invited one delegate each from the four countries in which Boerhaave's influence had been most strongly felt: Germany (Professor Paul Diepgen), Austria (Professor K. F. Wenckebach), Scotland (Professor J. D. Comrie), and me representing the United States. The meeting took place on September 23 and 24. The political situation was as bad as it could possibly be. On September 19 Britain and France had accepted Hitler's demands for a quick surrender to Germany of all predominantly German areas of Czechoslovakia. The following day Benes had declared that the Anglo-French plan for a partition of the country was unacceptable. On September 21 Prague, under tremendous pressure from London and Paris, had agreed to cede Sudeten German areas to the Reich and on September 22 Chamberlain had flown to Godesberg for a second meeting with Hitler.

34

War seemed imminent but at that time we acted as if the world were perfectly normal. What else could one do? These two days in Holland will remain unforgettable to all who attended the functions. The weather was perfect, beautiful autumn days with silvery mist. There were still flowers in the fields and Dutch hospitality was unsurpassed. There was an atmosphere more cordial than ever before because we probably all felt that we might never meet again or certainly not for a long time. During the day we forgot the world and remembered Boerhaave, but in the evenings we grabbed all the newspapers we could find. On September 23 Benes ordered general mobilization of the Czechoslovak army and Paris prepared for partial mobilization. On September 24 Chamberlain flew back to London. Mussolini assured Germany of his support. Britain and France sped their defenses. On the twenty-fifth my meeting was over and I wanted to go to Paris as we were scheduled to sail back to the States on the twenty-eighth. In my hotel in Amsterdam I was told that no trains were running to Paris as Belgium had mobilized its army and did not let any trains through. I went to the station nevertheless and the train was running. In Belgium every bridge, every tunnel and highway was guarded by the army, but the train got through to Paris almost on schedule. The next day my family was to join me, coming from Switzerland. I went to the Gare de l'Est to meet them, but the station was guarded by police and soldiers, and thousands of refugees were streaming in from Alsace and Lorraine. They remembered 1914 and abandoned their homes to escape foreign occupation.

On September 26 the tension had grown so much that President Roosevelt appealed to Hitler to negotiate. On the twenty-seventh the British fleet was partially mobilized and President Roosevelt made a second appeal to Hitler. On the twenty-eighth we were to sail on the *Queen Mary* but at the office of the Cunard Line in Paris they had no idea whether the ship would sail or whether it had been mobilized for the transportation of troops. Cunard had provided for boat trains, however, and advised us to go to Cherbourg and see what would happen. We had a lot of luggage and the difficulty was to find taxis. I managed to get hold of two of them and we reached the station hours before the trains left. The trains were crowded as dozens of people tried to escape to America although they had no reservations whatsoever. In Cherbourg every tenth passenger had his luggage examined minutely and the rumor was that some people were trying to smuggle out gold. We were not among them and all that could have been found on us after a long summer in Europe would have been a few very small travelers cheques. But gold was shipped out. After we had been herded on the tender we saw men carrying small but apparently very heavy boxes and heard that this was gold bullion, millions that were being shipped by the French government to the States.

After hours of waiting the tender left the harbor between mines one could almost grasp. We waited and waited not knowing whether the

Queen Mary would come at all, but all of a sudden there she was, resplendent with all her lights on, and when we boarded her the whole nightmare of the past few days vanished and we felt safe, at home. The Munich Conference was on—Czechoslovakia was betrayed by her allies, Hitler marched in, and World War II was postponed for another year.

It had been an extremely strenuous summer and I was very tired. I had conducted a travel seminar through the USSR, had visited eleven countries, and sailing home I decided that the following summer I would keep very quiet. For six consecutive years we had rented a lovely chalet on the Lake of Lucerne, in Kastanienbaum, and I thought that I would spend the next summer reading, writing, and fishing there. When I came to my office in Baltimore I found a huge pile of letters and the first I opened was an invitation to be South African Universities Lecturer for 1939. This was an invitation I could not possibly refuse as it gave me an opportunity to study the social-economic structure and the medical services of a semi-colonial country. And so I bought a pile of books on South Africa and spent the winter studying its history, reading its statistics, and getting prepared for a grand lecture tour. My friends thought that I was mad, that I was running into the war. Of course I knew that war might break out at any time. I had known it for the last ten years, but nobody could predict the exact date and in the meantime we had to continue acting as though conditions were normal.

Next summer I left New York on the *Normandie,* spent five beautiful days in Paris. The hotel for the first time had posters indicating the next shelter in case of air alarm. On June 9, 1939, I left the city of my birth and love, and was not to see it again for seven long years.

EDUCATION IN ZURICH

In 1901 I completed four years of preparatory school, and if we had stayed in Paris I would have entered the *lycée* in the autumn. It would in all probability have been the Ecole Alsatienne, the Protestant *lycée* of Paris, which was attended by many Swiss and had such famous graduates as André Gide. Our life, however, took a sudden turn through the fatal illness of my father. He was taken ill in the autumn of 1900. He had worries with his company. People he had trusted

had misused his confidence. A law suit had resulted which he won with
flying flags a few months before his death. But these worries weighed
heavily on his mind, and his condition turned out to be cancer of the
stomach. He did not want to see us stranded in a foreign country and
since his ties with his company had been severed anyway, we moved to
Switzerland and settled in Zurich, my mother's home town.

We lived in a large, comfortable flat in a newly built house on the
shore of the Lake with a superb view of the mountains and next to the
Municipal Theatre. There, after much suffering, my father died in the
early summer of 1901 at the age of forty-two. I was ten years old, my
sister seven, my mother was in her middle thirties. A child of ten has
no judgment of a parent and I think I knew my father very little, but
I remember him as a righteous and very kind man, hard working,
very generous, and very good to his employees. From remarks my
mother made I gather that he was perhaps too much open to flattery and
inclined to trust people more than they deserved. He was much attached to
his family and home town, Schaffhausen, donated money to the town and
had a house built which he presented to his sister. He left us well provided
for so that I had the enormous privilege of being able to study what
I wanted, and as long as I wanted, without having to look for an
immediate job. It sounds paradoxical, but I think it is much more
important to have some money when you are young than when you
are old. The only capital on which you can rely through life is the
education you get in the home, in school, in the theatre, traveling, and
in general in intercourse with your fellow men. If you can acquire this
without financial worries and without having to waste time doing odd
jobs it is a tremendous asset to you. Later, when you are old you can
reduce your material needs considerably and by then you have acquired
a philosophy which lets you look at life very detachedly.

My first recollections of Zurich, once we had settled there, were of deep
humiliations. I was ten years old, to be sure, but I was and felt a
Parisian. I was used to being called *monsieur,* and when I went out
I wore a bowler hat and kid gloves and had a cane with a silver handle—
fashionable in Paris, but apparently not in Zurich. Whenever I went
out alone boys would crowd behind me, laugh at me, call me insulting
names, and throw stones at my beautiful bowler hat. In the stores
nobody called me *monsieur,* but sales girls looking down on me
would ask: "What do you want, *chline,*" which in Swiss German
corresponds to "kiddo" in American. I could have cried at this lack
of respect, and finally I persuaded my mother to buy me the clothes that
the boys in Zurich wore so that I might look like a native. She did it reluc-
tantly and always preferred to have my clothes made in England.

My language was French. I understood and spoke some Swiss German
dialect, but not High German. With my sister I spoke French for many
years. Our French maid had come with us to Zurich. My mother very
wisely decided to send us to a private school where we would learn

good High German, and we went to the best school a child could possibly have anywhere in Europe at the beginning of this century—the von Beustsche Privatschule. Dr. Fritz von Beust was an educator of genius. His father, a Prussian, had come to Switzerland as a refugee after one of the abortive German revolutions in which he had been deeply involved. He opened a private school which his son continued and developed.

Switzerland in those days was a haven for political refugees. The University of Zurich, founded in 1833, was a stronghold of liberalism and did not hesitate to offer some of its most important chairs to Germans who were persecuted at home for political reasons. Whoever had trouble abroad because he was a democrat, or a socialist, or an anarchist in the autocratic states, looked to Switzerland, particularly to Zurich and Geneva. Plekhanov, the theorist of Russian Marxism, was residing—I almost said was holding court—in Geneva, surrounded by Russian refugees to whom his words were pure gold. In Zurich, if you stroll through one of the older sections of town you find two neighboring houses in the Spiegelgasse, simple working-class houses. The ground floors of both of them are taverns today. One has an inscription which says that in this house lived and died Georg Büchner, a revolutionary, biologist, and great poet whose works, *Dantons Tod, Leonee und Lena,* and *Wozzeck* are still performed today; some of them have been set to music. He had taken an active part in the struggles that took place in Hessia in 1834, had written a socialist pamphlet, *Der Hessische Landbote* with the motto "Peace to the huts, death to the palaces," whereupon he had to flee. Zurich gave him not only asylum but an opportunity to teach biology at the University. But he died at the age of twenty-three.

The house next door has a marble plate which says that in this house Lenin lived from 1916 to 1917. Here he had a room in a cobbler's flat, here he wrote his *Letters from Afar* in which he commented on the events of World War I and paved the way for the Revolution. He kept away from Swiss socialists as much as he could because he knew well enough that he would soon be needed in a much larger theatre. He never missed an opportunity to learn. One of my uncles had a maid from the French part of Switzerland who once by chance met a Russian by name of Ulyanov, Lenin's family name. He liked the girl and was anxious to practice his French with her. So on Sundays he used to take her on long walks in the lovely hillsides that surround the city of Zurich. I do not know what they talked about, but I am sure that it was not the Revolution. He used to write her postcards and short notes to inquire whether she was free, and years later I tried to trace the girl in order to find out whether she still had some of these Lenin autographs which I wanted to present to the Marx-Engels-Lenin Institute in Moscow. I failed to find the girl and she probably would not have kept these notes as the name Ulyanov was not more to her than the memory of a foreigner who was kind to her. From this house Lenin went to Russia in the historic sealed car. The Secretary of the Swiss Socialist Party, Fritz Platter, had made the arrangements with the German government.

Years later I spent several evenings with him in Moscow and we recalled and discussed the heroic days of 1917. The German generals thought that with Lenin in Petrograd the war on the Eastern Front would end sooner than without him. It did, but the German generals had not anticipated that not much later the German soldiers would revolt also, would beat up their own officers and tear the epaulettes from their shoulders. Generals are the poorest statesmen in the world. They grow up in military academies where they learn to obey orders and to give orders without asking questions. They are told what conditions in the world are and are expected to believe it. Today, moreover, most of them are narrow specialists, one for heavy artillery, another for tanks, a third one for anti-aircraft guns. It is no wonder that these men fail whenever they are given an embassy or some other important government position.

In 1935 I went to Russia for the first time and in Leningrad was shown the house of the dancer Kshezhinskaya where Lenin took up residence and from the balcony of which he addressed the crowd for the first time. When he arrived in the sealed car he was received enthusiastically with flowers, was brought to his residence in triumph, was asked to speak and everybody expected to be thanked and congratulated for having carried out the February Revolution so successfully. But Lenin on the contrary scolded them for having made the wrong type of revolution. "Peace, Land to the Farmers, All Power to the Soviets" became the new programme of action and we all know what happened thereafter.

And so in Zurich two modest houses recall the memory of two revolutionaries, almost a century apart, and since they both have taverns on the ground floor you may first drink a glass of beer in honor of Büchner, then a second one next door in honor of Lenin. These two modest houses to me are at the same time a great monument to the liberalism and tolerance that prevailed in Switzerland until after World War I.

The University of Zurich was the first Western European university that admitted women as medical students. The story is interesting enough to be recalled here. These first girl students came from Russia. Under pressure of the strong liberal movement that swept the country in the eighteen sixties, women were admitted to higher secondary schools in St. Petersburg. Once they graduated they wished to enter the university and particularly to study medicine as this was the best way to get close to the people. The only medical school in St. Petersburg, however, was the Military Medical Academy. In spite of the military character of the school a group of women was admitted but a few years later the political tide turned. Years of dark reaction followed and the women medical students had to leave the Academy before having completed their studies.

Looking for a place where they might be permitted to do this they looked to Switzerland, particularly to Zurich. The University there was a state university and so they approached the government asking whether they might be admitted to study medicine. There had been no women in medicine in Zurich before, but the government was a liberal one and had no objection. It was only afraid of the faculty. Would the professors be willing to teach men and women together? The nineteenth century was still a puritan age, or rather, bourgeois morals might be rotten but an effort was made to maintain a decent façade. The faculty had no objection either but passed the buck to the students. Would they be willing to study medicine together with women? They were, and so one day a group of Russian girls arrived, with bobbed hair, smoking cigarettes, and from then until 1917 Zurich always had a number of Russian medical students, women, socialists, revolutionaries. I knew quite a few of them in my student days. Most of them were impecunious and hard working. They might be materialists philosophically but were great practical idealists, ready to sacrifice themselves for the benefit of their people and I always had a great respect for them, their life was so hard compared to ours.

I know that America admitted women to medical schools earlier, but the number of women admitted is still limited today. There is still discrimination against them in hospitals and in other appointments. The number of women physicians hardly ever exceeds 10 per cent, while it is up to 50 per cent in the USSR. The ministers of health of India, China, and the Soviet Union are women today (1954), and these three women are responsible for the health and welfare of over one billion people.

Until World War I Switzerland was a haven for political refugees. It still was all through the war. As a student I used to go to the Café Odéon almost every day. The European *café* is not a pub, not a drinking place, but one where you go to read the newspapers of many lands and technical journals, where you write a letter while you are sipping a cup of coffee that costs you a few cents. At the Odéon during the war, Frank Wedekind, the German dramatist, could be seen almost daily as well as James Joyce, Ferruccio Busoni, and other famous refugees. In another *café* not far away the Dada movement was initiated at that time.

Switzerland's liberalism and tolerance in the nineteenth and early twentieth centuries are some of the most glorious pages of its history, all the more so since conditions have changed radically today. Before World War I the old democratic countries felt strong and safe. The socialists were noisy, but harmless and a handful of foreign anarchists were not considered a threat to the security of the state. Most Western countries were prosperous. There were minor economic crises to be sure, and from time to time a bank failed, but these were normal occurrences in the process of the concentration of capital. In the decades before 1914 the world seemed pretty stable, and my father used to say that one should never spend more than 50 per cent of one's income, the other half should be invested for the benefit of the family. Today after two world wars, after revolutions and an economic crisis that shook the world, no country feels secure and fear breeds intolerance. Citizens are spied upon and persecuted in many lands, not for religious but for political or economic heresies, and heretics have a hard time finding any asylum such as Switzerland was in the past.

The von Beustsche Privatschule where I was to spend three years was small but had a very international student body. We had come from Paris and my sister and I spoke French together. The children of Friedrich Erismann spoke Russian together. Erismann was one of the great pioneers of public health. A Swiss by birth, he had a brilliant career in Russia, in St. Petersburg and in Moscow, where he held the first Russian chair of hygiene at the University of Moscow until he got involved in some revolutionary activities with the students. He had to leave Russia and came back to Zurich where he held various positions in the health and educational administration of the city. Other children spoke Spanish or Italian, but Dr. von Beust saw to it that we learned good High German. I have only pleasant reminiscences of my classmates with one exception, a thoroughly vicious boy, the only really vicious child I have ever encountered. He was mean and debased in all his actions. When we had a snowball fight he put stones into his balls and he liked to torture his classmates. I was his favorite victim for some time. We had lost our father, were very sad about it, were in mourning. Whenever he saw me alone he would come crawling, put on a big smile and say: "Sigi's father has died!" Whereupon he laughed madly. Of course it hurt terribly. I should have hit him in the face, but I always had a horror of violence and would rather suffer than hit back. He seemed the incarnation of all that is evil, poor lad, and what he needed was psychiatric treatment, but a few months after I entered school he was expelled from it.

Dr. von Beust was an enthusiastic scientist, a botanist by training, and an atheist as many scientists were in those days. There were no prayers in his school, no religious instruction. His very correct idea was that religion was a matter of the family, not of the school. I do not know if the term "progressive education" existed in those days, but I know that my education from 1901 to 1904 was infinitely more progressive than that of my children thirty years later. We had no home work; classes met in the morning and on four afternoons, and Dr. von Beust thought this was quite enough and that the rest of the day should be free for recreation. We worked more intensively in school, and instruction was always combined with manual work. Science, and particularly botany, had a central place in the curriculum; we all had herbariums and at the age of twelve we were expected to be able to diagnose a plant to the family. This was not meant to burden us with names, but to teach us to observe nature; is not the *saper vedere* of Leonardo, "to know how to see things,"

41

essential not only in science but in life in general? Dr. von Beust's enthusiasm was contagious and through him we not only learned to see nature, but to love it, to have a personal relation to it, feeling that we are in nature, a part of it. I did not become a botanist, but I have rarely lived without flowers and I still prefer not to eat than to eat at a table without flowers on it. This is not a question of luxury as a simple daisy or scabiosa from the fields will do. I hate the mass slaughter of flowers so common in our countries, the bunches of two or three dozen carnations, the armful of Canterbury bells. We can learn a great deal from the Chinese and Japanese in this respect and I fully agree with them that one or two flowers in a good vase or bowl are infinitely more beautiful than huge bunches. I also agree with them that when a flower has died it should not be thrown on the rubbish pile with potato peels, but should be buried or entrusted to the river. Here in Pura, all through the year, I have my flower grave where flowers go back to the earth from which they came. Looking back I think that my love and respect for flowers originated in my early school days.

Geography was also taught in a way that was different from that of other schools. Switzerland is a mountainous country; we all had jig-saws and cut out altitude layers of cardboard, pasted them on top of one another, poured wax of different colors over them and thus got beautiful relief maps of various regions of the country. In geometry we made cubes, cylinders, cones and other bodies the contents of which we had to calculate. In order to demonstrate that the earth was moving in an ellipse we made a sun dial in the garden consisting of a pole and bricks that marked the hours. After a while we noticed that the bricks were no longer at the right place.

Today's reader will think that these methods of education are obvious because most elementary schools adopted them in the course of time, but they were far from obvious in 1901, and coming from Paris where education was most formalistic and knowledge was squeezed into you from books, we loved our new school, were deeply attached to Dr. von Beust and called ourselves proudly Beustianers. Today still, after fifty years, when old classmates meet incidentally, we fondly recall our school and the memory of our teacher. When he died the school was continued by the staff for a while, but the driving spirit was no longer there and after a few years the school closed. I owe a great deal to this school where I learned to love and observe nature, where I learned not only to read books—I was doing this passionately anyway—but also to work with my hands.

I left school in the spring of 1904 and entered secondary school, which as a Greek reminiscence was called a Gymnasium. There was little gymnastics involved, only a few hours a week and we hated it. Switzerland, like most European countries, had different types of high schools: an ordinary secondary school of from two to four years; a humanistic Gymnasium with emphasis on classical studies with six and a half years of Latin and five and a half years of Greek; a division of the Gymnasium with Latin but without Greek and more modern languages; an industrial school where mathematics was particularly emphasized; and a school of business economics. I know that America is strongly opposed to having specialized secondary schools for fear that they may train an undemocratic *élite*. I thoroughly disagree. These schools are open to all free of charge except for a registration fee and even that may be waived. And there are a number of subjects that one never learns unless one starts early. It is almost impossible to learn Latin well unless one begins at the age of ten or twelve. In my own profession I must read Latin books of up to five hundred pages all the time and also Greek books, and this I could never do unless I had the solid foundation that my old Gymnasium gave me.

But learning Greek and Latin is not primarily a question of languages. These are merely keys to the civilizations of Greece and Rome, the foundations of our Western world. I know that one can read the ancient classics in translation but what a difference between Homer in Greek and Homer in English. I never travel in the Mediterranean without having my old school edition of the Odyssey with me. Nobody has ever depicted the infinite charm of the Mediterranean better than Homer or whoever the poet was. We see the sea that has the color of violets with the white foam from which Aphrodite was born, with dolphins playing around the ship, and if we listen sharply we may hear the song of the Sirens—maybe as Debussy wrote it down. There are still witches like Circe on Mediterranean islands and sweet maidens like Nausicaa who will be friendly to a stranded foreigner. The Cyclops, I think, have disappeared and this reminds me of my professor of Greek, who was very interested in physics and explained to his class that Polyphemus, when he threw a rock at the ship of Odysseus, missed it because he had only one eye and therefore had no perception of depth. A student, thereupon, drew the attention of the professor to the fact that Polyphemus not only had just one eye, but that this one eye had been destroyed by Odysseus, so that he was completely blind. The professor yelled: "Sit down, you ass, *das kommt dann noch dazu*—this was an additional factor."

In the nineteenth century and at the beginning of our century many people in Europe and America had this same type of classical education. This created a common ground on which people met and understood one another. When I made a study of the beginnings of social insurance in Germany in the eighteen eighties, I had to read volumes of minutes of the meetings of the German Reichstag and was amazed to see on what a high level the discussions were carried on. Conservatives, liberals, and socialists argued while quoting Plato and Aristotle. At international diplomatic conferences the participants were always courteous because they all had a common educational background. Today they have nothing in common. They insult one another, their manners are bad, their speech vulgar—with exceptions, of course—and the result is poor politics.

Classical studies fascinated me, particularly Greek, and every day I got up one hour earlier than necessary to review my Greek and read books on the subjects we studied, and this was very early because in the summer classes began at seven in the morning. I devoured the books of Fustel de Coulange, Gaston Boissier, Camille Jullian, and many others. For many months I read the biographies of Plutarch while having breakfast, and my copy still has stains of egg and marmalade on it. At the age of twelve I saved money for a long time until I had the then formidable amount of sixteen francs with which I bought a beautifully illustrated book on Greek culture that was very popular at that time. I studied it very thoroughly, made profuse notes from it; it is in front of me now and I still consult it occasionally. At fourteen I planned to read the entire ancient literature preserved, in the original if possible, or otherwise in translation. It was a boy's dream and I, of course, did not succeed in reading every line, particularly as other interests interfered a few years later, but I managed to read a great deal. This was made easy because Greek and Roman classics could be bought for a few cents in Reclams Universal Bibliothek, in a most convenient pocket size format, so that you could always have a volume with you. Some were available in slot machines in railway stations. Thus at a tender age a world opened itself to me, fascinating and alluring, colorful and dramatic, Greece and Rome, Homer and Hesiod, Plato and Aristotle, Herodotus and Thucydides, the Roman poets, great figures—Alexander, Caesar, Augustus, and Marcus Aurelius, And I saw their everyday life reading the letters of Cicero, Pliny, and Seneca.

I was also fascinated by the conflict between Christianity and the state to which Boissier's *La fin du paganisme* was an ideal introduction. I read the Church Fathers and the extraordinarily interesting letters of Emperor Julian. The parallel with our own times is striking. Christianity came into the world as a religion which found its strongest appeal with the down-trodden and poor since it promised equality and a better life. It was a highly subversive doctrine in that it attacked the very foundation of the state, the divinity of the Emperor, and was opposed to all aspects of the Roman way of life.

I was a bookworm and my mother often worried about it. Even in the summer holidays which we regularly spent in the mountains, I took piles of books and my Greek grammar along. My mother insisted on physical exercise. I played tennis with great pleasure and I particularly liked fencing. We had an Italian fencing master in Zurich and for many years I went several times a week to practice fencing with a floret. A motley crowd was there: a Venetian count; a Swiss officer who intended to challenge a fellow officer, who had insulted him, to a duel and wanted to cut him up. But first of all there was a son of Gabriele d'Annunzio, the great Italian poet. I think the son was studying engineering at the Federal Institute of Technology, but to all of us he was *figlio del poeta,* son of the poet. These were still the days when in most European countries the poet was at the top of society. Nobody was more deeply respected and even worshipped than Gerhard Hauptmann or Stefan George in Germany, Paul Valéry in France, Verhaeren in Belgium, d'Annunzio in Italy. They might be dark as Mallarmé had been, drunkards like Paul Verlaine, or might have moral defects, but they were poets, men who had the great gift to express in words what we feel, our joys and sorrows, our hopes and fears. In their poems we find ourselves and we are grateful to them for saying what we feel. I remember that in my student days an American was asking a European student what he considered America's greatest contribution to civilization. The immediate answer was Walt Whitman's poems. And this is still the true answer today, for Whitman's poems will survive all the machines America has ever produced and will continue to stir and elate people all over the world.

After fencing I took up horseback riding, but I never really had time for sports. Books were my passion, and to get me away from books at least for a few weeks every year my mother took us on a trip during the spring vacation. We went to France, to Germany, Belgium, and more and more often to Italy. Going to Italy was not just an ordinary voyage, it was treading on classical soil, was to us what entering the Holy Land was to the medieval pilgrim. The journey was easy enough with the St. Gotthard railway. It was much longer than today, but still much too fast. I envied Goethe's slow traveling on horseback. Like him we felt the nostalgia for

> *das Land, wo die Citronen blühn,*
> *Im dunklen Laub die Gold-Orangen glühn.*

But we did not experience the terror of the Devil's Bridge, and instead of seeing an old breed of dragons in caves, we were welcomed at the entrance to the tunnel in Göschenen by Ernest Zahn, a poet famous for his novels of peasant life who at the same time was manager of the station restaurant. The train stopped for half an hour, the *table d'hôte* was set, and after a hearty meal one went back to the train and entered the tunnel. The line is electrified today and you pass the tunnel in twelve minutes. Formerly it took much longer and this was a period of great tension. You had left the Germanic lands and on the other side was Italy and the south, Switzerland still for a while, but Italian Switzerland, the country's beautiful balcony that looks to the south. And indeed here it was all of a sudden, Airolo, a deep blue sky, some wooden structures still in Alpine style, but also stone houses, pink and blue and yellow, and palm trees, and the deeper the train went down the valley, the Leventina, into the plain, the richer the vegetation became, the milder the air, the more colorful the houses which often surrounded a small Romanesque church. It was overwhelming, this transition from one world into another and still is to me today although I cross the St. Gotthard at least a dozen times a year. And when the first camellias bloom in my garden I feel the same emotion that I used to feel as a child when during the spring vacation we entered Italy.

Traveling has lost much of its charm today as it is far too quick. The transition from one world to another, from one landscape into another is too abrupt to be fully realized and enjoyed. We travel more often than people did before there were railways, but we see and experience less. Formerly people prepared for a trip sometimes for years and perhaps even learned the language of the country they intended to visit. Then they took time off, months, a year, or even more, kept diaries, visited with people in the foreign lands, and such a journey was an inspiration for life. There were hazards to be sure, coaches broke down, horses ran wild, and there were bandits, but I am sure that the fiercest bandits of Terracina were harmless compared to the reckless drivers who infest our roads. Today we lock our desk, take an airplane, and a few hours or a day later we find ourselves in Greece, Egypt, or India. I myself fly whenever I have a chance, have done so ever since World War I and have covered tens of thousands of miles in the air on four continents, but I am aware that flying is not traveling. It is transportation, is like being thrown into a letterbox with a tag and being delivered at the other end.

Italy was one of the great experiences of my boyhood, not only because it was classical land, the country whose literature I was studying every day and whose monuments were overwhelming even in ruins, but also because we had a history teacher who evoked a warm enthusiasm for Italy in all of us—Otto Markwart. A thick-set short man, with a goatee, who always wore heavy boots and a cape, he had been a student of Jakob Burckhardt, that great humanist, and the spirit of the master was alive in the disciple who was able to convey to us some of its sparks. Markwart was a bachelor and one might have thought that he was married to Italy, for Italy was his everlasting love. He spent every vacation there, spoke Italian like a native and collected an endless number of photographs that he had carefully mounted on cardboard and showed to his students on every opportunity. He also saw to it that our classroom had good large photographs of classical sites on the wall, so that the Forum Romanum and the temples of Paestum were as familiar to us as the monuments of Zurich. His teaching was most inspiring. Discussing a stormy session of the Roman Senate he jumped up addressing the class: "You are the Roman Senate. What are you going to do? You have defeated Carthage but again she raises her head threateningly. You there in the corner are Cato. Get up and tell them what they shall do" And the boy, Cato himself, addressed the Senate passionately, ending his harangue with the ominous *Ceterum censeo*.

From Markwart I learned that history is not a dead subject but a living force that determines our life. He taught us to think in terms of historic forces and developments. In his broad approach to history that embraced all aspects of civilization he passed on to us boys the teachings of his master, Jakob Burckhardt, whose works we devoured.

I also owe it to Markwart that I learned Italian at an early age. French, being the second national language of Switzerland, was a compulsory subject in our school for many years, but since it was my mother tongue I was exempt from attending classes for the first few years. Then came the choice between English and Italian and as I could easily persuade my mother to let my sister and me learn English at home with a private tutor, I took Italian in school and made quick progress. Today I speak four languages every day without being aware what language I am talking at the moment—German with my wife, English with my secretary and my daughters when they are at home, Italian with the maid and the villagers, French with the neighbors and many visitors. I read Spanish without any difficulty and Russian with little difficulty. I mention this not in order to boast but to show that knowledge of languages is nothing unusual on the Continent. My present secretary is British and her main language obviously is English, but she speaks German, French, Italian, and Czech fluently. The secretary I had before was a citizen of Israel, educated in England, a graduate of the School of Interpreters of the University of Geneva. Her main language was English which she spoke with a broad Bloomsbury accent. But in addition she had a perfect command of German, French, Spanish, Italian, Hebrew, and Arabic, and I could dictate letters to her in any language without even mentioning what language was coming.

A command of foreign languages is not only convenient in everyday life and when you travel in that it makes human contacts more easy, but it opens up the literature of many lands for you. I read newspapers in five languages and feel better informed on world affairs here in a small village than I ever was in America. And the great literature of many countries is available to me without the unavoidable distortion that every translation necessarily involves.

My dream was to see Greece but I had to wait many years before it became true. In 1931 my book *Einführung in die Medizin* was published, which was to be translated within a few years into seven languages including Chinese. When it came out I received a considerable royalty and I immediately told my wife that we should not have this money sink into household expenses, but should invest it in some great experience such as a journey to Greece. She immediately agreed. The International Congress of the History of Medicine was held at Rome that year. I had to attend it and was to meet my wife at Ancona from where we were to sail to the Piraeus on an Italian steamer. The Congress was brilliant. Mussolini was to open it but instead opened a sports assembly, football or whatever it was, at the Forum named after him. The Congress sent him a telegram, and the following day we were called into a room to listen to the answer received. It wished success to the Congress which once more would demonstrate the superiority of Italian science. Everybody applauded wildly except me and a few Scandinavian colleagues who found the telegram rather tactless. On a Saturday evening I went to Ancona where I enjoyed the excellent dry white wine of the region called Verdicchio. Sunday morning my wife arrived from Germany and our ship, the *Praga* of the Lloyd Triestino, a freighter that took a dozen passengers, was to sail for the Piraeus. My wife told me incidentally that her train had been late at the border station so that her trunk could not pass the customs, and had been sealed and would have to be inspected here in Ancona. We took a taxi and went to the customs house which we found completely deserted. After hunting around a long time we found a watchman soundly asleep. I woke him up as tactfully as I could by tickling his nose with a straw. When he shot up I put a coin in his hand to apologize for the disturbance and told him that we had a sealed trunk here that we needed as we were sailing for Greece in a few hours. He explained very politely that the customs house was closed on Sundays but that we certainly would get the trunk without difficulty the following morning. With a second coin I asked him what he would advise us to do. He had no suggestion to make and repeated that there was not a single custom's officer around. Of course I did not give up so easily and after a third coin he thought that the only possibility was to see the Director of Customs in person. Of course he would be very angry to be disturbed on a Sunday but, he added, it is your business to pacify him. I was not sure what he meant by this but decided I would try with rhetoric. We drove to the very handsome villa of the Director. I had my visiting card which stated that I was Professor of the History of Medicine at the University of Leipzig and asked to see the Director in a personal matter just for a second. He came after a while, I bowed deeply and my wife smiled enchantingly. Then I addressed him in best Italian:

"Sir, I have come from the mists of the North seeking the sun and the glories of Italy. You are a descendant of the Romans who have brought civilization and the vine, that noblest of all plants, to our barbarian regions. You are a descendant of the great humanists of the Renaissance, our constant source of inspiration, a humanist yourself as I have been told." This I made up on the spur of the moment. "Just a few days ago I had the honor of shaking hands with your great Duce in Rome." I had not but I might have and from that moment on the Director was interested. "It was on the occasion of a brilliant international gathering which revealed once more the superiority of Italian science. And now, Sir, I am on my way to Greece, the mother of us all, the cradle of our Western civilization. Our ship, a vessel of your glorious merchant marine, sails in one hour, and we have a miserable little trunk sealed in your customs house without which we cannot sail as it contains my wife's clothes."

"Ah," he said, "but the customs house is closed on Sundays."

"I know, Sir, and this is why I am here disturbing you. I came to Ancona yesterday, admired the beauty of your city, was amazed at the tremendous development your port has made in recent years. If you continue like this you will soon surpass all other Italian ports. Surely a man like you must be able to release the trunk of a lady on her way to the Parthenon, even on a Sunday."

"Have you a car?" he asked.

I had a taxi, had had it for hours and the meter was reaching astronomic figures.

"Let us see your trunk!" We drove to the customs house. The watchman had not gone back to sleep yet. He opened a door and here was our trunk, a nice cabin trunk, duly sealed.

"Have you a knife?" the Director asked. I had one and with an elegant gesture he cut off the seal and said: "Ecco, from one humanist to another. I certainly would not deprive Madam of her clothing. And now, *buon viaggio!*" We shook hands, were half an hour later on board ship and soon the whistles blew.

The voyage was delightful. The ship crawled. I do not know how many knots she made, but it cannot have been many as the trip took several days. I have crossed the Atlantic sixteen times, on the *Queen Mary,* the *Normandie,* and other fast ships, but the sea voyages I remember with greatest pleasure are the slow trips on small boats, one from Cape Town to New York in 23 days, trips from London to Leningrad on small but most comfortable Soviet ships, and this one on the *Praga.* Life on board was most informal. The officers were Triestini who had served with the Austrian Lloyd and spoke German with a broad Austrian accent. You could spend half the night on the bridge looking at the stars and at the Greek islands, at the home of Odysseus. We spent an entire day at Aigion, a small town on the northern shore of the Peloponnesus. We wondered why, but the explanation was very simple. Our main cargo was wood pulp that was shipped from Sweden to Greece where wages are low. There it was worked into paper which then was sent to Sweden. It sounds silly, but this is the way a capitalist economy works. Then came the Canal of Corinth. Our small vessel had no trouble passing it, although it is very narrow. But when we sailed back on a larger steamer, the *Stella d'Italia,* it seemed that the distance between ship and rock was only a few inches on each side, and the officers were decidedly nervous although the main responsibility was with the pilot.

And then we reached the Piraeus, we saw the Acropolis, all of a sudden. We were in Greece, in Attica, the mother of us all and were to spend a few weeks delving into the past but also enjoying the colorful oriental life around us. Athens was still full of refugees from Smyrna and at night, in the suburbs, you heard as many Turkish as Greek songs. When Greece suffered that terrible defeat at Smyrna in 1922, public opinion turned violently against the government and the members of the

Cabinet were simply lined up and shot. Nobody cared much about it because, after all, a few politicians more or less, what difference does it make? But world public opinion was outraged because one of the Cabinet members was shot while he was suffering from typhoid fever, and this was against the rules. A sick man must be cured first and then shot. One of my colleagues owed his life to this preferential position granted to the sick man in society. He was a member of the old Hungarian aristocracy, was arrested at the time of the Revolution and was to be hanged, but this was while the influenza epidemic of 1918 was raging and he was very sick, suffering from pneumonia in both lungs. So he was not hanged but sent to a hospital first to be cured before he could be hanged. By the time he had recovered the Revolution was over, and he lived merrily for many years thereafter.

This is obviously not the place to describe a Greek journey as this would require a whole book and has been done so many times before. But the reader will believe me when I say that it was an overwhelming experience. For years and years I had read the great classics of Greece; I had imagined the Greeks debating on the Agora, the market place of Athens, or walking in ceremonial procession to the Acropolis, or listening to a new drama by one of the great tragic poets in the theatre of Dionysus. And here I was, all of a sudden, on the Agora, on the Acropolis at sunset when I not only saw the pillars of the Parthenon but could touch the Pentelic marble which to the hand feels like old ivory; I sat in the marble chair reserved for the priest of Asclepius in the theatre of Dionysus; I saw the sun set through the temple of Poseidon on Cap Sunion.

The first impression of Attica is one of smallness. Countries that have given the world so much inspiration for thousands of years seem large in our imagination, yet the inhabited part of Egypt with its giant monuments was never larger than the territory of Belgium, and Attica was smaller than a small American state. I have a visual mind, I like to see things. The moment I see a landscape I understand what happened in it. One understands the great collective efforts of Egypt the moment one sees the Nile and a landscape drawn in broad lines with deserts east and west. And one understands Greek individualism and particularism seeing the small valleys, the rivers and brooks, dry in the summer, torrents in the spring draining the water into lovely creeks. One of my old friends, a most distinguished Hellenist, has never been in Greece, has never felt the desire to see the country of the ancient civilization to which he has devoted his life work. To him ancient Greece is fully alive. He sees it, lives in it, and does not want to see ruins surrounded by the squalor of modern slums, or the pretentiousness of modern villas. But I feel that I can write much better about Epidaurus once I have seen the valley with the holy precinct of Asclepius' temple which attracted thousands of pilgrims for centuries. I can write better about an oriental town when I remember its noises and smells.

The classical education my old Gymnasium gave me became the

foundation upon which I built my whole life, and the Greek and Roman classics remained a constant source of inspiration and happiness. Even today I hardly ever travel without having the poems of Horace in my pocket, and winter weeks in England would be unbearably cold—in the houses—without the *Bucolica* of Vergil which recreate warm Italian days far gone. This reminds me of a delightful experience I once had in Baltimore. It was at the time of the Spanish war. I was organizing a local committee for medical aid to Spain and was enlisting the interest of some of my colleagues whom I knew to have strong democratic convictions and who understood that the defeat of Republican Spain would invariably lead to Hitlerite aggression. I made an appointment to see our Professor of Pediatrics, Edwards A. Park, went to his office; the secretary asked me to wait a moment as the professor was seeing a patient. I sat down in a comfortable armchair next to which I found a beautifully bound old edition of Horace. I opened it at random; it was spring, and there it was:

> *Solvitur acris hiems grata vice veris et Favoni*
> *Trahuntque siccas machinae carinas*

It happened to be a poem that I knew by heart, the book dropped out of my hand and I kept reciting:

> *Nunc decet aut viridi nitidum caput impedire myrto*
> *Aut flore, terrae quem ferunt solutae;*

"Of course I do, who would not?"

The professor had come and had patiently listened to my mumbling verses. For an hour we discussed Horace and I almost forgot the purpose of my visit. When I told him about the Spanish War and the consequences it would have for the rest of the world including America, he said: "Look here, I know nothing about politics, but if you think I should be on the committee feel free to use my name." Park was one of the most delightful persons I ever met in America. A great pediatrician, a great scientist, he was at the same time a true humanist and, above all, an *anima candida*, a kindly warm-hearted individual who radiated friendliness and whom nobody could help loving.

Although I was in the humanistic division of the Gymnasium, mathematics and science were by no means neglected. We had mathematics and geometry throughout six and a half years, and we had excellent instruction in science. Zoology was taught by a student of Haeckel, botany by a student of Schinz who was the Professor of Botany at the University and the father of a classmate. We had excellent instruction in chemistry by a student of the Nobel prize winner Alfred Werner, and our instruction in physics imparted sufficient knowledge to us so that we passed the subject easily in medical school. This shows that it is possible to combine instruction in mathematics and the sciences with seven hours of Greek for five and a half years, and seven hours of Latin for six and a half years, but of course we worked harder and longer hours than American students do.

Every one of us had a hobby. Hans Schinz was a great botanist and at a tender age had a herbarium which covered the four walls of his room. He sold it later when he was in need of money—a chronic condition with him—and when he decided to go in for radiology. Hans Bodmer was a musician who later acquired the best collection of Beethoven manuscripts and studied medicine, although he did not practice the profession. Kittelmann was an ace stenographer who won many prizes, later became a lawyer, but whenever there was a session of parliament he was called to do the minutes in shorthand.

My hobby was the study of Arabic. Through my classical studies I became interested in the history of ancient Egypt and Mesopotamia and in the Orient at large. At the age of sixteen I walked into a bookshop and asked for an Arabic grammar. The book dealers said they had none in stock but would gladly order me one. I had no idea which grammar to get, but then I ordered the one by Harder that had a key to translate the exercises, and from then on I devoted my early morning hour to the study of Arabic. When the boys who were going into theology had to take Hebrew in the Gymnasium, I asked Professor Hausheer for the permission to join the group. He inquired why I wanted to learn Hebrew and I answered simply that I was studying Arabic. Later I entered the University to read the Koran with the commentary by Baidawi, and the Book of Judges in Hebrew.

II

Biographical
Papers

1910-1931

Although Sigerist's autobiography comes to a sudden stop with the incomplete chapter on his school days in Zurich, enough material exists in some of his published papers and in his extensive diaries for an account, in his own words, of the events of his life.

The inevitable and often difficult problem of choosing a profession was not an easy matter for Sigerist who, in 1910, took the Maturität and graduated from the Literaturgymnasium in Zurich. Even after entering the University of Zurich, his vacillations between the humanities and science were not easily resolved until one day it came to him that his broad humanistic background could best be combined with science in a relatively new and unknown field—the history of science and medicine.

The old Gymnasium in Zurich was a great school to which I owe infinitely more than I was aware at the time.[1] It had a great tradition of liberalism and all philosophies were represented among the faculty. It taught us how to organize our work and succeeded in challenging us and arousing our intellectual curiosity so that we could spend whole nights discussing Plato, Kant, Darwin, Haeckel, or Marx, and sometimes almost came to fist fights over problems of Russian literature or modern art. When we graduated at the age of eighteen or nineteen we were well prepared for the university.

After graduation I registered in the Philosophical Faculty of the University of Zurich as a student of oriental philology. I continued my studies of Arabic and Hebrew and took up Sanskrit. And since the latter course proceeded rather slowly I worked with a private tutor and at the end of the year we were reading the Panchatantra and similar texts.

In those days the University of Zurich was rather weak in oriental studies and this determined me to spend most of the year 1911 in London. I had some excellent courses at University College, and since I was the only student attending them learned a great deal. With Mabel Bode I read the Meghaduta and with H. Hirschfeld the Fakhri and

[1] Excerpts from the essay "University education," in *The University at the Crossroads: Addresses and Essays* (New York: Henry Schuman, 1946), pp. 13-19.

the Delectus Veterum Carminum Arabicorum of Noeldeke. At the same time I began the study of Chinese at King's College and devoted a great deal of time to it. My teachers were rather skeptical and repeatedly pointed out to me that it was impossible to embrace the whole Orient, that I would have to specialize either on the Near East, on India, or on the Far East. But I refused to specialize. I was interested in the East as a whole, in comparative religion and comparative literature, in the migration and transmission of literary subjects, and similar problems. And since I was very young I thought that nothing would be impossible to me.

I worked very hard in those years and always had some grammar in my pocket and a notebook full of Chinese ideograms. But the time came when I had to admit that my teachers were right. It could not be done. The task became so big that even physically I could not master it. But I still refused to specialize and since I had always been greatly interested in science I went back to the University of Zurich and took the science courses that were given to students of science as well as to medical students.

There, again, it was my good fortune to have a great teacher, the professor of zoology and comparative anatomy, Arnold Lang. He was a former student of Haeckel, a great expert in zoology of the invertebrates and in genetics. His lectures were entrancing and we never missed a single one. During a course he never attempted to cover the whole field but discussed only a few selected subjects, a few animal forms, elements of genetics or similar topics. These he presented in great detail giving the history of the problem and discussing general principles connected with it. He could spend weeks developing the structure of one animal, drawing it in colored chalks on the blackboard. And when, at long last, he had given the finishing touch his bearded face brightened up and felt like God after the creation of the world. He had recreated the worm, or the fish under our very eyes. And having watched this creative process we could never forget it. We had been allowed a glimpse into the workshop of nature.

At the end of the course he apologized for having covered so little ground but added that we could easily find the rest in books, and that if we had followed him we would be able to consult and use books intelligently. I never had an opportunity to talk to Professor Lang. He did not know of my existence. I was just one of hundreds of students who crowded his lecture hall. But I was tremendously influenced by him because I had the privilege of watching the working of his mind. And from him I learned how to teach. Much later, when I became an academic teacher myself, I remembered how he had presented his subject, built up his lectures and organized his courses. The European university has a great tradition of academic oratory, an art that is not taught in courses but passed on from master to student through example and by the mere force of personality.

56

My year in science was a happy one and for a while I considered remaining in science, but again the phantom of specialization arose. What was it to be: chemistry or zoology or botany? Medicine seemed the broadest field, and so I became a medical student and never regretted it. Medicine undoubtedly is one of the most fascinating academic subjects in that it leads the student through heights and depths of human life.

I studied medicine at the University of Zurich where I graduated in 1917 and at the University of Munich where I spent the summer of 1914. I had many excellent teachers during the six years of my medical course but two of them stand out far above all others: Friedrich von Müller and Ferdinand Sauerbruch. They were very different but great teachers both.

Friedrich von Müller was at the height of his career when I took his course. He was professor of clinical medicine in Munich, a dignified gentleman and a great physician and scientist with vast cultural background. He represented the best type of German professor. His task was to introduce the young student into the field of clinical medicine. Every morning he gave a clinic of two hours at which he presented one typical case. Four students were called upon and with them he examined the patient and discussed the case, while the others watched them with breathless attention. His presentation invariably began with the question: "What do you see, what strikes you when you look at the patient?" whereby he meant to develop our faculty of observation. He repeated over and over again that medicine was not difficult provided we had a thorough foundation in anatomy, physiology, and general patholo- gy. "You must know the structure of the human body, its function and the mechanism available to the organism to react against lesions. The rest boils down to observation and correct reasoning." And this was what we learned from him first of all: to observe phenomena and to reason correctly. I followed his precepts all through my studies and it saved me a lot of trouble. Von Müller's teaching was so impressive that to the present day I remember every individual case he presented during the course and even remember the face of many of the patients. The class- room was crowded with hundreds of students and a regular race for seats took place every morning.

Sauerbruch had an entirely different personality. He came from Marburg to Zurich in 1911 as professor of surgery. He was young, enthusiastic, and temperamental. Students loved him or hated him but nobody who ever came in touch with him remained indifferent. He was an intuitive type of man, a brilliant surgeon who in his surgery as well as in his researches showed a great deal of imagination and origi- nality. His clinic was inspiring and spectacular. Once, desiring to impress upon us the importance of the early operation of appendicitis, he demonstrated over twenty cases in one clinic, some of whom had been sent in for operation too late. Bed after bed was rolled in. The professor

57

hardly said a word but the difference between the patients was striking. All those who had been operated on early looked flourishing while the others looked very sick. It was a piece of showmanship but nobody ever forgot the lesson. Sauerbruch taught us infinitely more than surgery. He made us think—think in terms of biology. A student could pass an examination with him without many facts provided he was able to approach a case intelligently and to think properly. In his early years in Zurich Sauerbruch gave a course in general surgery that was attended by students of all classes, by the faculty and by the practitioners of the city. One had to be there an hour in advance to secure a seat. Every single lecture was a masterpiece, well-rounded, full of original ideas and challenging thoughts. It was certainly not by accident that Sauerbruch, like Müller and all great medical teachers I ever had, was deeply interested in the history of medicine and never missed an opportunity to make historical remarks. Men who made history were always aware of developments in which they were taking part. I was Sauerbruch's student for three years and came closer to him than to most of my medical teachers. He took a genuine interest in young people and kept an open house in which students were always welcomed.

I was an enthusiastic medical student, but remained interested in the humanities. In Zurich, medical school and university were on the same campus so that it was possible for medical students to attend courses in the academic division, which I frequently did. In Munich, once in the middle of the academic year I suddenly felt tired of the hospital and of medicine at large. I began skipping classes and spent the days in museums and art galleries, the nights in theatres and concert halls. I was in a turmoil and when quite accidentally I met a friend in the street who was leaving the same day for Venice I decided to join him, and spent several weeks in Italy. For a while medicine was entirely forgotten and I lived in a world of history and art. Then, one evening, sitting in a café of the Piazza San Marco I felt an irresistible longing for the hospital, and there for the first time it occurred to me that medical history and the history of science might be a field in which I could combine all my interests. I went back to Munich the same night in a state of great elation. The next morning I resumed my hospital work with enthusiasm. In the afternoon I went to the Library where I found *Isis*, the journal recently launched by George Sarton, and the various publications of Karl Sudhoff. In the next few days I made a plan to study the various periods of the history of medicine and science by reading the most important texts. A German publisher was issuing a series of historical source-books that included the history of science and I soon was collecting materials for a history of oxidation. But then the war broke out. We were all called for practical work and the book was never finished.

Here I must recall one school that taught me perhaps just as much as the university, although I was not fully aware of it at the time: the army. I served for nearly two years in the Medical Corps of the Swiss army. In Switzerland every citizen is trained to be a soldier and medical students are automatically enlisted in the Medical Corps at the age of twenty, where they are promoted to higher rank according to their professional status and length of service. At the outbreak of the World War the entire army was mobilized and kept under arms for the first eight months. After that time when it became apparent that the country was not immediately threatened only one-half of the army was kept at the borders so that throughout the war we medical men spent half of the year in army service while we could continue our civilian work during the other half.

The two years in the army were a valuable experience to me in many respects. Medically I learned a great deal. We were often stationed in far remote mountain valleys where we had to attend the civilian population as well as the troops, sometimes under very difficult conditions. Much of the work was practical public health work in which I became greatly interested. The Medical Officers Training School gave excellent instruction not only in war surgery but particularly in public health. In 1918 I had the good luck of being one of the first in my division to be stricken with influenza so that I was fit again when many of my fellow medical officers were sick. I spent most of the year treating influenza patients in a variety of troops and regions and worked for several months in the Influenza Bureau of the Surgeon General's office from which I was sent out to make epidemiological surveys all over the country.

But the army was a great school to me in other respects as well. So far I had lived the life of the middle class and had moved mostly in academic circles. I was interested in social problems but looked at them more from the theoretical and public health angle. In the army I came in close touch with the working class. In the cavalry to which I was attached for over a year the soldiers were peasants, in the artillery to which I was transferred later they were factory workers, most of whom were employed in several large metallurgical plants in the vicinity of Zurich. These anonymous soldiers became my teachers. They opened my eyes about many problems that I had not seen before and made me realize how little I knew about the world in which I was living. They made me visualize a field of research and activity equally important to the historian as to the medical man. They had confidence in me and on many evenings I went to the sickroom under the pretext of a late ward-round, sat on a bed and listened. They discussed their own problems and discussed the war. And it often struck me how much more convincing their interpretations were than those I heard in the officers' mess. Switzerland, neutral but surrounded by warfaring countries, was an ideal post from which to observe events. Information was obtainable from all sides and it was much easier to get at the truth than in those countries where unilateral heavy propaganda obstructed the vision. The imperialistic character of the war soon became apparent and it was

59

not difficult to realize the full significance of the Russian Revolution.

The armistice was signed and the war was over, at least nominally. I was twenty-seven years old. I had an all-round medical training and had acquired some practical experience in medicine and public health. During the interval between two service periods I had interned for a while in obstetrics and in my senior medical year I had done experimental research in the Pharmacological Institute of the University of Zurich under Professor Cloetta, as the result of which I had published my inaugural dissertation under the title "Experimental investigations on the effect of chronic camphor medication on the normal and sick heart." And now the question arose what the next step would be.

I knew what I wanted and felt no hesitation about it. My field of research was to be medical history. To most of my former professors I was a lost sheep. "Medical history," they said, "is a delightful hobby for retired practitioners but there is no career in it." I was no longer a child and knew better. And this time I was right. In all my previous studies I had felt the need for an historical approach to any given problem. I saw that general history must by necessity remain fragmentary and lead to wrong interpretations if it does not include the history of science. And I felt, although rather vaguely at the time, that medical history studied in a broader sense could be developed into a method that could contribute to the solution of urgent social problems of medicine. In medical history I found a field that was not a narrow specialty and in which I could combine my various interests. I was fully aware that I was not yet equipped for such studies and that I would have to go back to school for at least three years. And since I could no longer afford to make a wrong start I went to Leipzig in 1919 as soon as conditions permitted in order to consult and work with Karl Sudhoff.

In the early twentieth century a few men were demonstrating that medical history was not just "a delightful hobby for retired practitioners."

The best center for medico-historical research in Europe was at the University of Leipzig where Karl Sudhoff had built up an Institute for the History of Medicine. For postgraduate work in this field the obvious place to go was Leipzig, and the obvious man with whom to study was Sudhoff.

On a cold December day, in 1919, in the early morning, I arrived at the monumental station at Leipzig.[2] I had never been there before. The

[2]Excerpts from the essay "The medical literature of the early Middle Ages: A program—and a report of a summer of research in Italy," *Bulletin of the Institute of the History of Medicine,* March 1934, 2: 26-30.

war had been over for more than a year, but the conditions in Germany were still very bad. From Basel to Frankfurt the train was crowded. It made no difference whether you had first or third class tickets. In a compartment that had eight seats we were fifteen! I stayed two days in Frankfurt, and had the greatest difficulty in getting a ticket for Leipzig. Only a limited number of tickets was issued. I was at the station at five o'clock in the morning, and told the man at the desk that I was a Swiss doctor called to an urgent operation in Leipzig. I was a youngster at that time, and the man didn't believe me until I bribed him. Finally I got a ticket for the night train. The ride from Frankfurt to Leipzig was an ordeal. I travelled in a car the windows of which were broken, so that I was almost frozen to death. The light didn't work, and all we had was a stump of a candle that the conductor generously gave us. But finally we arrived at Leipzig. There was no taxi at the station, no porter. I was lucky enough to find a man willing to carry my bags to the hotel. But I was in Leipzig at last.

As soon as it could be done I went to see Karl Sudhoff at his apartment. He expected me. It was a great moment when I saw Sudhoff for the first time. We had corresponded for quite a while. When I decided to go into medical history I wrote to Sudhoff asking for his advice. It was during the war. I immediately received a very encouraging answer. And now I was in Leipzig to work under his guidance. During the war he had been an army physician, and at home he still wore his military tunic as a "Hausrock." I had hardly entered the room before we were already discussing problems of medical history. He showed me his unique Paracelsus collection; then, pointing to a large shelf he said, "Dies ist mein eigenes Gemüse"—"This is my own stuff," the innumerable books and pamphlets he had written himself. A few hours later we were in the Institute of the History of Medicine at the Talstrasse, at this time the only Institute of its kind in Europe. Coal was scarce in Germany, and only two rooms were heated—the seminar room where the students worked, and a small director's room. Generously, Sudhoff offered to share his own room with me. And there I was for many weeks. And every morning we put on our top-coats and went to the library of the Institute or to the collections, and Sudhoff, without ever getting tired, showed me books, photographs, objects, and told about them. And then he suddenly said, "By the way, what do you intend to work on?" I stammered that I was interested in Haller, and a good many other things. And he answered "That's all right, but look here, there is one period in the history of medicine we know very little of—the early Middle Ages. You ought to take up that period." And before I could say a word, I had a huge pile of photostats on my desk.

And so I was launched.

Back in Switzerland, I began studying the mediaeval manuscripts in which the Swiss libraries are so rich. The library of the monastery of St. Gall very kindly sent their manuscripts to Zurich, and there, for

61

many years, I spent most of my time studying the St. Gall Manuscripts, analyzing them, identifying the different treatises, making notes.

The history of medicine, however, is such a wide field, in all its periods so full of interest, that I could not possibly concentrate exclusively on the Middle Ages. I had a sentimental attachment to Haller which I cannot possibly explain. I suppose it is the 18th century atmosphere of a Switzerland without railroads and tourists, and with an unspoiled nature, that attracted me. I found a very interesting collection of letters written by Haller to his most intimate friend, Johannes Gesner, in Zurich, interesting particularly because it begins in Haller's student days, and runs without interruption to the time of his death, covering in this way a large portion of the 18th century. I published these letters, but it was a hard job that took much time, as Haller's handwriting was very difficult to read in his last years. More than two thousand notes had to be written in order to identify the many persons and books mentioned in his correspondence. Then I was interested in the Renaissance. I wrote several papers on the period, and translated Ambroise Paré's *Treatise on Gunshot Wounds*, from 16th century French into German, wrote an essay on Brunschwig, and started the *Monumenta Medica*.

Sudhoff had a watchful eye on me, however. He probably thought that I was deserting the early Middle Ages, and so one day a letter came inviting me to edit the Herbal of Pseudo-Apuleius. It took a long time to get the book printed, complicated indices had to be made, we had to raise the money for adding the plant pictures which are one of the most important parts of the book, and could not possibly be omitted; but finally, in 1927, the volume came out. And it made me realize that there was no escape from the early Middle Ages for me, and that I would have to stick to the job, until the whole period had been elucidated.

The ties between Sudhoff and Sigerist grew from a student-professor relationship into a warm friendship. In 1925, when Sudhoff was seventy-two years old, Sigerist was called to the University of Leipzig to succeed his superior in the chair of medical history and in the directorship of the Institute of the History of Medicine.

My appointment to the University of Leipzig came as a complete surprise.[3] I knew that I was *tertio loco* on the list. My competitors were much older and were Germans; why should the Ministry appoint a foreigner who had not yet completed his thirty-third year? I had rather hoped

[3]Translation of excerpts "Erinnerungen an meine Leipziger Tätigkeit," *Wissenschaftliche Zeitschrift der Karl-Marx-Universität Leipzig,* Mathematisch-Naturwissenschaftliche Reihe, 1955/56, 5: 17-20.

for a position in Munich where my former teachers, Sauerbruch and Friedrich von Müller, were pulling strings to have the Bavarian Ministry establish a chair for the history of medicine. In the winter of 1924 I had given guest lectures in Munich, which had been received with general approval, and so I justifiably had hopes.

Therefore my appointment to Leipzig was really a surprise. For four years, since 1921, I had been Privatdozent at the University of Zurich, for one year as titular professor. In the year 1923 I had written, or translated, or helped publish four books; I was editor of the *Monumenta Medica,* had published with my friend Charles Singer a *Festschrift* for Sudhoff, and until 1925 had done some forty shorter works. That was the total baggage I had to show.

I first went to Leipzig to receive instructions from Geheimrat Sudhoff and in our conversation I soon sensed that he himself was surprised at the Ministry's choice, sensed that he preferred me to the other candidates, for I was his closest student.

At the Ministry in Dresden my negotiations with Oberregierungsrat Ulich proceeded very smoothly—my demands were modest. When Ulich asked me my age and I told him, he said suddenly: *"Donnerwetter,* you certainly are young for this position." Upon which I answered: "Together with Napoleon I can say that this is my only fault which I am correcting with every hour."

He laughed and said: "That is my answer when I am asked about my age, for I'm also very young." He then sent me to the *Hofoper* where I heard an unforgettable performance of *Orpheus.*

So I came to Leipzig. I already knew the Leipzig Institute for I had worked in it for some time in 1919, and had also begun my dissertation there; a correspondence with Sudhoff had ensued which became more and more active. At the height of the 1923 inflation I had presented him with the *Festschrift* I already mentioned.

I still remember Sudhoff's seventieth birthday well. It was a shabby affair. Germany was poor. A simple celebration for which I had donated flowers brought the participants together in the seminar room of the Institute. Speeches were held in the name of the University by the Egyptologist Steindorff (whom I later found again in America), and in the name of the medical faculty by Dean Hertel. Others spoke, Master Sudhoff himself spoke. Afterwards some of us gathered in one of the Keller restaurants to a very modest dinner. No one could foresee that five years later, when Sudhoff's seventy-fifth birthday was celebrated, many of the celebrators would arrive in Horch or Mercedes cars, that the flower-filled auditorium would hardly hold all the guests, that the celebration would be opened and closed by a singer, and that we would afterwards meet, dressed in tails, for an elegant dinner at the Harmonie.

And now I was in Leipzig as Sudhoff's successor and was aware of my responsibilities. My aim was not to imitate Sudhoff's work, but to develop it organically. I had had the luck to read Sudhoff's *Kurzes*

63

Handbuch der Geschichte der Medizin in proofs, and had missed the sociological approach. Who benefitted from the great medical discoveries? All population strata or only the wealthy? What sort of an influence had the industrial revolution had on the health of the population? All these were questions which Sudhoff did not answer in his *Handbuch.* Already at that time I intended to write my own book—a history of medicine from a sociological standpoint. I did not know then that years would have to pass before I could think of executing my plan.

Over the next few years Sigerist's Institute in Germany became a European center for studying medicine in a historical perspective, and certain physicians in the United States were interested in initiating similar studies in their country. The Johns Hopkins Medical School and Hospital had been molded by historically oriented physicians like William Osler, Howard A. Kelly, and William H. Welch who had organized a medical history club and had encouraged the collection of old medical books. After his retirement in 1925 from the directorship of the Johns Hopkins School of Hygiene, William Welch directed his energies toward the creation of the first American Institute of the History of Medicine at the same university. It was formally opened in October 1929.

On a bright morning in the late spring of 1927, I met Dr. William H. Welch for the first time.[4] Dr. Welch intended to create a similar institution at the Johns Hopkins University; and he had come to Leipzig to discuss his plans with Karl Sudhoff and to see for himself what we were doing.

I had heard a great deal about Dr. Welch. I knew that he had contributed more than anyone else to the advancement of medical science in America. I was most anxious to meet him; and there he was, short, rotund, with a big cigar, a man whose great modesty and extreme kindliness captivated all who met him from the very first moment.

Those were pleasant days in the Leipzig Institute, showing Dr. Welch around, telling him about our work, what we had done so far, and what we intended to do in the future, asking for his advice, discussing the present situation in medicine. We agreed that modern medicine had become so specialized and so technical that some place had to be established in the medical schools where medicine would be studied, not from the specialist's point of view, but as a whole, as an entity—and in its relationship to the other sciences, and to society as a whole.

Dr. Welch never said much, but there was not a thing that he did

'Excerpts from *American Medicine* (New York: W. W. Norton & Company, Inc., 1934), pp. xi-xii.

not observe. He met our classes, went every day through the library and the collections. You never saw him with a pencil in hand; he never made a single note. But after a morning spent at the Institute you would find him in a nearby bookshop, ordering from memory hundreds of books, so many books, in fact, that there were later rumors that he had far exceeded his budget.

One day we had lunch in one of the historical Leipzig inns, "Auerbach's Keller," and it happened that we were seated at the same table where, more than half a century before, Dr. Welch had met John Shaw Billings. He looked around and suddenly said: "After all, this is the place where my career started." And he began telling me of his career.

He talked for hours. We were quite alone. I listened entranced, and certainly had no idea that five years later I would succeed him at Hopkins, and that my American career had started at the same table where he had once met John Billings.

Before leaving Leipzig, Dr. Welch invited me to come to Baltimore some day as a visiting lecturer, to give a few courses and to see what they were doing in America.

The Leipzig Institute had expanded tremendously, and the space problem was becoming acute.[5] We just did not have enough room to accomodate all the people. The plan to build a new institute was considered but could not be carried out because the financial situation was becoming catastrophic. One day I found out from my Institute janitor that behind my back our rooms had been promised to the Mineralogical Institute before new space had been secured for my Institute. Of course it was obvious that the terms under which I came to Leipzig were not being met if I had to vacate our present accomodations without receiving a similar amount of space.

Several projects were finally under consideration, projects which I usually heard about from my Institute janitor or by way of the Mineralogical Institute. At last I was ordered to the rent office on December 19, 1930. I was shown completely new plans for a smaller institute and was made to understand that I had to agree to these plans right then and there without having time to discuss the matter with my assistants. After Geheimrat von Seydewitz yelled at me and blamed me for harboring evil intentions—after all I had done for the Institute—my patience was at an end; I handed my resignation to the Ministry in a long and carefully considered letter, with a bleeding heart, for I was very attached to the Institute and its members. But I saw no future ahead of me. The economic depression was in full swing, and the political sky was becoming visibly darker. I was seized by great despair and lost all courage.

Oberregierungsrat Ulich smoothed the matter over again and persuaded me to take back my resignation. He also permitted me to take

[5]Translation from "Erinnerungen an meine Leipziger Tätigkeit," p. 20.

a leave of absence so that I could spend the winter semester of 1931-32 in America. The idea of a lecture tour through the United States fascinated me. To me, as a student of the history and sociology of medicine, a trip through the United States held the promise of a great experience. Having lived and worked in a good many different countries, I was thoroughly familiar with the medical conditions in Europe, past and present. What would they be in America? How would they compare with the European conditions?

In September of 1931 I left for New York.

III

Diaries

To write a diary is to stop an instant every day, to
reflect, to think of what one wanted to do and of what
one did not do; the effect is very salutary.   H.E.S.

1931-32

SEEING AMERICA

The travel journal of his lecture tour through America in the winter of 1931-32 was the beginning of a long succession of diaries. Such a fascinating adventure for a European obviously merited being recorded, and for this special trip Sigerist had a beautiful leather-bound volume of thick paper made with the Institute's signet stamped in gold on its cover. The entries were made in long-hand, in German; only the most interesting reflections are translated and presented here.

1931

Hamburg

A line is drawn. A book is finished. A new one begins. The task lies clearly ahead of me: a sociology of American medicine as seen through its evolution. I can already see the main trends—the beginnings, the Mayflower, Puritanism, the pioneer days, the industrial upheaval, the Civil War. How does medicine fit into these movements? How is medicine formed by them?

I am leaving for America with the same feelings as if I were going to Tibet on a mission—to get to know and understand the medicine of a foreign culture. I am asked: will you like it in America? As if that mattered. I want to see, hear, discover. Time is short and will have to be used to best advantage. And the many lectures which will not move anybody. I am not a benefactor of humanity, have not invented anything, have not exceeded any records. I will speak of medicine and its growth, of the laws that control its development, of great doctors and great errors, and of cultural and intellectual patterns. But will this interest people who only live for the moment or look at the past snobbishly?

SEPTEMBER 16

The "Albert Ballin"

Farewell to Europe. Everything is grey in grey, fog everywhere. People are crowded together on the shore. They wave and cry. A horn madly blows the Siegfried motif. Finally everything is ready and the boat moves slowly. We are also moved. How will we find Europe when we return? Divided as before? Moving from compromise to compromise?

I buy an American journal, anything, *Harper's* magazine. The first article I happen to notice: "The Crisis of Medical Service." At once I find myself in the midst of the problem. Medicine has become too expensive, has become a commodity that can no longer be afforded. A new system of medical service must be found. The author concludes: America is facing a problem which is as large and difficult as the building of railroads or the development of the automobile industry.

SEPTEMBER 17

The morning is sunny and mild. I sit on the top deck with a book, but am not reading. For hours I simply look. I should be working on my lectures, but I am not ready yet. My cabin is too small and terribly hot. I am still tired from my last book and not interested in my lectures. I am oriented only towards the present and everything new that will confront me, and not toward the past and the subjects I have discussed a thousand times before. I will rest for two more days, and then make a start.

SEPTEMBER 19

New York

One day the crossing came to an end and we reached our destination. New York. A taxi takes me to the Shelton Hotel on 49th Street. My room is on the nineteenth floor. I step to the window and for the next hour remain there, motionless.

The impression is overwhelming. Babylon. This is how Babylon must have impressed the soldiers of Alexander. Skyscrapers all around me. To the right, the new Waldorf Astoria rises in terraces, endlessly tall, ending in silver cupolas. To the left, the massive building of the New York Central with its golden roof. Next to it, the slender tower of the Chrysler Building with its scaly roof ending in a long point. And next to it and in between one skyscraper after another, smaller and larger ones, narrow and wide ones, some which could be in Moscow, others with Romanesque, Byzantine, or Gothic ornaments. Marble, gold, silver brightly illuminated by the sun.

This is great art. What do historical reminiscences matter? They fade when faced by such masses. A tremendous will has found its artistic expression. And I experience a solemn hour the like of which is seldom given to us in our life.

SEPTEMBER 25

Dr. Canby Robinson, the dean of the Cornell Medical School, visits me and invites me to dinner. American hospitality is wonderful. I am often quite ashamed that new acquaintances whom I saw only for a short while in Leipzig, receive me here like an old friend. Robinson tells me about his school and his students. He invites me to a lecture. And I am suddenly thrilled. For the first time my lectures assume a tangible form, cease to be a burden, and become something to which I look forward: once again to talk to young people, entirely different young people, bring them some points of view which will perhaps be new to them. After one week I also feel more at home with the language. Robinson has read my *Einführung* very carefully, and tells me which parts he particularly liked. I am very astonished how well my book is known.

OCTOBER 1

We drive up Riverside Drive and stop before Riverside Church, a new Baptist church, a caricature of Chartres. Over the west portal are some famous scientists, Faraday, Pasteur, Lister, and the Jew Einstein in ancient robes, a terribly funny sight. In the inside, which we could not see because of a wedding, Robert Koch is supposed to be enthroned with Christ. A pity that one wing is not devoted to movie stars in gratitude for the illusions they give us. They would look very well as angels. A psychological puzzle is the enormous popularity Einstein enjoys all through America even though no one understands his theory. OCTOBER 3

Rockefeller Institute. Many laboratories equipped with all the latest fancy equipment. Little mechanization. People are more important, but a strict hierarchy. Simon Flexner[1] surveys the whole and sees that the work is done. All facilities are present, but for God's sake, something has to come out of it. There are cells in the library where people write. Experiments must be clothed in literary form. Smoking is permitted, of course, but in spite of all the facilities, no telephones are to be found in these cells—concentration. The books are so arranged that not one step is wasted. Good. If only the intellect is present. Lunch is eaten together. Exchange of ideas. Jokes are probably told.

The Institute is good, is excellent, is ideal. It is precisely what such an institute should look like. But why do I have such a strange feeling? Because:

1. A really creative person is completely independent of such institutions. He will always and everywhere find the means with which to follow his ideas.

2. Genius can never be bred even if the working conditions are perfect and every unnecessary step is saved.

3. It is not good to separate research from teaching. The closer a human being is to life, the easier it is for him to think of something. Pasteur studied the diseases of wine and of the silk worm. In the future I will expect more from the neighboring house, from Cornell.

Such an institution is good for small, everyday jobs. By chance someone may perhaps hit on a great invention. It will not be more than chance. OCTOBER 7

[1]Simon Flexner (1863-1946), brother of Abraham Flexner; prominent pathologist, Director of Laboratories when the Rockefeller Institute for Medical Research was organized in New York; Director of the Institute, 1920-35.

New Haven

My lecture is in the big auditorium which is jammed full: Medicine of the Renaissance. After several cocktails I read my lecture with great enthusiasm. The applause is so prolonged that, like a tenor, I have to rise several times to acknowledge it. And yet I am dissatisfied. I have the feeling that many in the audience were somewhat surprised by my overly poetic way. One simply should not read lectures. Too much is said in too literary a fashion. One should speak freely, even if not quite so correctly, and say the same thing three times. Then people will understand you. OCTOBER 27

Baltimore

Today I gave another lecture about Greek medicine, and I was completely satisfied. I spoke as in one of my best German lectures, absolutely free, and thoroughly didactic. Everyone else was pleased. OCTOBER 29

Long talk with Garrison[2] about medical history in the United States. My opinion: the interest is enormous, much greater than in any European country. A great deal is published, but most of it is very amateurish. The task of the Institute in Baltimore is to break the way for really professional work. It will have to be done very slowly and nicely, without hurting feelings, more by example than by criticism. But where is the right person? Garrison is a bibliographer, Oliver[3] has the wherewithal but not the time, Cushing[4] would be a drawing card and suitable for raising money. But the money is here. Missing is the alkalizing force.

In the evening I was the guest of the Saturday Night Club, a musical circle, almost all of them German-Americans. The Club meets in the shop of a violin maker and until ten o'clock music is played very seriously: a Mozart symphony, the Tragic Overture by Schubert. Then we went to a member's house, and the fun began—beer, sauerkraut, sausages, and great abandon. Today was Halloween and the whole room was decorated accordingly. Brooms and witches everywhere. The members are all well-known intellectuals—Henry L. Mencken, Raymond Pearl, Deebjen, Broedel, and several musicians from the conservatory. Much song and laughter. OCTOBER 31

[2]Fielding H. Garrison (1870-1935), first Librarian of the William H. Welch Medical Library, Baltimore, Md., and author of *An Introduction to the History of Medicine* (4th ed., Philadelphia, 1929).

[3]John Rathbone Oliver (1872-1943), Baltimore psychiatrist and Associate in the History of Medicine, Johns Hopkins University.

[4]Harvey Cushing (1869-1939), famous neurosurgeon who wrote *The Life of Sir William Osler* (2 vols., Oxford, 1925), and collected an extensive medico-historical library which today forms part of the Historical Library of Yale Medical School.

Annapolis

Lunch with Riesman. I am sitting next to his daughter and we talk about Proust, and about the Renaissance. Suddenly she says: "Why don't you write a book about the Renaissance in the style of Marcel Proust." The idea hits me like lightening. Proust pictured the society in which he lived with a perception and clarity that few possessed before him. Why not depict a period of the past in like manner? No chronological build-up, but simply by associations lead the reader in zig-zags into all nooks and crannies, so that in the end a living picture is evoked, and the reader knows the characters forever, just as we know the Baron Charlus, la Duchesse de Guermantes, Albertine, and Françoise. The idea is captivating —a new style of historical presentation.

Or why not picture America in this way: three hundred years ago a continent of enormous proportions, jungle, and a handful of Indians. And today. In three hundred years a world was built. Tremendous forces at work, felling trees, shaping, creating. And now the machine functions. Voices are singing—the Negroes sing by the Mississippi, the cowboys sing, the workers on the Pacific railroad sing in time with their hammers. Music would be the language of such a work, a symphonic poem, a hero's life. Music in words. American fantasy in major. The mighty beginning: New York. First movement: the East. Second movement: Westward ho! Movement, continuous movement. An endless procession rolls westward. Carts, ox carts, horse carts, pullman cars. Westward ho! Ten thousand, ten million. Then a pause, a breathing space. An intermezzo in minor: Hawaii. Back again, and the third movement: the West, California, Spain, and the Jesuits. Fourth movement: the South, plantations, slaves, the Civil War, Virginia. Final chord: New York. If only I could succeed in finding such a way into literature. A liberation from the narrowness of the German university, away from this stuffy professorial atmosphere. Freedom in America. Why not?—I have a little fever, not much, only a hundred. NOVEMBER 14

Baltimore

Welch is in his eighty-second year. He is a great man in addition to being charming and kind. He does not work any more but carries his fame with dignity. Everybody raves about Popsie. What he does not like to hear, he does not hear. It simply glides off him. He is now living for posterity. He finds it important for others to know that he was a baseball player. He recounts much from his life. He has a marvellous memory which is aided by his diaries. No one has ever entered his apartment.

Nobody knows where Popsie sleeps,
Nobody knows where Popsie eats,
Nobody knows what girl he keeps,
For such is our Popsie.

So sing the students. He wants to have Harvey Cushing as his successor. Why? Because Cushing wrote Sir William Osler's biography in two thick volumes. Now he is supposed to write Welch's biography and Welch would give him material.   NOVEMBER 22

Farewell from Baltimore. The Negroes in the Club: we got so accustomed to you. In the evening with Welch at Garrison's. It was an excellent stay. The lectures were a complete success. I have come to know an American faculty well. The lectures made quite a different impression from what I had expected. The interest in cultural matters is enormous and the respect for education very great. It is much more gratifying to travel with medical history than with physiological chemistry because here there are many good chemists but no medical historians. Everything I brought was new.

So the projected book has been pushed into the background for the lectures have demanded much time. More than that, the country has affected me deeply. First the country, epic America, and then medicine, which is only a small part of the whole.

And now the travels are about to begin, the train through the continent, westward, following the trail of the pioneers. The bags are packed, eleven of them, like a film star. The camera equipment has been checked. Now I can begin.   NOVEMBER 23

Boston

Harvey Cushing is operating. Although only 62, he is an old man, graceful, sickly. We change our clothes and wash. He has been operating all his life, but before every operation he is nervous. It must be that way. We enter. The chief physician has already opened wide the cranium. The patient is a sailor, a Hercules. He is lying on his stomach and is so restless that he finally has to be anesthetized. Cushing begins, opens the *dura mater*, feels his way slowly with the electric cautery in his hand. He dissects. The tumor must lie in the occipital lobe. There it is, a meningioma, enormous. He is bleeding, a flash, and the blood is stilled. Again, again, and again. A young girl, the anesthetist, is buried under the patient. She spends hours in this cave. Suddenly she puts out her hand and signals with a sharply falling motion. It is a matter of life and death. A blood transfusion is given. Cushing continues, stills blood, penetrates further. Hours pass. Again the hand with the downward curve. Another transfusion. Will he last? The curve of the hand rises. On. Cushing works with a light on his forehead, like a cyclop. Finally the tumor lies exposed, is detached, leaves his host, travels to the pathologist and becomes a collection item. Six hours have passed. Cushing is at the end. The head physician finishes. And down in her cave the anesthetist still perseveres, bathed in perspiration and covered with blood. Once more she has to give the signal for alarm. Then the operation is finished, but the struggle with life or death continues the

74

whole night. A doctor and a nurse stand watch. Finally nature triumphs, and the fight is won.

Meanwhile the time has come for me to go into action. I am supposed to speak on culture and disease at Harvard. After the great performance I have witnessed, I am supposed to give an intellectual talk. There action, here words. It is difficult but it must be done. First a faculty tea, stiff and formal. Then the lecture in a large auditorium. The talk seems to fascinate, for the ideas are new.

Another day, another operation. A man has gradually become almost blind. A tumor of the pituitary gland presses on his visual nerves. The tumor must be benign, for the patient's history goes pretty far back. Again the skull is opened wide, this time in front. Again Cushing proceeds, step by step, dissects, lifts up one of the frontal lobes, and works his way to the tumor, sucks it out, cleans the nerve. The patient is fully conscious, talks with us and while he is talking under his cloth we look into him. The nerves which transmit our voices to him lie exposed before our eyes. Pale and clean the optic nerves lie before us. We hold his brain in our hands—a preparation, but a living preparation which talks and groans and excuses himself for his groaning. The operation lasts only a few hours and tomorrow the patient will be able to see again.

A last lunch with Harvey Cushing and we part as friends.

NOVEMBER 28—DECEMBER 2

Minneapolis

A disturbing day even though it was spent in my chair. Confused emotions. Welch appeared, cheerful and composed as ever, and brought me an appointment to Johns Hopkins. A unanimous decision by the faculty. Fine that a faculty exists anywhere which backs me unanimously. How different it was in Berlin! What now? The decision is between science and politics. Here I have again begun to enjoy research, and would have the means. In Germany there would no longer be any question of research. Every year I would have to write a popular book as a living, and otherwise—politics. Strangers we would remain in both countries, but a small house in Switzerland would serve as a *pied-à-terre* where I would have my library, a garden by a lake, carefree summer months in my own country in which I have my roots. A retreat where I could retire any time.

A quiet and lonely day. A year has come to an end. What has it brought? Misery, unrest, uncertainty, not only as a result of the war. The war itself is only a symptom of a great crisis. But what kind of crisis—of capitalism, of democracy, of materialism, of the machine, or of the West? Who knows! And the cure? Nobody knows.

Personally: *The Great Doctors* and some success in America, rather cheap success because what I brought was new here, and so it continues, work and more work and we shall see what will happen.　　　DECEMBER 31

A terrifying screaming of the sirens tears me from my work: the New Year has begun. All factory sirens screech, cars honk, fireworks and paper horns on the street. Noise. With noise comes courage. One feels strong when making much noise. In other countries church bells ring in the New Year, the bells of the church in which no one believes, but it is still more beautiful and solemn. One does not feel courageous, but light.

But not all Americans begin the New Year with noise. A friend told me that he and his friends had spent the evening listening to chamber music. During a Beethoven quartet the old year finished and the new year came in. And everyone was very happy, more than with making noise.   JANUARY 1

St. Paul

Lunch with Dr. Arnold Schwyzer in St. Paul. He is from Zurich, came over in 1892 and was immediately so successful as a doctor that he was not allowed to go back. Today he is one of the most prominent surgeons of the whole region. A pioneer. In the afternoon we drove to visit his brother, Gustav Schwyzer, also a surgeon. Two brothers, both outstanding surgeons. A little farther south another pair of surgeons, the brothers Mayo. The first pair is Swiss, remained individualists, and accomplished remarkable things. The others were also outstanding surgeons, but they were American. They organized and commercialized the profession, and the Mayo Clinic resulted.   JANUARY 2

San Francisco

The second week in San Francisco begins with the arrival of a letter from President Ames with my official appointment to Johns Hopkins and the approval of the Board of Trustees. Now it has become public. There is general rejoicing among the medical historians and especially among Hopkins people. They all hope that I will accept the call and I myself am more and more tempted. An enlargement of my activities: first Switzerland, then Germany, and finally the American continent. The possibilities are enormous. The Institute is a superb instrument which has only to be tuned and played. Then the Old Ladies' Home will amount to something.   JANUARY 26

Honolulu

My last day in San Francisco passes without the usual excitement before an Atlantic crossing, for no customs inspections have to be made, no formalities. In the middle of the Pacific we are still on American territory. On awakening I see the coast, a mountain—Diamond Head, green and red. Slowly the boat heads for port. A flock of brown boys

76

swims toward us, diving for nickels. We approach the port and the pier. From the land we hear Hawaiian melodies. A colorful crowd, people of all races in light summer dresses await us with flower wreaths in their hands and the welcome greeting, Aloha, on their lips.

I land and am met by Dr. Fennel and his wife who welcome the Malihini, the stranger, with strongly-scented wreaths of carnations. It is as warm here as in August. The Royal Hawaiian Hotel has a magnificent garden, cocoanut palms, banana trees, papayas with melon-like fruit, bread-fruit trees with heavy fruit. And especially flowers, everywhere, strange colorful exotic plants of silk and velvet, some like fireworks. And the queen of the flowers—the hibiscus—blooms in all colors of the rainbow. Hedges of hibiscus which grow like weeds.

JANUARY 28

In the afternoon Dr. Wayson, the director of the leper station, has a clinic in the leprosorium. He shows me the early symptoms of the disease, explains the diagnosis. The disease is a mystery. The seat of the irritation is known, in the skin at the edge of the spots, or in the ear lobe, or in the nasal partition, but the disease cannot be bred or transferred to animals. One does not know the path of the infection. Wayson assumes that the infection travels through the respiratory system, Fennel believes by way of the gastro-intestinal canal. But these are only speculations. The patient is isolated and as a result hides himself and is treated only years later. It must have been the same in the Middle Ages. In Japan lepers are not isolated, and yet leprosy is decreasing.

JANUARY 29

Molokai, Kalaupapa
I am sitting in a house which is "clean." Entering the enclosure, I had to wipe my shoes on a rug drenched with lysol and wash my hands with lysol soap and alcohol. Outside the enclosure is "unclean" territory. We are in a leper colony, a small group of "clean" people surrounded by 450 lepers. We are in the house of the directing physician, Dr. Lorenzo P. Luckie from Alabama. What contrasts! I spent the morning with Mrs. Fennel in the Academy of Art, a magic island in the middle of Honolulu.

Then an adventurous excursion to Kalaupapa. Dr. Fennel, Kugler (the superintendent of leprosy), and I took a plane and after three quarters of an hour we land on the island Molokai. A car, an ancient Packard, is waiting for us. It is raining, and the drive starts up-hill over bumpy roads which remind me of Greece, through holes and puddles, and we are more shaken up than in the plane. Finally we are at the top of the mountain, the Pali. Horses are ready with strangely ornamented saddles. And we continue on horseback, at first through gorges on level ground, and then suddenly we are at the edge of a precipice. The side of the mountain falls off perpendicularly 1,600 feet, below us the roaring sea, and the peninsula with the leprosy settlement as on an airview picture. The rain has stopped, but a fierce wind is blowing. We are supposed to descend on a stony, steep path hardly wide enough for one horse, a path which has become slippery with the rain, on one side of us rises the wall of the mountain, on the other side—the precipice. (Once when we were students we climbed the Säntis. The path was narrow and the precipice steep. I felt miserable, but there was no going back. Dizziness had to be overcome. Don't look, loosen the inhibitions with cognac, and distract yourself. I recited the prologue from *Faust*, started over and over again, tried various intonations, walked on and on; a thunderstorm threatened, thick clouds, singing, just don't stop, and the last bit—the final rocky wall, steps, and finally the hut was reached with thunderous singing. At last we had overcome the difficulties. The thunderstorm broke, but we were safe and the return tomorrow was down the other side.)

We have already gone part of the way, sliding, slipping, but it gets worse and worse.

"Should I not get off and lead the horse?"

"For heaven's sake don't do that" calls the Japanese guide. "The horse goes, let the reins loose."

Of course he is right. We go on, for an hour. The horse smells the ground, finds the best way to go, steps and slides. These horses know every stone, take the same road every day and know nothing else. The surf comes closer and can now be heard. The brush gets thicker and—at last we are down. A Ford is waiting for us and takes us to the doctor's house. Whiskey tastes marvellous, better the second drink, still better the third. It has become dark and we sit down at table. After dinner we drive to the movies. In the intermission the light is turned on. Fennel and I have to appear on the stage and Luckie introduces Fennel as a member of the Board and me as a foreign professor who has come from far away to study "our troubles." Fennel speaks, and then it is my turn. I raise my arm: "Aloha, friends!" And then I see them all, with the terrible lion faces, their noses eaten away, the wasted claw-hands, many bandaged all over, many blind—a terrible sight. And while I am speaking I cannot take my eyes off these marked faces, and the ending almost sticks in my throat: "And so I wish good luck to you all. Aloha oe!" Is it not ridiculous to say that? But they clap politely, those who still have hands, laugh, and the movie continues about platinum blondes sought after by handsome men. Outside it is stormy. The palms rustle. FEBRUARY 6

In the east of the peninsula, in Kalamao, is a little Catholic settlement. Three Franciscan lay brothers tend the sick. Here worked Pater Damien who himself became a leper and died a martyr. Yet the disease is much less contagious than tuberculosis. But he was, said Fennel, what you call in German *ein Schweinehund*, smoked the same pipe with the lepers, ate with them from the pot. According to another version he was

78

already sick when he arrived and was sent for that reason. The settlement is run down, damp, and is supposed to be torn down eventually.

Not far away are some very beautiful buildings, but they are uninhabited and are deteriorating visibly. Some mystery, which I could not quite fathom, is connected with these buildings. One day the federal government wanted to put an end to leprosy. Hawaii was to see how this can be done. A model settlement was erected at great cost. Only the lepers were missing and did not come. They refused to come and preferred to remain in their miserable huts on the other side. Why? I was told that the government had sent an old army doctor who was afraid of the disease, who only spoke with his patients through a glass window, only touched the lepers with gloves, and above all was of the opinion that all lepers should be sterilized. Of course they did not want that. Oh, no! And the lepers have power, have the vote, and in a thousand ways are connected with the other islands. The government had to abandon its plans. I wonder if there is not more to it?

In the afternoon we go from house to house and visit the sick. Rosina, a pretty Portuguese girl, receives us amiably, yes doctor, no doctor. She lives with three men under one roof and manages the household. She has had five children with five men. The children are taken to Honolulu and brought up by the state. Each child costs the state $10,000 and Rosina's fertility knows no bounds. She is an expensive patient. Here is a Hawaiian girl, barely eighteen, who just got married.

"How long have you been here?"

"One year."

"How long have you been sick?"

"Oh, I was very small."

Always the same story. The curse of isolation. One isolates because of history, because of the Bible, and not for rational reasons. As a result the sick hide themselves and forego treatment.

At night we sit with our whiskey in the doctors' house and talk. About leprosy, of course. What is the best book on leprosy? There is no such book. Well, let's write one. The people are here—marvellous, self-inclosed material for observation. Wayson will write the clinical part, Fennel the sociological, and I the historical. A piece of paper, a pencil, here is the outline. We were so sleepy after our strenuous day, but now we are wide awake. More whiskey, and at one at night the book is ready before us. The doctors are lonely on this island. If they need a book it takes a month for it to come. They live and work from day to day, the climate is mild, and the sun shines always—almost always. It takes a push, and now they are enthusiastic about this new book.   FEBRUARY 7

My seven months in America had made a deep impression on me, and with this impression I went back to Leipzig.[5] But there was something else I carried with me. In Minneapolis Dr. Welch had knocked on my door, had come to ask me to join the Johns Hopkins Medical School, to succeed him in the chair of the History of Medicine, and to take charge of the new Institute of the History of Medicine. I was entirely unprepared for such an offer, and being on leave of absence from the University of Leipzig, I could not decide while still away.

I was aware of what I would have to give up: Karl Sudhoff's chair, the best-equipped Institute of Medical History in Europe, a group of students to whom I was profoundly attached. I would have to adopt another language, which to a writer is a serious matter. Once before I had shifted from one language to another, from French to German, so I knew what it meant.

On the other hand I saw great possibilities for the development of my subject in America. The science of medicine knows no political boundaries. Its discoveries fly like sparks from land to land and over the ocean itself. But the conditions for creative development, that great sum of material and imponderable factors which bring the seed to flower, are seldom found simultaneously in one country. Padua brought forth Vesalius, witnessed the beginnings of clinical instruction, gave the decisive stimulus to Harvey, and finally became the working-place of Morgagni. After 1700, Leyden, with its Hermann Boerhaave, was the post-graduate school of European medicine. Scotland and England followed. The center of gravity continued to shift: to Paris, to Vienna, finally, about the middle of the last century, to Germany. Almost all the important European countries have in their time been the leading voice in the concert of medicine. Whose turn will it be next? To the historian it must seem that it will be America's.

Wherever I had been I had found a keen interest in the history of medicine. I had further found great social problems in American medicine that had to be approached historically. Medical history in most countries was a purely antiquarian subject. My approach was somewhat different. Although I had gone through a strict philological school, and although I am still doing a good deal of philological work, I was always primarily interested in all the general problems of modern medicine; investigating the past in order to get to a clearer understanding of our own time, and to help in preparing the future; studying history in order to make unconscious trends conscious, so that we can face and discuss them openly. I felt that an Institute founded by Dr. Welch, backed by his authority, could not but be a vital Institute, an ideal place for such studies.

[5]Excerpts from *American Medicine,* trans. Hildegard Nagel (New York: W. W. Norton & Company, Inc., 1934), pp. xvi-xvii, and translation from "Erinnerungen an meine Leipziger Tätigkeit," pp. 17-21.

Personal considerations helped my decision—my attachment to Dr. Welch, the strong appeal the country had made to me, its dynamic vitality, its courage, its optimism in spite of depression, and last but not least, the fact that here one was constantly looking into the future, preparing for it rationally, while Europe is becoming more and more reactionary and mystical, losing that freedom of thought without which there can be no scientific research.

However, I could not reach a decision before I had consulted the Saxon Ministry. On my return to Germany I found a completely changed political situation which in these seven months had become considerably worse. I knew that my name was on all the black lists and that I could not remain in Germany if Hitler came to power. In the summer of 1926, in Weimar, I had participated at the meeting of republican university professors who had decided to support, and not to sabotage, the German Republic. I had helped to publish the *Neue Blätter für den Sozialismus;* and in the summer semester of 1932 I myself had thrown out two fat Nazis who appeared in full uniform in my lecture room, contrary to the rector's rule that party shirts could not be worn in the lecture halls. This was a clear case of provocation. I knew what was ahead of me and that I could expect no mercy from the Nazis.

I asked for an interview with the Ministry. Oberregierungsrat Ulich, who just happened to be in town, invited me to have tea in one of the parks and tried to persuade me that I should refuse this distinguished American offer and remain. He pictured to me what would happen if all decent men were to leave the sinking ship. My arguments were that the battle was already lost, that German *Wissenschaft* was in grave peril, and that in America I would try to save what was still worth saving. I would take along my Privatdozent Dr. O. Temkin and build up a nucleus of German learning in foreign lands.

Suddenly Ulich took a different stand and said: "So far I have spoken in the name of the Minister. I was under instructions to persuade you to stay in Leipzig. Now I will talk to you as a friend. Accept the appointment. Save whatever is still salvageable of German learning. Continue the traditions of German *Wissenschaft*. The situation will become much worse than either you or I can imagine."

In April, 1932, I accepted the offer of the Hopkins, and was back in America a few months later.

1933

THE FIRST YEAR AT JOHNS HOPKINS

With January 1, 1933, begins a series of yearly diaries which were systematically kept, day-by-day, without many periods of interruption until the onset of Sigerist's illness in 1954. Sigerist arrived in Baltimore in the fall of 1932. From then on the diaries were kept mainly in English, although German and French were occasionally used. The entries in the first year (1933) were begun in German and by a deliberate act of will continued in English which at first sounds somewhat stilted and awkward, but improved rapidly with practice.

P*Baltimore*
rovided I have another ten years of good health and maximum working capacity I will be able to accomplish something. The foundations exist, and a certain *aequanimitas* has been achieved. Now I must produce. *Einführung in die Medizin* and *Die Grossen Aerzte*[6] are the beginning, the America book will follow, and then Russia. In between, as a rest, a little philology, a Latin grammar, and the medieval studies as a stabilizer.   SUNDAY, JANUARY 1

I have made a five-year plan. At my age one has to plan. It is a good plan with many books and tempting trips. But first of all the book on American medicine has to be finished. I read my section on pioneers, but I am still too close to the work to be able to judge it. I write a few pages. The new chapter is going well and I see it clearly before me.

SUNDAY, FEBRUARY 12

A record: thirteen pages on the book (once it was twenty). I began in the morning, finished at night. Of course not much otherwise. In the afternoon I was interrupted in my work and had to identify a Vesalianum. At 6:15 a radio lecture about the plague, five minutes. I tried to speak an Oxford, not an American, English. The old ladies in

[6]These two books were translated into English as *Man and Medicine* (1932) and *The Great Doctors* (1933).

1933

Baltimore, my admirers, must have pricked up their ears. How silly!

Nine pages written about Cornell at one sitting, as in a trance (whiskey helped, good rye with ginger-ale, the best drink imaginable). What is better than to write, to work, to create. A true act of birth. I have a terrific cold, but it is all forgotten when I write.   THURSDAY, FEBRUARY 16

Suddenly the news that Dr. Welch is dying. It is unspeakably sad.

SATURDAY, MARCH 18

I pay a visit to Dr. Welch. I want to see him once more. The nurse admits me to his room. He is weak and numb, his face waxen, *facies hippocratica.* He recognizes me, says he is pretty comfortable. I tell him how much we all miss him. He: "I still have that catheter." He speaks softly and with effort. In a few weeks he completely went to pieces, not any more the former Dr. Welch, but an old organism which is mobilizing its last reserves in the battle against decay.   FRIDAY, MARCH 17

42 years old. At that age my father was already dead. A period of his life had come to an end, and a new one would have begun had he lived. I remember him well, as young as I was at the time. I often wonder what kind of a relationship we would have had together. My mother was alone for a long time.   FRIDAY, APRIL 7

Today I realized that our public health is barbaric. Medicine is still in its first, the therapeutic, period. For the next, the preventive period, a social revolution is needed. Under the capitalist system—even less in a fascist state—preventive medicine is not possible. Russia therefore signifies the beginning of a new epoch in medicine also.   MONDAY, APRIL 17

In Cambridge, Mass., with George Sarton.[7] Finally we meet each other. We have been corresponding for many years. We have so much in common, and have gone along similar paths, but always missed each other. Now I went to Cambridge to see him. A very pleasant *milieu,* his wife a painter, the daughter an actress with Eva LeGallienne. We discuss endless topics, interrupt to play classical music on a splendid phonograph. In the afternoon a walk through Cambridge and the campus of Harvard University. Spring is only just beginning here.   SUNDAY, MAY 14

I am finished with my book *Amerika und die Medizin.*[8] I can hardly believe that it is really ended. The bibliography still has to be brought

[7]George Sarton (1884-1956), leading historian of science.
[8]*Amerika und die Medizin* (Leipzig, 1933) was translated into *American Medicine* (New York, 1934).

83

up to date, but that is purely mechanical work. In 1930, when I heard of the possible invitation to America, I began the preparations for this book. Then I travelled six months, and wrote for a year. Three years in all. And now Russia. But I am tired today and cannot work. An hour with Popsie [Dr. Welch].   MONDAY, MAY 27

The academic year draws to a close. The balance is good, could not be better:

1. The America book is finished. The rest of the manuscript was sent off today.

2. The medieval studies are in swing again, and if everything goes well should be terminated in a few years.

3. The student body has been won over. At present it is only the first year students, but they are enthusiastic and that is essential. The rest will follow.

4. The first assistants who want to devote themselves entirely to history are present.

5. The foundations for organizing the Institute have been laid.
                                                      WEDNESDAY, MAY 31

Good-bys, the whole day good-bys, and good-bys are always painful. Farewell from the Institute, from the usual rooms, from Dr. Welch—how will we find him again. And another farewell, which makes me particularly sad: farewell from the German language. For thirty years German was the language in which I thought and wrote. And now this has come to an end. It must be so. In Nazi Germany I have no following any more. The contacts are lessening from day to day. My future lies here, here in the Anglo-Saxon world. My last German book is finished. And now I must change, transform myself completely, think in English and become an English writer.   THURSDAY, JUNE 1

So let's go on, in English. Vacations! It's hard to realize, after the tension of the last eight months. A period has come to an end, our first year of American life. It was extremely pleasant, couldn't have been more satisfactory. And now for four long months the adventure of travelling.   FRIDAY, JUNE 2

Paris

I cannot resist the temptation to go and look for old books although there is very little chance of finding something worthwhile. And yet I was lucky and got a perfect copy of the *Orthopédie* of Andry for 35 francs, at the Quai Malaquais.   THURSDAY, JUNE 15

Basel

A publisher came from Berlin to see me. A year ago he had decided to publish a handbook of the History of Medicine under my edi-

84

torship. The situation in Germany made it impossible for me to start such an international undertaking particularly as a good many of the contributors were to be Jews. But my man knows the trick. He has established a Swiss firm and this will publish the book. He's a clever fellow. And then, says he, in two years, when the book begins to appear, the situation may be quite different.   FRIDAY, JUNE 23

I want the children to realize that Switzerland once was a Roman province. We drive to Vindonissa where we visit the amphitheater and the museum. New excavations have been done since I was there. *Thermae* were unearthed and I am very interested to see that a mere *castrum* had such huge baths. Then Augst, Augusta Rauracorum, and the theater which is rather well preserved. Tea in Bad Schinznach, a historical place also, flourishing once, famous through the foundation of the Helvetic Society, dying today in spite of a golf course.   SATURDAY, JUNE 24

Milan
In Italy! It is three years since I was here, a very long time. It was in 1930, I had just finished the *Einführung* and spent a delightful week in Perugia, then the International Congress in Rome, Ancona, and Greece. It's like a dream being here again. In between the United States twice, the Hawaiian Islands, two new books. And now again Italy and everything is unchanged. I am a few years older and yet much the same, still a student and interested in everything. The trip from Basel to Milan was very nice in spite of the bad weather. I remember so well the thrill it gave me when I passed the Alps the first time. It must have been about 1905 on our way to Nervi. I don't feel that thrill any more. The trains are too fast, the scenery too familiar and yet it's a grand thing being here again.   JUNE 25

Venice
The best way to lengthen your life is to enjoy every single day, to live every day consciously, to have it filled up with creative work and artistic emotions. It is only four days ago that I left Basel and yet it seems ages.
Today is a great holiday—San Pietro. Crowds on the Piazza San Marco, crowds in the Palace of the Doges. I take a boat to the Lido. I have lunch in a garden overlooking the sea and there I sit for hours reading proofs of my book. It always is a queer sensation to see your own book printed, queerer still to read those pages on America here in front of the Adriatic Sea. Near by is San Lazzaro; the first article I wrote that was ever printed was on San Lazzaro. It appeared in the *Neue Zürcher Zeitung*[9] and I was very proud of it. Again a thunderstorm in the evening and when it stopped the band played on the Piazza. *Buona sera.*   JUNE 29

[9]August 30, 1910.

Vicenza, Padua

Castiglioni's assistant took me for a walk. He knows every stone of Padua. We went to the Arena first, to Giotto. Then to Gattamelata and to the Santo, to the salone where I saw Pietro d'Abano, the relief I had reproduced in *The Great Doctors*. We walked through the narrow streets of the city and saw many delightful medieval houses. It is a funny city. The students are still the lords of the place. I went to one of Castiglioni's exams and was amazed to see how much the students know. Of course in such surroundings it is impossible not to be interested in the history of medicine. JUNE 30

Bologna

To the Library, but which? I know that there is a manuscript of Dioscorides here. I have the designation but I don't know in which of the two libraries it is. So I try the Biblioteca Communale first. It was the wrong one. Never mind, for the Library is in the Archiginnasio, a gem in itself and there is the anatomical theater of Levanti with its wonderful wooden sculptures. Then to the University Library and there I find the manuscript. It was noon, however, the Library closed, so I went to the Pinacoteca that gives a splendid view of the Bolognese school. Particularly appealing to me was a sweet Madonna of Carracci, the pathetic Guido Reni. Many Sebastians, a very interesting one by Guido Reni without arrows. The whole afternoon in the Library. TUESDAY, JULY 4

Florence

I began my work at the Laurenziana. The surroundings are fascinating. You pass a beautiful courtyard from which you have a splendid view on the Duomo. Then you pass the unique collection of miniatures, and you work in a circular room seated on high chairs. The manuscripts are brought to you one after another — splendid material. I am full of my work. I decide to make it three volumes instead of two. The first will contain the catalogue and the plates, each important manuscript being represented by a full-page illustration. The second volume will be a collection of texts whenever possible in critical editions. The last volume finally will give the history of this literature. If I succeed, this will be a piece of work that will last a century, just as we still consult Angelo Mari and Fabricius. My other books are written for the day and will not survive me long. MONDAY, JULY 10

Sils Baselgia, Switzerland

And so the first part of my Italian tour has come to an end. It was extremely pleasant and very successful. Italy is a wonderful country. I lived in constant ecstasy. After a winter of hard work in America it was so very refreshing to dip into Italian art. No country in the world where you can find so many artistic creations on such a small space. My medieval work is well started now. I found beautiful material, enough

86

to keep me busy the whole winter. With the exception of Pisa and Siena I carried out my schedule. I am looking forward to being back in Italy soon.   TUESDAY, JULY 18

It is thrilling to be a historian today when all over the world history is being made. But it is difficult to stay critical and detached. Being a Swiss and therefore not being entangled, it is somewhat easier for me to keep *au dessus de la mêlée*. If I were younger I would probably want to play an active part in the development. Now my field of action is in literature and teaching, and I hope that by just being detached and critical I can influence the development at least in the limited field of medicine.   JULY 20

The first of August, the Swiss National Day. I feel rather miserable. I cannot yell with the others. I cannot believe that this country is superior to others, that the Swiss are better than other people just because I happened to be born of Swiss parents. It is a beautiful country, no doubt of it, and there are delightful people here as everywhere, but I cannot help seeing the drawbacks, the utter conservatism, the slowness, the narrow-mindedness of the Swiss in general. And I cannot help being glad that my field of action is in a larger and more progressive country.
The weather was awful, the fireworks very poor, the band played badly, and the whole performance was a failure.   TUESDAY, AUGUST 1

I began reading Hitler's *Mein Kampf*, the most stupid book of a political dilettante I've ever read. It is incredible that a man with such a superficial knowledge of history, such a wrong view of social problems, such a primitive theory, could attain such power. It was possible only in a country that was politically entirely undeveloped.

WEDNESDAY, AUGUST 2

The last day. Packing. While I was packing, the last proofs of my book came. I corrected them immediately and now I'm definitely through. My God, what a relief this is! In 1930, expecting an invitation as visiting lecturer to the Johns Hopkins I began studying American medicine. For three and half years this kept me absorbed. Now I am through with it. I wonder what the reaction of the medical public will be in Europe and in America. And now to Russia and Russian medi-cine.   FRIDAY, AUGUST 11

Perugia

A revolutionary government constantly feels the need of justifying and advertizing its doings. Italy has drained the Pontinian swamps, has obtained some new territory in this way and founded two small cities there. A terrible fuss is made about it. During the same period of time Holland has dried up the Zuydersee which was a much more difficult task. Nobody speaks about it. Why? Because this has been accomplished by an ordinary democratic and liberal regime. What a noise would have been made if this had been done in Italy or Russia.

SATURDAY, SEPTEMBER 9

A few days ago, in Florence, I bought a copy of J. P. Muller, *Il mio sistema.* I hadn't seen the book since 1905. I was an enthusiastic follower of Muller then and practised his exercises daily. Now, after nearly thirty years I feel that I have to do something. I'm getting fat and stiff. So I began today, and from now on I will do some calisthenics every morning in order to be able to carry out the two next five-year plans. At the same time I will cut down my smoking which is my greatest vice.

SUNDAY, SEPTEMBER 10

Rome

Rome, after three years Rome again. The city is hardly to be recognized. I saw the whole development since the beginning of the fascist regime: 1923, 1925, 1930, 1933. And the work isn't completed yet, far from it. The changes are enormous. Where a few years ago there still were slums, now we find the Via dell'Impero from Piazza Venezia to the Coliseum, the imperial fora beautifully excavated. I went all over the Forum Romanum, then after dinner to the Exhibit of the Fascist Revolution, a very impressive show in the Russian style. And finally, tired as I was, I went to the International Poultry Exhibition not on account of the chickens but because the exhibit was in the Mercati Traianei that I wanted to see.

MONDAY, SEPTEMBER 11

My bible just now is Jakob Burckhardt's *Welthistorische Betrachtungen*, a splendid book full of ideas, the reflections of a great historian at the end of his life. It is extraordinary how much he anticipated.

SUNDAY, SEPTEMBER 24

The "Albert Ballin"

Looking back. What was the result of these four months? First of all, my America book was set into type, corrected, printed, and finally it appeared. The English edition of the *Grosse Aerzte* must be out by now too, so that I will come back to America with two new books.

Then I learned some Russian, not as much as I hoped for, but the Russian work is well started and all I have to do is to keep it going for three more years.

My most important task for this summer was the manuscript work. I hoped that I would be able to get through with the Italian libraries. I did not. I worked in 10 libraries, examined 22 manuscripts, ordered 646 photostats, and 58 ordinary photos. But I still have to visit, in Italy, the libraries of Naples, Monte Cassino, Rome, Arezzo, Pisa, Lodi. This will have to be done next year. The reason why I didn't fulfil my programme is that the preparation wasn't quite accurate enough, that there was too much material, too scattered. Time was too short for such an enormous mass of material. Still, the results are not bad. I have very important material on which I can work the whole winter and I learned the technique of doing such work. Next year it will be much easier and require much less time. Regardless of manuscripts the Italian trip was extraordinarily inspiring. From Milan and Venice to Rome I saw all the great cultural centers, learned a great deal about the past and about the actual development. My historical views have undoubtedly been broadened and deepened.

For the Institute I bought hundreds of Alinari photos, a good beginning of a collection. Many of these pictures deal with Aesculapius and will be helpful for my monograph. All in all it has been a very good summer. SATURDAY, SEPTEMBER 30

Looking forward. First of all, I am very glad to be back in America. America is the only country in the world where, at the present time, studies like mine can be done effectively. In the fascist countries there is no interest except for nationalistic history, and all the money available is being spent directly or indirectly for war preparations. In France and in England very little is done for medical history. There, like in the small countries (Switzerland and Holland), we find that narrow bourgeois spirit of self-satisfaction. There are no dynamics in medicine. Europe has a glorious past but no future. In America a great revolution is taking place and I feel that in my field I have a part to play. Next winter's tasks will be the following:

1. To consolidate and develop the Institute. We have a good educational programme. I have fewer lectures than last winter. Therefore I will be able to prepare them more carefully. Our *Bulletin* is established and running, and now I'll start the different series of publications.

2. To write the Latin grammar the idea of which is to broaden the young students' general education.

3. To write a dozen smaller papers. Last year there was hardly time for papers but I have much material ready for publication.

4. To combine the medieval work so that the three volumes will be ready in 1937.

5. To continue collecting materials for the future books, Russia, Aesculapius, etc. TUESDAY, OCTOBER 3

Baltimore

I spent an hour with Dr. Welch. I found him quite unchanged, mentally very alert, interested in everything. It is splendid how stoically he stands the long ordeal of a disease from which he must know that there is no escape at that age. SUNDAY, OCTOBER 8

A great addition to our life. I bought an excellent phonograph and records of the 4th symphony of Brahms. It sounds splendid, I'll build up a collection of records and will have all the great musical creations at home. THURSDAY, OCTOBER 12

This was one of those days on which everything goes wrong. Waking up sneezing and coughing with a new cold. Snow outside at this time of year. Mrs. Broemer didn't get through with the letters. I started dictating a paper when Fuller, the printer, came. He hasn't got the type we want, hasn't done a darned thing. The whole morning is wasted. With great difficulty and constantly interrupted, I worked an hour on the Milan manuscript. Then the lecture on Harvey which was the best part of the day. But then—o God—I couldn't open my car, the lock was broken. More than that—the motor had been running the whole day. Finally, I found a mechanic who succeeded in opening a window. At home everybody was in a bad temper. We were to go to a fine concert, but I just couldn't. And now I find my pen rotten and am longing for the old pen. TUESDAY, NOVEMBER 14

It is rare to meet a man you feel is a genius. And yet I spent the whole evening with such a man, Professor Forrer,[10] a Swiss, visiting lecturer at Hopkins, an oriental scholar, the man who discovered and deciphered the Hittite inscriptions. He is full of ideas, has an entirely new approach to all these problems, and will certainly revolutionize linguistics. I do hope that he will stay in this country. SUNDAY, NOVEMBER 19

Rotten day, disturbed all the time. The curse of an Institute are the visitors that you have to show round. A lady came and as I asked her what I could do for her, she answered, "Oh, I just wanted to meet you." As if I were a wild animal in the zoo. Then two old generals came, army surgeons, just to see my rooms. I was fixing up the exhibit, but finally I got wild and my secretary never saw me in such bad temper.
TUESDAY, NOVEMBER 21

Worries about the financial situation of the Institute. Once before I saw my work breaking down, in Leipzig. I would hate to see this repeated and, of course, would hate to leave this country. In Leipzig, at least till 1930, the Institute meant everything to me. Now, fortunately, I'm detached. It is my work that counts. I will stick to it in spite of all difficulties. And if it cannot be done at the Hopkins, I will do it somewhere else. If the few thousand dollars that are required cannot be raised it proves that America isn't ripe for such work. SUNDAY, NOVEMBER 26

[10]Emil Forrer, formerly professor at Berlin and later at Chicago, author of *The Hittite Ideographic Writing* (Chicago, 1932).

A very great pleasure: I was presented with the Sudhoff medal. A beautiful diploma accompanied it with two pages written by Sudhoff in long hand. It pleased me because it comes from the hands and bears the signature of my venerated master and because it shows that I'm not forgotten yet in Germany.   MONDAY, NOVEMBER 27

A great day in American history today, the eighteenth amendment has been repealed, an experiment "noble in purpose" proved to be an utter failure and one had the courage to admit it (depression, of course, helped a great deal).   TUESDAY, DECEMBER 5

And so this year has come to an end, but it doesn't mean an end to me. My new year begins in October when I land in New York.

We had a big party, eighteen in all. Here in America one begins the new year by making noise to frighten the evil spirits. I thought it would be nicer to call the good spirits. Hence, at 11:25 I had everybody sit down and began playing Beethoven's *Quartet in C Sharp Minor Opus 131* on the victrola. The plaintive melody of the first movement. A year is dying. Then at midnight sharp the last movement was being attacked, so vigorous, so full of optimism, so joyful. It was a good start.

SUNDAY, DECEMBER 31

1934

RESEARCH IN EUROPE

Sigerist spent the summers of 1933 and 1934 working in European libraries where he studied medieval manuscripts for his projected history of Latin medical literature in the early Middle Ages. His impressions are a charming mixture of personal and impersonal history, of reminiscences about the past and the present, of sights and sounds. The delight of traveling and gastronomic pleasures were combined with work. As usual, his aims exceeded human possibilities.

Baltimore

And so the new year began. It began with a great deal of work. I have just read two papers in Boston and have to prepare two more papers for New Haven, one of which is very difficult as I have no idea yet what I shall say. It is a formal address for the hundred and fiftieth anniversary of the New Haven County Medical Association. Cushing was to deliver it. As he was sick they asked me and I had to accept.   MONDAY, JANUARY 1

I went to see Cushing at the hospital. He was, or at least seemed, very cheerful smoking a pipe and listening to the radio, but everybody is worried about him. He has a big stomach ulcer or at least we hope that it is an ulcer and the foot is healing very slowly.   FRIDAY, JANUARY 5

Seminar on surgical diseases. Work on a Florence manuscript. Visit to the Enoch Pratt Free Library, a luxurious building. I wonder if the result corresponds to the costs involved. Of course, a library here has many of the functions of a Volkshochschule in Germany. But still, the luxury is exaggerated—a monument of the post-war boom period.

I have subscribed to a good many Russian periodicals. The *Moscow News* came today. I try to keep in touch with Russian things this way.

TUESDAY, JANUARY 23

1934

Dictated a report on the activities of the Institute and a second one on the Sudhoff Exhibit. In other words I am taking over the publication of the *Bulletin*,[11] although the finances are far from sound. But we must have the *Bulletin*. It is the backbone of the Institute. SATURDAY, JANUARY 27

Long talk with Dr. Hume,[12] the founder of Ya-Li, Yale in China, a very sympathetic old gentleman who certainly has done splendid pioneer work in the East. After Russia, China. When I'm through with my Russian work I will attack the field of Chinese medicine, will survey the country and start an Institute for the History of Chinese Medicine there. SATURDAY, FEBRUARY 3

A very good day, the result of yesterday's rest. I began writing Notes and Comments on the Teaching of Medical History. It is a blessing having the *Bulletin* again. Since 1925 I have always had my own journal through which I could address a large audience. I would miss it badly. MONDAY, FEBRUARY 12

Plans for a new book. My Haller collection[13] is developing very slowly as I have the most common editions now and it will take some time to find the rare ones. So I thought it would be nice to start a new collection. An excellent object would be the *Schola Salernitana* as there are so many editions in so many languages. And besides, the book is an extremely important document of the history of hygiene. To study it with all the commentaries and additions would be very worth while.

SATURDAY, MARCH 3

I think I discovered an essential reason for the success and charm of American life. It is its instability! If it is winter today, it may be summer tomorrow. If you like snow, enjoy it now. If you hate it don't bother, it may be hot tomorrow. We have a fine Institute now. It may blow up next year. I have a good job now, I may lose it in a few years (if the funds break down). I have my own journal. How long? Therefore: *carpe diem*. Don't wait, do things and enjoy them now. And if everything comes to the worst, don't worry. You may get an even better opportunity the next day. European life is essentially static, American life dynamic.

SUNDAY, MARCH 11

[11] In 1933 and 1934 the *Bulletin of the Institute of the History of Medicine* was published as a supplement to the *Johns Hopkins Hospital Bulletin*. Thereafter it became a separate publication under the aegis of the Institute. With volume 7 it was renamed the *Bulletin of the History of Medicine*. Sigerist was its editor until 1947 when he returned to Europe.

[12] Edward H. Hume, who wrote *The Chinese Way in Medicine* (Baltimore, 1940).

[13] Albrecht von Haller (1708-1777), Swiss anatomist and physiologist who wrote many books on literary and scientific subjects. The extensive Haller collection which Sigerist assembled was finally sold to the Yale Medical Library.

93

My birthday—43 years old. A good thing in America is that age does not mean anything. There is no problem of the generations here. A "Jugendbewegung" is inconceivable. Whether a "boy" is twenty or sixty makes no difference whatever. What he accomplishes counts. My students are not younger than I am, nor am I older than they are. The whole country is young. I suppose that only countries with old civilizations feel old and therefore worship youth and overrate it.

SATURDAY, APRIL 7

Dr. Welch is 84 today. I went to see him. He was very cheerful, told me of his early days in Germany. He enjoyed the many flowers and telegrams he got.   SUNDAY, APRIL 8

I started a new seminar on the Social Aspects of Medicine. There seems to be much interest in it, the room was crowded with third and fourth year medical students. I gave a general introduction and traced the development down to the Middle Ages. I will repeat this course every year and develop it. Some day it may become a book. This is the line I am most interested in at the present time.   MONDAY, APRIL 9

I must improve my English and have started a new scheme to that purpose. I'm reading Huxley's *Point Counter Point*, two pages a day, analyzing every sentence and making notes of every word and every idiomatic expression that strikes me. I hope to improve my vocabulary in this way and to acquire a better style. No English writer appeals to me as much as Huxley.   TUESDAY, APRIL 10

Dr. Freeman[14] came to lecture me about my health. His recipes are certainly good—slow down, eight weeks vacation, etc., but hard to follow once you are entangled in your work. Still, I will slow down. First of all I will accept fewer lecture engagements next winter and, in order to protect myself, will charge a rather high fee. The money earned in this way will be spent on a vacation trip in the middle of the academic year. That will help.   MONDAY, APRIL 16

There are days—fortunately they are rare—when you feel sick of America. Today was such a day. I was reminded that I had been cheated shamelessly by my automobile dealer. I opened the newspaper and saw nothing but political scandals and crimes. I went downtown in order to buy a pocket diary (mine went to pieces) but the stationers laughed at me. There are no diaries at this time of the year. I wanted to buy silk shirts with detachable collars, but was told that "nobody" wears such, that collars are always attached. You suddenly feel that you are a European after all. In despair I went to a cinema. Thank God it was

[14]Allen W. Freeman (1881-1954) was at that time Dean of the School of Hygiene and Public Health and Professor of Public Health Administration.

an English film, *The Constant Nymph*. The girls were not pretty, no Hollywood dolls, just human beings speaking real English. Reconciled with the world I went home and read *The Tempest* and the sonnets.

SATURDAY, APRIL 21

At 7:00 p.m. Miss Broemer telephoned that Dr. Welch had died. It was not unexpected. We heard this morning that he was suddenly much worse. After his birthday he broke down. He was unconscious during the last days and passed away without suffering.

MONDAY, APRIL 30

We are all terribly depressed about Dr. Welch's death. It was bound to come and it is a blessing that he could pass away peacefully without suffering acute pain. Yet it is hard to realize that we won't see him again. He isn't dead, his spirit will be alive as long as there is a Hopkins, a Rockefeller Institute, any of his many foundations, and he will continue to give guidance and inspiration. The many stories illustrating his character will go from mouth to mouth, from generation to generation, and he will always be remembered as a great man, lovable for his extreme modesty and kindness of heart.

TUESDAY, MAY 1

At three o'clock was the funeral service for Dr. Welch at the old St. Paul's Church. An illustrious crowd was assembled. The service was as simple as possible yet terribly conventional. The old man would have chuckled if he had heard the credo recited for him. Everybody agreed that the right thing to do would have been to have a non-religious, academic service in the Welch Library, yet the trustees would have been shocked, there would have been newspaper gossip. So one had to submit to the conventions.

WEDNESDAY, MAY 2

The President's office sent me some extraordinarily interesting documents—the correspondence between Gilman, Cohnheim, Billings, and Dr. Welch during the years 1883-1885.[15] Dr. Welch had not changed much. He was exactly the same, with the same characteristics in these early days as he was half a century later.

MONDAY, MAY 14

I worked the whole day on the manuscript and finished the preparation of the summer's work. I am ready to start this year's field work, including Italy, France, Belgium, Holland, and Switzerland. The material is overwhelming. If I can investigate 502 manuscripts, it will be a fine result.

FRIDAY, MAY 18

[15]Daniel C. Gilman (1831-1908), first President of the Johns Hopkins University; John Shaw Billings (1838-1913), developer of the Army Medical Library and the creator of its famous Index Catalogue, one of the major planners of the Johns Hopkins Hospital and Medical School; Julius Cohnheim (1839-1884), Professor of Pathological Anatomy at Leipzig with whom Welch studied in Germany. He recommended Welch for the chair of pathology at Hopkins.

And finally the last day has come. I feel quite different from last year. Last year I had finished a book, something was over, I was relieved from a great burden and was looking forward to having a radical change. This year everything is just going on, there is no stop and I am rather apprehensive about Europe. I know that I will be irritated constantly about the political situation. Yet the work is tempting, the escape from the routine. Farewell to the Institute.

TUESDAY, MAY 29

The "City of Newport News"

There we are, leaving Baltimore for four long months. The weather was fine. At 3:30 we went on board. The boat is small but very pleasant. We had quite a crowd to see us off. The cabins were full of *bon voyages*. At five we sailed down the Bay passing Gibson Island, Annapolis, down into the night after a beautiful sunset.

WEDNESDAY, MAY 30

The chief result of last year's work is the consolidation of the Institute. It is firmly established now, is known and appreciated all over the country. The teaching has passed the experimental stage. It works and works well. The publications are started. Volume I of the *Bulletin* had 480 pages, Volume II will have about 600 and the journal will soon be independent. It has a definite function in the country—to publish the results of original research, to propagate medical history not as a hobby but as a science, a historical discipline. A further advance was made in broadening the basis of the Institute in the sociological field. This line, I am sure, has a great future.

SATURDAY, JUNE 2

Tomorrow we shall be in Paris. The idea to be in Europe again rather bewilders me. I am sorry to leave this hospitable boat which, after all, is still American territory. The transition is so sudden which would not be the case had we sailed on a foreign boat. I wonder what the political situation in France is. Toward 6:00 p.m. we saw land, Bishop's Rock. We passed numerous boats—Europe.

FRIDAY, JUNE 8

Le Havre, Paris

Delightful weather. The coast of France. The pilot. Le Havre. There we are, landing at 11:00 a.m. The city seems tiny, the houses like doll's houses, but people are charming, very friendly and helpful. Three and a half hours ride to Paris, passing Rouen. In Paris dinner at Rougier facing Notre-Dame.

JUNE 9

Packing and leaving Paris at 2:00 p.m. It is always a great joy to be in Paris, particularly at this time of year. The only thing that disappoints me is that we do not stay on the Left Bank where I feel so much more at home. But, after all, it is perhaps better this way. The two springs

96

that I spent there in 1930 and 1931 were a period of their own and one shouldn't try to revive the past.   SATURDAY, JUNE 16

Basle

Today I started the manuscript field-work season, at the University Library. Basle is very poor in early medieval material, but I had the glorious idea to have three St. Gall manuscripts sent to Basle. They arrived safely and are waiting for me. The Library is at Schönbeinstr. 20, a very convenient building, a courteous staff. So it was a pleasure to start the work. I developed the technique last year so that I could go ahead without hesitation.   MONDAY, JUNE 18

A letter from Johns Hopkins University telling me that the board of trustees decided to designate the occupant of my chair as the William H. Welch Professor of the History of Medicine. Nothing could give me greater joy.   SUNDAY, JUNE 24

Geneva

I spent yesterday afternoon at the Library in Geneva where I had to examine a manuscript. Klebs showed me a photo of Dr. Welch that was taken in his New York time, the picture of a handsome, energetic, clever young man, clean-shaven. It explained much, for example, his popularity among Broadway people.   JUNE 26

Montpellier

My alarm clock rings. Where in the world could I be? It is warm, the sun pours in through my shutters, the bed is enormous. Oh yes, Montpellier. A narrow courtyard with palm trees. I'll take it easy today, begin with having a good breakfast and dressing very slowly. The town is charming, narrow streets, boulevards with old trees where the walls once stood, the Promenade du Peyrou, seventeenth to eighteenth century, full of twentieth century babies, an enormous botanical garden founded by Richer de Belleval in 1593, full of babies too. You don't notice the decreasing birth rate. The Medical School is in the building of the old Benedictine abbey next to the Cathedral. The library is there too where I spend the afternoon working on a MS.   WEDNESDAY, JUNE 27

Late afternoon in the botanical garden. It is examination time. Groups of young men and women with books studying the plants, as we did at that time, as Haller did in Leyden, as endless generations of young medical men did for centuries, investigating nature in order to cure sick fellow-men. The continuity of the profession, the great medical brotherhood. They are Frenchmen these boys and girls from the southern provinces, some speak Provençal—but among them are Negroes from the colonies, Mongols from Indo-China. I am a stranger among them, yet not a stranger—we are all brothers, comrades fighting the same fight, in different languages with different weapons—the same fight.

FRIDAY, JUNE 29

Vendôme

I am literally exhausted after a long and very hot day spent in Vendôme. The library is particularly important, having three eleventh century medical manuscripts the origin of which is unsure. They were written in the Abbey de la Trinité in Vendôme. Unfortunately the library is open only on Sundays and Thursdays from one to three. That leaves very little time. I arrived at 11:15, went to see the Trinity church, an amazing Gothic building, very flamboyant; the town is early Gothic and particularly good; then the ruins of the castle and the charming City Hall. At one I was at the library and worked very hard. The manuscripts are in very bad shape, badly preserved.   SUNDAY, JULY 8

Angers

I arrived at 1:00 p.m., went straight to the library but the janitor told me that it was closed till September 1, in the process of being repaired and rearranged. I must have looked very disappointed particularly when he told me that the manuscripts were all locked up in the bank. Finally he advised me to go upstairs and see if I could find the assistant librarian. I found her, a very energetic young woman, and she gave me the good news that the MSS. had just come back and that I could see them. She was extremely kind and helpful and so was the curator who came later. Surrounded by carpenters and other craftsmen I did my work.   TUESDAY, JULY 10

Vendôme

In Vendôme again. At 1 o'clock sharp I was at the library this time armed with my camera. I worked terribly hard as the time was so short but in two hours I photographed more than 200 pages. I developed two films in the evening and they seemed to be quite good.

THURSDAY, JULY 12

Brussels

From Paris to Brussels in an excellent train that takes only 3 hours, Pullman cars, Étoile du Nord. No troubles with the customs. My cousin Bruno is at the station and drives me to his home in Genval. I just found that it is about 28 years since I was here. I remember the time very well. We went to Mainz first, then down the Rhine to Cologne and then to Brussels. I was young and full of enthusiasm (how tired and depressed I am today). I remember what I saw and what I read at the time. I must have kept a diary. Flemish paintings made a deep impression on me.

THURSDAY, JULY 19

Brussels

I finish my work at the library, place my order for photostats. At noon I am through. It is just a month since I left Basle. I have not done all I wanted, but still the score is not bad: 29 manuscripts examined, 544 photostats ordered, 30 ordinary photos, and about 200 Leica pages. It is more than last year and I have the month of September still.

TUESDAY, JULY 24

Kastanienbaum, Switzerland

I arrived in Lucerne in the morning, and we drove to our house in Kastanienbaum, called Utohorn. The place is enchanting, could not be more delightful. An enormous garden, a wood, and the lake of Lucerne. The house is very comfortable, furnished with old furniture. I have a very nice study with a superb view onto the Rigi mountain. The house is very big so that everybody can retire when he feels like doing so. There are three rooms for guests. The great advantage of Kastanienbaum is that it is not a village, not a community of its own. It consists of a small hotel, a tiny post office, and a few country houses buried in big gardens. No railroad, no traffic whatever, thank God. An ideal place for a vacation. I am sick of hotels. The fishing is very good here. My father was very keen on fishing, and so are all the Wiskemanns. I inherited the inclination. Nothing thrills me more than fishing.

WEDNESDAY, JULY 25

A trip to Gstaad, passing the charming lake of Brienz that is so untouched and unspoiled, then two hours in Interlaken which always reminds me of the two summers we spent in Beatenberg. It was in 1923. I was still rather weak after the bad pneumonia I had had the summer before, and we rented a charming little Bernese chalet for the whole summer. Nora was one and a half years old and a cute kid; Erica was five and quite a botanist. I did some work and received there an invitation to give lectures in Munich, which was the beginning of my German career. We went back to Beatenberg in 1924 but it was not the same.

MONDAY, AUGUST 6

Back in Kastanienbaum Bruno Hauff, the German publisher, was waiting for us. The sale of my books is rather bad in Germany as I had expected. The American book has sold only about 500 copies although the reviews were excellent. It is obvious that Nazi Germany has no time for, and no interest in, such subjects. But the books don't get old. They can wait for better times.

WEDNESDAY, AUGUST 8

I went to Zurich to consult Dr. Th. Haemmerli. He is an excellent physician and treated me years ago. He examined me for more than an hour very carefully, made an X-ray and electro-cardiogram. The result was very satisfactory. I have a high blood pressure that will have to be watched, but otherwise the heart is o.k. The hypertension is the result of a family disposition. Three Wiskemanns died of angina pectoris, and a fourth had his first attack recently. As I have the Wiskemann constitution it is better to be careful. I will go once a year to Haemmerli for a check-up. If I live reasonably—and why shouldn't I—I may go on for quite a while. The future of medicine is prevention! WEDNESDAY, AUGUST 29

Italy again. Italy and yet on the way home. The ultimate goal of this trip is Baltimore. A month from today we are due in New York.

Lodi was on today's programme. The municipal library has a manuscript of Apuleius. It is a late fifteenth century manuscript, in all probability a worthless version. Still it has to be seen and furthermore you never can tell what the MS. contains besides Apuleius. So we went to Lodi, but we had bad luck, the library being closed from August 27 to September 8. There was nobody there, nothing but an iron gate safely locked. But Lodi is a nice city with two interesting churches. MONDAY, SEPTEMBER 3

Vicenza

Vicenza again, a successful morning. Last year I examined a manuscript, ordered photos and could not get them in spite of repeated letters. So I had to make the pictures myself. The librarian, a nice and inefficient fellow, was called by phone, granted the permission and in a very short time I had all the pictures I wanted. THURSDAY, SEPTEMBER 6

Rome

I worked this morning at the Biblioteca Casanatense, a very agreeable place, well run with a delightful special reading room for rare books supervised by a charming young lady. The family was in St. Peter's and the Vatican and had a hell of a time because the children had on short stockings. Every woman that enters the church is carefully inspected as to how much skin she shows. Sex and money—this is the Catholic Church. Placing sex in the center of everything, fussing about it, magnifying its importance—and money with which you can buy everything, absolution from sin and even the paradise. MONDAY, SEPTEMBER 17

Naples

The *rapido* to Naples. The first impression is dirt, picturesque filth, slums and rats, the ideal place for epidemics. But the sea and the surrounding hills are beautiful and there are big boats in the harbor. Where are they sailing to? Egypt? China? The boats are white and the sea is blue, so blue. In front of our hotel is the Castello dell'Ovo, the island Megaris. The villa of Lucullus stood there. And today there are clubs and elegant restaurants, people singing songs—and inside the castle there are prisoners, in heat and filth. They hear the songs and dream of women. But there is a wall between them and the life outside.

TUESDAY, SEPTEMBER 18

By car on the autostrada to Pompeii with a very nice guide. For 25 years I have longed to see the place and here I am finally. It is even more than I expected. I have spent so much time studying antiquity, have lectured on Greek and Roman life for so many years. This integrates the picture. A Roman city becomes alive. But it was not Rome—a small provincial town yet all aspects of everyday life are represented: working and resting, amusement, excitement, religion, law, medicine—not to forget the sexual life that does not impress me as cynical but just as natural.

THURSDAY, SEPTEMBER 20

The "Vulcania"

Palermo, Almeria, Gibraltar, the Atlantic. It is hot still, and yet the summer has passed and it is autumn now. In a few days I will be back in America, at the Institute, and the academic work will start again.

Looking back: 43 medieval manuscripts were examined in 18 libraries. Ordinary photos were made of 30 manuscript pages with miniatures, 814 pages were photostated and 310 photographed with the Leica, so that I have photographic records of 1,154 manuscript pages—enough to keep me busy for the whole winter. It has been a good summer.

Baltimore

I had a great idea. I decided to go twice to Russia, two months next summer and two months in 1936. The first time I will try to get a general impression and to make contacts, the second year I will check impressions and complete my studies. This will be much better and besides it will leave me time for the medieval studies. I would hate to interrupt them entirely.

SATURDAY, OCTOBER 6

Readjustment of the five-year-plan. It had to be readjusted. The two next winters will be devoted to *Civilization and Disease*. 1936-37 I will write the Russian book and then spend two winters in completing the three volumes on the early Middle Ages. This should be enough. But it is not too much, it is possible.

SUNDAY, OCTOBER 7

My first lecture. I am always scared before delivering the first lecture of the year. Thank God that I am. A big crowd, the whole first-year class. I gave a general introduction and spoke on paleopathology. For more than ten years I have never delivered the first lecture without being handicapped by a terrible cold.

TUESDAY, OCTOBER 9

I am perfectly mad about my publisher. He rushes me in the most shameful way. He writes letters and wires saying that the book (*American*

Medicine) has to be out by the middle of November, that he has committed himself to booksellers, reviewers and the profession. What do I care? He is not a publisher but a grocer, a sausage dealer. I hate this American way of publishing, this silly advertising, idiotic reviewing. My next books will go to another press. It is the first time that I am entangled in this publishing racket, but certainly the last. My whole day was spoiled   WEDNESDAY, OCTOBER 17

The Maryland Society for the Improvement of Gastronomy and Oenology held its first meeting of the season at my house, and the preparation kept me busy nearly the whole day. I cooked most of the dinner myself. Here is the menu:

1. RUSSIAN INTRODUCTION
   Romanoff Beluge Caviar   *Vodka USSR*
2. SWISS ENTRÉE
   Fondue Neuchâteloise *(eaten standing
   in the entrance hall)*   *Zeltinger 1931*
3. FRENCH SUITE
   Bouillon en tasse
   Canard à l'orange   *Réserve des Papes 1929*
   Glaces. Gâteau Avelius   *Bolinger 1926*

It was an eclectic dinner but proved to be a great success.

FRIDAY, OCTOBER 19

Robert Ulich, my old boss, former *Ministerialrat* in the Saxon Ministry of Education, spent the day with me. He resigned as soon as the Nazis came into power and is professor at Harvard now. I was delighted to have him here. He always backed me in Leipzig and whatever I have achieved was done with his help. He deserves all the credit for what the University of Leipzig did in the post-war years. The others in the Ministry were perfect fools.   SATURDAY, NOVEMBER 3

Today I started work on *Civilization and Disease*, a new book that will keep me busy for two years. The subject is fascinating but difficult. I worked the whole evening in preparing a general scheme. It may have to be modified but at least I can start. It may be a fine book. Aldous Huxley anticipated it. Whenever I think I have an original idea, I find it in one of Huxley's books.   MONDAY, NOVEMBER 12

American Medicine is out. The first copies came in today. There they are on my table. A ridiculous jacket with the caduceus of Mercury, "Gott der Kaufleute und Diebe" (which includes the publishers). A hideous title page with snakes and stars. Why not angels and clouds? The girls are very excited and would like to see me thrilled. Why should I be? It is old stuff to me.   FRIDAY, NOVEMBER 16

102

Again endless routine and no work whatever done. In two months I wrote two pages of the new book and worked on two Montpellier manuscripts. The Russian preparation is progressing very slowly, and I have not written a single paper. In other words, two months were just wasted. I don't know what is wrong, insufficient preparation and lack of concentration. I suppose too many evening engagements. This has to be changed radically. Seminar on Benjamin Rush. We have an outstanding collection of his works, part of the Jacobs Collection. I did not expect it.

THURSDAY, NOVEMBER 22

Lunch at the Club. One hour at the Walters Art Gallery. I decided to spend an hour there every Saturday. It is so near the Club. The gallery is magnificent, a little bit of everything, but good specimens, just what a city like Baltimore needs. We saw the ancient collections today and it was a great pleasure.

SATURDAY, NOVEMBER 24

The new book is terribly difficult. I struggled the whole evening and did not write a line. At one moment I felt like giving it up. But it would be absurd. I have good material and a few ideas that are good. I must stick to it. It is just the beginning that is so upsetting—the generalities. Once I get to facts it will be easier.

TUESDAY, NOVEMBER 27

Very exciting day. News came that the Trust Fund is interested in my sociological scheme. They would like to have it put on a national basis. Well, if they see big I can see big too. I worked feverishly the whole day on the memorandum, asking for funds sufficient to provide $25,000 a year. I will not start before I get at least $15,000 annually. If I am successful I may be able to create something really great, a new and promising venture. A great deal of medical knowledge is wasted because it cannot be applied. The social adjustment is the coming problem of medicine.

WEDNESDAY, NOVEMBER 28

Saturday is a bad day. I am always so tired at the end of the week. This was the case today. I intended to do much and did very little, some Russian, a few letters—and that was all.

The political situation in Europe is very tense. A conflict between Yugoslavia and Hungary demonstrated how poisoned the atmosphere is, loaded with hatred. I wonder how long the war can be postponed. It is inevitable, became so the day the Treaty of Versailles was signed, the most imbecile document in history.

SATURDAY, DECEMBER 8

Orpheus and Eurydice broadcasted from New York. While listening I played the piano part. I remembered one evening in Dresden in the spring of 1925. I had been called to succeed Sudhoff and had seen Ulich in the afternoon. In the evening I was the guest of the Minister of Education in the former royal box of the opera. I was tired and had that warm feeling of having accomplished something. A new period of my life was beginning. I saw great possibilities and was just 34 years old. Well, the future was different from what I anticipated.

SUNDAY, DECEMBER 9

The daily routine. I am so tired of it, yet it has to be done.

I am reading Romola Nijinskii's book on her husband. It is fascinating and it reminded me of the pre-war days when I saw the ballet in London, 1911. What a queer world this was, so very remote now.

Somebody asked me why nobody dared to oppose Hitler openly in Germany. There is a new factor in history. People do not mind dying but they dread torture. The human organism is so frail. The twentieth century revolutions have reintroduced systematic torture. Medical care for everybody, but torture if you disagree politically.

WEDNESDAY, DECEMBER 19

1935

THE FIRST TRIP TO THE SOVIET UNION

During the summer of 1935 one of Sigerist's great ambitions came to fulfilment. For years he had prepared himself for a study of health in the Soviet Union. At times his ideas were tinged with emotional overtones for here he thought he had at last found a society where injustice and inequality between human beings were being eradicated, and where a planned economy was avoiding the haphazard processes of capitalism.

Yet most of the time the scientist and rationalist in Sigerist was speaking. After an investigation of European and American medicine, the medical services of a socialist economy attracted his attention just as later South Africa, Saskatchewan, and India were to claim his interest. In his introduction to Socialized Medicine in the Soviet Union *he wrote:*

All my life has been devoted to the study of developments in the medical field and I have approached the problem of Soviet medicine as a historian from the perspective of history, studying and analyzing it as a historical phenomenon, in the same way as I approached the problems of ancient and medieval medical history before. I endeavored to understand Soviet medicine, its principles, its implications, its significance, its position in the history of medicine.

His attention to Soviet affairs was often misunderstood.

Few personal observations were made during the strenuous study tour in the Soviet Union and this accounts for the gap in the present narrative. After June 19 his diary consists of detailed professional notes about the many institutes, clinics, hospitals, factories, rest homes, and nurseries he and his group visited. These notes he later used for numerous articles and for his two books, Socialized Medicine in the Soviet Union *and* Medicine and Health in the Soviet Union.

No other diary entries were made after June 19 until his return to America on October 8.

Baltimore

There are two types of men, scrappers and non-scrappers. Cushing is a scrapper, and so am I. All historically-minded people are. I wish I had started a scrap-book earlier in my student days. THURSDAY, JANUARY 24

A contribution to the psychology of "primitive" people: if you give your colored cook a recipe and ask her to execute it, she will do so. But if you give her specific instructions asking her to modify the recipe, adding this or omitting that, she will disregard your instructions and cling to the printed text. To her a printed text has magical power. It cannot be altered. It is as if you would ask her to say the Lord's Prayer omitting certain commandments. It cannot be done. If you have special wishes write a new text; it will be a new magical formula.   SUNDAY, FEBRUARY 3

While I am writing late at night the newspaper boys are selling a special night edition announcing the verdict in the Hauptman trial. There is no proof that he has killed the Lindbergh baby, but he certainly is an uninteresting, vile individual, useless to society. The newspapers made him a national hero. For weeks he was a headliner and his example will encourage other crimes. But Hearst made money on him and this is what counts.   WEDNESDAY, FEBRUARY 13

The first thing I read this morning in the paper was that the delegates of the A.M.A.[16] had unanimously rejected the President's sickness insurance plan. This, of course, was to be expected. It would have been against the historical rules if it had been otherwise. In all countries the organized profession, i.e. the medical politicians (old generation), opposes social progress. It won't make any difference.   SUNDAY, FEBRUARY 17

Chicago
Breakfast with Dr. C. W. Poynter, Dean of Medicine at Nebraska, and his wife. Mrs. Poynter asked me why I had not mentioned women in medicine in my American book. I don't know. It is an omission, but why did I omit it? It preoccupied me. I think the explanation is this: to me man and woman are so absolutely equal that when I speak of physicians I never think of their sex. In my children's education I never think of their being girls.   TUESDAY, FEBRUARY 19

Baltimore
Seminar on Social Aspects. The audience is still increasing. The Dean, Alan M. Chesney, the State Commissioner of Health, J. Mason Knox, quite a few interns attend the course. I like it; I am so full of that subject, have so much to say that I speak passionately and this carries the audience. I discussed capitalism today, its essence, rise, and influence on medicine, then the German social insurance. I had the people in my hands, by God. They may disagree with many points, but all of them will think differently and will have clearer conceptions at the end of the course.   WEDNESDAY, FEBRUARY 20

[16]The American Medical Association.

One more week and I will start working seriously. In the coming week I will liquidate all the routine work. I have to write 54 German letters myself as none of my secretaries know enough German. Everything must be ready for the coming struggle. I started in my study at home, cleaning up all the drowsy, painful work. I found a letter that my father wrote me for my tenth birthday, blessing me. Three weeks later he was dead. Letters and documents concerning the early days of the children. Something is wrong with me that I am stirring up the past. I dreamed heavily all these nights.   SATURDAY, FEBRUARY 23

I had a hell of a time in the seminar today. I spoke on medicine and fascism and I had just started condemning the regime when I noticed that three fascist students, Italians, were in the audience. I did not want to offend them. Still, they attacked me with stupid arguments. It is a hopeless mentality.   WEDNESDAY, MARCH 6

Social seminar on Soviet medicine. We had to move to the lecture hall and it was filled to the last seat. There was quite a good discussion.

A student came home for dinner and for a talk. He is from Little Rock, Arkansas. His father is member of a clinic that has a very good insurance scheme. He told me much about the appalling conditions in the rural districts where fee-splitting is the rule, where a physician sells his patient that has to be operated on to the surgeon who will pay the highest commission. I could write a second book on American medicine, the back side of the medal.   WEDNESDAY, MARCH 13

The newpapers are full of sensational news from Germany. Everybody knew that Hitler was rearming, but now he has admitted it openly and challenged the whole world. One more scrap of paper. France and Italy are ready for war, England apparently not. The situation is very tense and war may break out at any time. This would be the end of the old European civilization—and perhaps the beginning of a new era, of a new and better world. But the price will be terrible.   SUNDAY, MARCH 17

Dr. Freeman told me that a rumor was being spread that I was a communist. It is perfectly absurd. I was never a member of any political party and never will be. I am a historian, a student of historical and sociological events and am studying Soviet Russia as such. It seems that people begin to be hysterical.   MONDAY, APRIL 1

The Maryland Legislature just passed a bill according to which all teachers in state schools or schools partly supported by the state have to take an oath of allegiance to the United States. It is fascinating to watch how history follows iron rules. The same causes have the same effect all over the world.   TUESDAY, APRIL 2

I did practically nothing today. I am deadly tired of the daily routine. I was lucky in having an excuse for doing nothing. A lady sent me a Haller bibliography that she had written and I was so fascinated by it that I spent the whole day with my Haller collection checking the bibliography. It is a good collection but it is growing very slowly now. Many items are extremely rare. WEDNESDAY, APRIL 3

Temkin and Edelstein[17] are very excited over the teacher's oath bill. Aliens cannot take an oath of allegiance. Therefore all foreign professors would be fired on June 1. It would wreck Hopkins. The Homewood faculty, the war veterans, the student body, the medical school sent telegrams to the Governor protesting against the bill. I cannot take it seriously as I have experienced how little laws mean to the citizens of this country. THURSDAY, APRIL 4

With Weed[18] in New York "money-raising." God damn it! How I hate that business. It was the social scheme again and this time we went begging to the Commonwealth Fund. We were humble and apologetic. Such a great, sound, timely programme, but it has to be "sold." Mr. Barry Smith was most gracious and he and the members of his staff seemed very interested. But what does it mean? We bought a lottery ticket and this is all. We lost on the Keystone ticket and what the chances of this ticket are nobody knows. MONDAY, APRIL 22

Vallery Radot, the grandson of Pasteur, came to the Institute and was very much impressed in seeing the Jacob's collection. I had a photo made of him and Dr. Jacobs—the grandson and the collector of Pasteur. Lunch at the Hospital. At 5:00 Vallery Radot gave his lecture on Pasteur, a grand talk, not only extremely interesting but profoundly touching. Dinner for our guest at the Country Club. I had to give a talk in French. He gave our Institute a splendid autograph of Pasteur that I will publish in the *Bulletin* soon.[19] THURSDAY, APRIL 25

Spent the day with Vallery Radot. Lunch at the Club. Then I showed him the city, Fort MacHenry, Federal Hill, Walters Art Gallery, tea at Miss Cone's[20] to see her Matisse collection. A great Van Gogh, a landscape in waves. Matisse in all periods. Good Picassos. An amazing collection stuffed into two small apartments. SATURDAY, APRIL 27

I have often been asked how many languages I know. I have just

---

[17]Dr. Owsei Temkin and Dr. Ludwig Edelstein were members of the Institute's staff.
[18]Dr. Lewis H. Weed (1886-1952), Professor of Anatomy and Director of the Medical School.
[19]Autograph published in the *Bulletin*, February 1936, 4:153-157.
[20]Miss Etta and Miss Claribel Cone, the Baltimore art collectors.

figured out that I have attempted to learn 14 languages. I still consider French my mother tongue. I thought in French until I was 16. I still count in French and think in it whenever I am tired. Then, of course, German became my language and I learned to master it thoroughly. I learned Italian in school and worked hard on it. I always loved this language. In the Gymnasium in Zurich I learned Latin, Greek, Hebrew, and Arabic privately. After graduation, in 1910, I took up Sanscrit and, in London, Chinese. Then, going back to the University after 1917, I studied Persian and Syriac. In 1921 before going to Spain I learned some Spanish, and now it is Russian. I started learning English very late, before we went to England. While in England in 1911, I was so busy studying Oriental languages that I had little time for a serious study of English.   WEDNESDAY, MAY 15

Weed called up to tell me that the Commonwealth Fund cannot consider a grant at the present time. I am profoundly discouraged because it means that this winter was really lost. It is my fault. I had the wrong policy. You have a choice between two things: either you stick to your individual work and give up the department, or you devote yourself to the department and sacrifice your own work. I attempted to save the department first hoping that I would be able to go back to work later. I was wrong. The country is not ripe for such an Institute. Next winter will be different.   THURSDAY, MAY 16

We are leaving for New York today, sailing Monday. I will be in Russia soon, realizing an old dream.

I am leaving this book here. I will travel through so many different countries, communist and fascist, that such a book could be embarrassing. But I will keep a travel diary.   SATURDAY, MAY 25

London

And so I am starting a new book. Four years ago I was sitting alone in a hotel room in Hamburg ready to sail, to explore a new continent. I am part of that continent now and again I am sitting alone in a hotel room, ready to sail again, to explore a new world but looking east this time. A crowd in the streets, church bells ring, the king is passing followed by the spectacular mounted guards. The crowd cheers the way they would cheer for a film star. Circuses. What will this new world mean to me? The last time I sailed I expected very little and found a great deal. Now I am expecting very much, too much perhaps. I am sailing full of enthusiasm for that new world about which I read so much. Will I find what I am looking for, hopes realized, the promise of a better future, a world built on rational foundations with justice for all? To be disappointed would be a great shock. But I will endeavor to be objective. I am aware of my responsibility. Many people are waiting for my judgment with confidence.

A cab to London Bridge and I am entering the Soviet Union on the M.V. "Sibir." The storm that raged for two days suddenly subsided. Shortly after six the anchor was lifted—and we are sailing now, sailing under the red flag, that symbol of revolution suppressed everywhere, freely hoisted here—sailing down the river on a mild summer evening. How peaceful the world could be. I firmly believe in the fundamental goodness and honesty of man. Give him social security, a chance to work and his share in the goods of life and he has no reason to be wicked. Christianity came into the world as the religion of love, and failed. It was adopted because man was afraid of life. If you are not afraid of this life you need not wait for a hypothetical hereafter. Christianity failed to create satisfactory economic conditions. It did not prevent man from exploiting his fellow-men and therefore sowed hatred instead of love.

The channel, endless lights. How peaceful the world could be.

JUNE 8

The "Sibir"

The boat is delightful, spotlessly clean, just the right size. I am alone in a two-berth cabin and even have a writing desk. I could not be more comfortable. What makes the boat so pleasant is the spirit that reigns on board. No servility, no hunting for tips. The crew, the passengers in the three classes are one big family. No barriers that separate the classes. Everybody talks freely to everybody. We are all united by our common goal: the Soviet Union in which we are all interested. The sun shines, it is warm and soon the whole boat is one big debating club. Economics, social problems, wages, strikes, the coming war are eagerly discussed. Our group could not be more heterogeneous, workers, school teachers, returning Russians, English trade-unionists, professional people, yet we all speak the same language, use the same Marxian terminology and understand each other splendidly. Long talk with a Californian worker, member of the party. He has exceedingly sound views. He must have worked hard to gain such an understanding of economics. He thinks that a fascist move is unavoidable in America. I am disturbed to hear that everybody expects it, takes it for granted, accepts it with resignation.

The Dutch coast, many boats, one certainly does not feel lonely. In the evening we reach the entrance to the Elbe Canal. A Nazi pilot comes on board.

JUNE 9

Leningrad

We arrived in the early morning and had to wait quite a while for the customs. But we waited in a comfortable Intourist building and everybody was perfectly courteous. I have a nice room in the Astoria Hotel.

Sightseeing tour, great historical places from which a new period of world history started, Finliandskii Voksal, Smolny, the Winter Palace.

110

The place was covered with red flags—a gymnastic festival had been held yesterday. The people in the streets are much better dressed than I expected and they undoubtedly look happy with the exception of a few old people, probably members of the former bourgeoisie. Our guide told us that she had attended a boarding school in Brighton and had studied in Oxford in 1911-12. She makes a good living now. If she had emigrated she would be washing dishes in Paris or New York, or would be an old prostitute in Shanghai.

Remarkable how many parks and gardens there are. Wherever a corner was available, trees and shrubs have been planted and children are playing there. The welfare of every individual counts.

Evening at the Opera where a ballet was given, *Esmeralda*. The music was rather cheap but the dancing was exquisite. The story was Victor Hugo's *Notre Dame de Paris*, and Vencheslova danced and acted the girl with utter grace. The audience was very appreciative. It was interesting to observe the audience: two groups of people, one rather well-dressed, obviously intelligentsia, engineers, doctors, etc.; the other, factory workers, sailors, etc. In every society there will be two groups, the leaders and the led, but while in capitalist societies the leaders have all privileges, here both have equal rights. Both groups are enjoying this ballet tonight and as a matter of fact the latter group is much more numerous. There are no workers in the Metropolitan Opera.   JUNE 13

New health resorts are systematically planned, an estimate being first made of the capacity of the spring. No financial interests to interfere. But it takes time and there are difficulties, sometimes very trifling ones, due to the backwardness of many races, e.g. some people have to be educated to use a water-closet properly.

A German theatre will be opened in Moscow with Piscator,[21] Friedrich Wolf[22] and others. A German intellectual and artistic center will develop in Moscow.

The new subway is luxurious with marble walls, etc. More luxurious than any subway in the world. Hannes Meyer, formerly of the Bauhaus Dessau, has to add columns to his buildings. Is this necessary? Is this luxury not a reminiscence of the bourgeoisie? I think it is justified, the idea being that the proletarian state can do just as well as other states. The worker who formerly lived in darkness and filth may be surrounded by marble now. The new state did this for him. If the new state consisted of intellectuals, pillars would not be necessary, but to workers and peasants they are a symbol.   JUNE 14

I went to see the Prophylactorium of the Volodski District. There is as much therapy there as prophylaxis, but it is good to emphasize the word

[21]Erwin Piscator, prominent German stage director.
[22]Friedrich Wolf (1888-1953), German dramatist and writer.

prevention. The institution was erected in 1928. It is a complete health center that can take care of 10,000 people. It is a combination of hospital, dispensary, maternity center, venereal station, night sanatorium for adults and children. The ideal health center for complete medical service as it was recommended for America by the Commission on Costs of Medical Care. The doctors are mostly on a part-time basis, also practising in the district. There is one physician for a group of blocs. If a patient is bed-ridden the doctor will see him at home. When the patient is better he will go to the Prophylactorium and see the same doctor there.

In the night sanatorium a man may stay for 35 nights. Four beds in one room. Nice, airy dining-room. The children's night sanatorium was closed as the children had gone to the country.

Most of the apparatus, X-ray etc. were made in the Union.

The pharmacy, in spite of a small staff, can take care of 1,500 prescriptions a day.

In a room where medicinal baths were given, four women were naked in bath tubs. They were not embarrassed at our visit. Why should they be?

Much education will have to be done still. Everywhere there are tanks with filtered water. Two sets of glasses, unused and used. But I saw several people drinking from the same glass. It was too much trouble to put the glass at the right place. A matter of education.

All in all a splendid institution.

Evening at the Opera, *Sadko* of Rimsky-Korsakov, beautifully staged in gorgeous colors. Good voices with the exception of one. JUNE 16

The Hermitage, an amazing collection. Many minor baroque masters for whom I did not care so much. But a great Raphael, excellent Rembrandts, and a jewel, a Domenichino. Two El Grecos and two most impressive Luis de Morales, new to me.

St. Isaac, a pompous church that cost as much as two Dnieprostroys, now an anti-religious museum, with good material, but badly presented.

Delightful evening at Professor Bykov's home. They are four (or five) people living in four rooms, small rooms but space enough for a piano, a library, collections. Highly cultured people who live in an intellectual and artistic atmosphere. Professor Kupalov and Dr. Goldberg were there, Mrs. Bykov, two daughters, one a musician who played preludes of Shostakovich, the other preparing for the University, another lady, head of a library. We spoke German, English, Russian, but mostly French, discussed the history of science, literature, art. A real Russian supper. Bykov has a splendid collection of books. Academia publishes all the world classics in new Russian translations in beautiful illustrated editions. The classics of science are being published in editions of 10,000. Bykov has translated Harvey, and Goldberg is translating

Galvani. There is a regular hunger for books in the Union, and the largest editions are exhausted in no time. JUNE 17

Moscow

The first impression of Moscow is overwhelming. A big city, a great city. Leningrad is a mere village compared to it. I should not have stayed there so long. Here is the heart of the Soviet Union. I was met at the station by a charming English girl, representing the Open Road. I have a most pleasant room at the Hotel National with a big writing table. In Leningrad I was lost. Here I am taken care of and everything is prepared for me and made so easy.

In the afternoon I went to Voks and had an extremely pleasant hour there discussing the American situation with two clever women, one of them a doctor. They are very helpful and will even give me a special guide. Things could not be better and I feel quite elated.

Evening at the Kamerny Theater, *The Cherry Orchard* of Chekhov. I must confess that I did not understand much. JUNE 19

New York

Exhausted in New York. The boat—a filthy old bus—the *Berengaria*—was late and the immigration and customs inspection were the usual ordeal. First impression—the overwhelming good service in the Pennsylvania Hotel. It will take Russia fifty years to develop such a hotel. The comparison is not fair. Neither France nor any other European country has such service and, in all probability, no country outside the United States will ever have. TUESDAY, OCTOBER 8

Baltimore

Back in Baltimore, back to the Institute. It is very different from other years. Other years I was exultant. I am not now. I have changed. I have been in the Soviet Union and look at things differently. The Institute seems a palace to me, my rooms luxurious—but I know how difficult it is to work here. I know that I will be an administrator and that I will be fortunate if I can steal an hour or two late at night for research. Besides I am tired. I had hardly any vacation this year. WEDNESDAY, OCTOBER 9

The whole day in the photo laboratory. My photography is very poor. People find the pictures nice and that is all. But now I will fix up my laboratory properly and will improve my technique. Photography is a great art and it certainly gives me a great deal of pleasure. It is so different from my usual work. SATURDAY, NOVEMBER 2

An American movie, *The Mutiny on the Bounty*. What would Eisenstein have made of such a subject—a great fresco of human stupidity, brutality, exploitation, and finally rebellion. Here everything was commonplace and dull, just brutal. SATURDAY, NOVEMBER 30

Today I committed a sin. I consented to talk for money. A group of Baltimore society people—what in Leipzig was called the *haute volage*—invited me to talk on Russia offering $100 and I accepted. Of course it was hard to refuse. But I would not have accepted if I had not been tempted by the money. It came so easily; without any effort. Still, I am deeply ashamed. They applauded wildly as they would a tenor, and were thrilled. One was honest when he said: "It was a terrifying picture you gave us." It was, for them. MONDAY, DECEMBER 16

1936-38

TEACHING AND RESEARCH:
BALTIMORE AND EUROPE

For a few more years, until the beginning of World War II, Sigerist's pattern of living was continued: eight months of teaching, lecturing, writing in the United States, four summer months in Europe travelling, working, and least of all vacationing in Switzerland. Twice more, in the summers of 1936 and 1938, Sigerist spent time in the Soviet Union, verifying his earlier studies and adding new knowledge. Again his diaries of those summers are silent about his experiences.

During the pre-war years the tensions and pressures on Sigerist increased greatly. An astute follower of political events, Sigerist expected the outbreak of the war and watched its dress rehearsal in Spain. Personally, also, tremendous demands were made on him. He knew that he was contributing to a greater awareness of past and present problems, and he was unable to refuse the numerous public engagements that drew him into the fray. He complained that "people take me for a slot machine: you press a button and the machine spits out a lecture, or article, or statement."

Although he undoubtedly enjoyed this participation in public affairs, he was also beginning to realize the difficulties of maintaining both the life of a scholar and the life of a public servant, difficulties which were to lead ten years later to a renunciation of his leading position in the medical world. "Under the present system," he wrote, "the scholar who succeeds becomes an administrator and can do research only at night after a long day spent on trifles."

1936

Baltimore

I see the way that I have to go quite clearly. I have to write two books, a History of Medicine, and a Sociology of Medicine. The History will be quite different from all existing books. It will give a picture of medicine as one aspect of civi-

115

lization, as a social institution. It may be a one or a five volume book. And the Sociology will establish a new medical field. This is my goal, will be my life-work, my contribution to medicine. All I am doing now is merely preparation. And when I am through I will retire. I will have said all that I have to say. I only wish that my health will be good enough.   WEDNESDAY, JANUARY 1

I played a joke on the Institute. When I came this morning my parking place was taken, as it so often is. Well, I had the car full of books and felt sick with a congested sinus. So I drove home again and telephoned that I would not come unless they could guarantee me a parking place. General consternation. I will repeat this whenever my place is taken. How can one build a public library without providing parking space? After all, the longer I am at home the better work I can do.
                                SATURDAY, JANUARY 4

A funny experience today. I was at the Court House as chairman of a committee for the examination of candidates for the position of interpreter to the court. A rabbi to the right, a Catholic priest, a Pole, to the left, *das Weltkind in der Mitten.* We examined eighteen candidates in Yiddish, Polish, German, Italian, French, and half a dozen other languages. The best joke was that I was the only expert in Russian. I bluffed so that all were convinced that I was a perfect Russian. It was great fun and besides brought in $100.   WEDNESDAY, JANUARY 29

A South African, Dr. Gillman,[23] from Johannesburg came to see me and to ask me if I would be willing to make a study and lecture trip to South Africa. They have some interesting social problems to solve and need some stimulus. As I seem to be a professional stimulator they would like me to come. I am delighted. Nothing could please me more. I know nothing about South Africa. Being entirely unprejudiced I would very much like to survey the field. It is a young Commonwealth attempting to become culturally independent from England and I am very interested in all young countries.   MONDAY, MARCH 23

My birthday, 45 years. How short a time it was and yet long because the years were well filled. I had the privilege to live in a most interesting period of history without being crushed by events (so far). My field of action broadened steadily: Switzerland, Europe, America, the Soviet Union. I feel in the middle of my career and I hope I will have the health to complete it. I do hope I will live long enough to see the triumph of socialism in the world, the beginning of a new era, the promise of civilization at last.   TUESDAY, APRIL 7

[23]Dr. Joseph Gillman of the University of the Witwatersrand, Johannesburg.

Good lecture on American medicine. The whole course is particularly pleasant this year. As a matter of fact the whole year was good. I did not write any book but a good many papers, some of them worthwhile, and first of all, all over the country the interest in problems of social medicine has been greatly stimulated which certainly was due to a certain extent to my activities. It is a great pleasure to get reports on new developments from many schools.   THURSDAY, MAY 14

Back in America after a very good summer. June and July in the Soviet Union where I felt quite at home and where I completed my material—mostly in Moscow but with a delightful Volga trip to Kazan and Gorky. Then two great months in Kastanienbaum where I launched my book, writing the first 206 pages. It was a great joy to be able to concentrate on one subject, to work rested after a long night's sleep, at leisure. I worked throughout the summer but feel perfectly rested.
                                                    TUESDAY, OCTOBER 6

I have a new daily schedule. My chief task this winter will be the Soviet book. This must be done. The manuscript has to be ready on May 1 at the latest. So I will work on it every morning and will not go to the Institute before 12. This will give me 2½ hours for writing every morning. So I will be sure that no day will be lost. Then:

12-1   reading correspondence, seeing people
2-3   dictating letters
3-4   papers
4-5   teaching or work on Russian,
Evening: writing, preparing lectures, etc.   THURSDAY, OCTOBER 8

Election day. We spent the evening with friends where we found a wild crowd of enthusiastic New Dealers (pretty drunk as it goes). At 9:30 it was sure that Roosevelt was re-elected by an overwhelming majority. I was sure that he would be re-elected but I did not expect such a landslide, 46 states! It was decidedly a class vote and as there are many more poor than rich people his election was sure. I am delighted with the result. Now we are going to have four more years of liberal common sense administration. Landon was just a harmless fool, but the men behind him were crooks.   TUESDAY, NOVEMBER 3

My remedy for colds never fails me and after a good night's rest I feel fine today. The whole day was very satisfactory. I wrote five pages on the book and devoted the whole afternoon and evening to a South African physicians' group sent by the League of Nations to study public health conditions in America and Europe. They came to the Institute where I told them what our work is and where I gave them a tea. They seemed quite impressed.   WEDNESDAY, NOVEMBER 11

117

Every morning at breakfast I read the newspapers and every morning I feel quite sick after having read the news from Spain. It is an outrageous situation, a gang of capitalists and officers fighting the people to preserve their class privileges. But what a heroic resistance.   THURSDAY, NOVEMBER 12

Alumni dinner at the Belvedere. Hundreds of our medical alumni from the South. I had to talk on the Library and the Institute and—I don't know how it happened, I was hardly prepared, it was all a matter of atmosphere—I struck the right chord and found an amazingly warm response. This is so exceedingly encouraging—I do not make any concessions but stick to my line and say openly what I consider the truth whether it hurts or not—and yet the people like me and respond to my message. It was a most happy evening.   THURSDAY, NOVEMBER 19

I sat next to Victor Heiser yesterday. His book, *An American Doctor's Odyssey* was a tremendous success, sold 140,000 copies in no time and is being translated into many languages. I felt embarrassed because I had not read the book but ordered it today. Can a good book be a best-seller? I am not sure. Heiser feels he is a missionary propagating public health among the public.

Evening at the Ford Theater, a Chinese, or rather pseudo-Chinese play, *Lady Precious-Stream,* charming, well acted but rather puerile and I don't think it has any resemblance with the original, but the stage setting amused the people.   FRIDAY, NOVEMBER 20

New York

My lecture tonight may save human lives. I spoke on social aspects of medicine before the New York chapter of the Phi Beta Kappa, an audience of about 200. In introducing me the chairman mentioned that I was serving on the committee to provide medical supplies to the Spanish government and the audience cheered wildly. So I knew where they stood. I spoke for 1¼ hours and they applauded endlessly. Then one young man rose and said that applauding was alright but not enough, that the audience, to show its appreciation, should collect money for the Spanish government. A short time later they handed me over $30 which buys a good deal of serum. I felt elated.   MONDAY, NOVEMBER 23

Baltimore

Dinner at Hamilton Owens,[24] a purely English dinner (veal and kidney pie) "in honor of Mrs. Wally Warfield Simpson," the Baltimore national heroine. The general opinion is that the king should marry her. I feel differently. I do not care with whom the king fornicates. Monarchy is stupid but if you have it, stick to the rules of that silly game. It is hard

[24]Editor of the newspaper the *Baltimore Sun*, 1938-43; editor-in-chief, the *Sun-papers*, 1943-56. Mrs. Simpson was born in Baltimore.

118

to say whether the sympathy for the king is not merely the result of the antipathy to Baldwin who is a curse to the country.   FRIDAY, DECEMBER 4

Sarton, the poor devil, had another break-down and has just left for a three-week trip to the West Indies. How I envy him. I would not mind the break-down if it would result in such a vacation trip. *Hélas,* I am too robust and besides I haven't the money. His secretary sent me a memorandum that he wrote on the necessity of the organization of an Institute of the History of Science. I agree with him whole-heartedly and I worked till late into the night on the presidential address I am going to deliver next spring in Atlantic City where I will discuss all these problems in great detail and support Sarton strongly.
                                                     MONDAY, DECEMBER 7

A sideline on the solidarity of the American working class. Arriving in Baltimore today I heard that the Diamond cabs are on strike fighting for the permission to join the truck drivers' union. I took a Yellow cab and asked the driver why they did not join the strikers. His answer: "No, Sir, we are not so foolish as to lose the Christmas business. Let the Diamond boys fight it through. If they succeed in building up a strong union we'll be glad to join them. Yes, Sir."   TUESDAY, DECEMBER 15

Our financial situation is bad this year. Expenses are increasing and income is low. It is time that I stopped lecturing. Not only does it cost time, but it costs money as well. Most universities are too broke to pay honorariums or even expenses. I never got a cent from Harvard, Yale, or Columbia.   THURSDAY, DECEMBER 31

1937

Baltimore

A new year is beginning. First I will have to finish my Soviet book. It looks pretty safe, but it will be a terrific effort to complete it before May 1. Then I will write the Addresses and Essays on Medicine and Society. After that I should be ready for some new travelling—South Africa, Russia again, China. And soon I will start preparing my *magnum opus,* the History and the Sociology, 5 volumes.
                                                     FRIDAY, JANUARY, 1

I am tired. I gave up eating lunch in order to have one more hour. After dinner, I cannot help it, I go to sleep in my chair for a few minutes. It is usually 2:00 a.m. when I finally sleep. At 8 I get up again. But the book must be done and done well. It must be a real contribution, must stir the people's minds, must arouse the young generation.
                                                     THURSDAY, JANUARY 7

The political situation is getting more and more tense. The Germans have made the biggest possible blunder by fortifying Ceuta and antagonizing England. The next war will be a war between democracy and fascism, but democracy will be supported by very different forces, socialist Russia, France of the Front Populaire and ultra capitalist England. England is an unreliable customer and the government is pro-fascist at the bottom of its heart. If war breaks out I will enlist in some army. I cannot sit here, write books, and make speeches while the future of Western civilization is being decided.   FRIDAY, JANUARY 8

Most distressing news from Switzerland. The Federal Council has passed a law empowering it to suppress all radical opinion. It is amazing to see how old democracies, when they have the choice between democracy and socialism, and capitalism and fascism do not hesitate to throw democracy overboard.   SUNDAY, JANUARY 10

New York

Mass meeting at the Metropolitan Opera House for Spain, a farewell party for the ambulance corps that will leave Saturday. A most inspiring meeting, 2,500 people, tremendous enthusiasm. I spoke for the Medical Bureau, others spoke. $6,000 was contributed in half an hour. Surgeons and nurses in uniform were introduced to the audience, endless cheers. A great evening.   THURSDAY, JANUARY 14

Ten blocks up, ten blocks down Lexington Avenue. Lights all over. The air is crisp like in early spring. I walk rapidly, breathe deeply, and feel full of vitality shaking off the sickening atmosphere of the meeting of the Council of Learned Societies. I can't get accustomed to the American system of waste, to that stupid *Kulturpolitik* of committees on a charity basis. Chinard[25] suddenly said: "Au fait qu'est-ce que nous foutons en Amérique, quand on serait si bien à Paris?" I wonder. Well, let's see the real America, a burlesque, Minsky's, and a colored review, *Harlem in Uproar*. Superb music, olive girls dancing furiously. That's America at its best.   FRIDAY, JANUARY 29

Invitation and banquet at Alpha Kappa Kappa. I had to speak and discussed why we consider the Greeks our medical ancestors: the myth of Aesculapius, the two great discoveries they made—disease a natural process, the healing power of the body—and I ended by recollecting Friedrich Müller, the days in Munich. The key to medicine: observation and correct reasoning.   SATURDAY, FEBRUARY 6

There is more begging in America than in any other country, including the Orient. It is not done in the streets but by mail, on good stationery.

[25]Gilbert Chinard, Professor of French and Comparative Literature at Johns Hopkins.

Not one day passes that I am not solicited to give money, for crippled children, for tuberculosis, the Red Cross, for hospitals, conservatories, libraries, universities, for fires and floods. Half of the population is begging to support the other half. What a shameful procedure for a civilized country. Thousands of women are spending all their time and efforts in begging. What a waste of energy and intelligence.

FRIDAY, FEBRUARY 12

Madariaga gave a lecture in Homewood on Spain and Peace. He is a Catholic and an old-school liberal. So you knew in advance what he was going to say. His recipe for peace was: international trade and world citizenship. We heard this for more than a century and the result was communism and fascism. So there obviously must be other factors involved but he did not mention them. He spoke brilliantly but it did not mean anything. These men won't save the world.   MONDAY, FEBRUARY 15

Albany and Saratoga

Greatly surprised by the beauty of the Hudson. Comfortable train following the river for three hours, on a glorious spring-like day. Yet the river carries ice. Hills, a silver mist, villas of wealthy New Yorkers, and convents. Not the romanticism of the Rhine, something more powerful, more savage, reminding me of Indians, reminding me of the Volga. Albany, the ambitious small capital of a great state. Union Medical College, a good new hospital with a good staff and a group of students. I spoke to them and to a crowd of pretty nurses on the history of the concept of disease.

Then drive to Saratoga Springs with Dr. Hunt. Dr. McClellan[26] showed me the spa which is beautifully equipped. The State of New York erected buildings for 8 million dollars in exquisite style. The spa compares very favorably with European resorts. Dinner at the hotel with the local doctors, after which I gave a lecture on Soviet medicine to the County Society. Back to New York on the night train, and back to Baltimore, Saturday morning.   FRIDAY, FEBRUARY 19

Baltimore

Roosevelt speaks on the radio about the Supreme Court, an excellent talk, clever, honest, convinced of the cause. There is no choice, he must get rid of the old dodos who live in a world that is gone.

I wrote a few pages for the new medical students' journal.[27] Once more "Worte an die Medizinische Jugend," passionate still but this time more diplomatic. Still, I have the same interest in the young medical generation as I had in Leipzig.   TUESDAY, MARCH 9

When Mrs. Bauernschmid was a young girl she once asked Osler what syphilis was. And Osler entreated her never to mention this name in

[26]Dr. Walter S. McClellan, Medical Director of Saratoga Springs Authority.
[27]*Journal of the Association of Medical Students.*

121

decent society. "Perhaps," he said, "when you'll have white hair, it will be possible to discuss the disease openly." Well, Mrs. B. has white hair now, a campaign has been started against syphilis and everybody speaks of it. So Mrs. B. gave a big dinner inviting the people engaged in the campaign, the Surgeon-General Parran[28] and his charming wife, Earl Moore, Huntington Williams[29], school people, and President Bowman.[30] Mrs. B. recollected Osler and I had to give an impromptu speech on syphilis.   TUESDAY, MARCH 16

Freeman comes and tells me that he is worried about my various activities. Yet when we discussed them he had to admit that I was right. For a moment I thought of publishing my book in Europe only, forbidding an American edition so as not to contaminate the American medical youth! But Freeman found as I do that this would be foolish.

I dictated five pages, prepared five more. If I had the evenings free every day it would be child's play to finished the book.   MONDAY, MARCH 22

I am very much upset about a new happening at the University. One of their best students was refused Phi Beta Kappa because he is an active member of the American Students Union. And what makes it worse is that it was the medical school members who brought the chief pressure.
                                                    SATURDAY, APRIL 3

My forty-sixth birthday celebrated by attending a superb concert of the Philadelphia symphony.   WEDNESDAY, APRIL 7

Big banquet in honor of Adolf Meyer[31] to celebrate his seventieth birthday (which was last year) and the twenty-fifth anniversary of the Phipps Clinic (which will be next year). Meyer throughly enjoyed the affair. All his students past and present were assembled and endless speeches were held. Meyer is a most lovable character and has done a splendid job in America. The trouble with him is that he cannot express himself. As a matter of fact, nobody actually knows what his philosophy is.   FRIDAY, APRIL 16

Student Conference, the fourth—but the first convention of the A.M.S.[32] In spite of bitter antagonisms the students met in Baltimore, 375 of them representing 33 schools. Lunch in the Great Hall. Formal opening. Chesney[33] gave an excellent talk. He does not believe in the A.M.S. and his address was ironical without being offending, very

[28]Thomas Parran, Surgeon-General of the U.S. Public Health Service, 1936-48.
[29]Huntington Williams, Commissioner of Health of Baltimore since 1933.
[30]Isaiah Bowman, President of Johns Hopkins University.
[31]Adolf Meyer (1866-1950), Professor of Psychiatry and Director of the Henry Phipps Psychiatric Clinic (Johns Hopkins Hospital).
[32]Association of Medical Students.
[33]Alan M. Chesney, then Dean of the Hopkins Medical School.

cleverly done. Then John P. Peters of Yale spoke, very well also, attacking the foundations, the "philanthropic bosses."

I felt sick and went to bed so as to be able to talk tomorrow.

SATURDAY, APRIL 17

I have 38° temperature, cough and can hardly talk but I have to go to the meeting. The students expect me, many of them are my friends, the left wing of the student body. The convention was in full swing when I came towards 11:00 a.m. The constitution of the A.M.S. was being discussed. There are pros and cons. There were spies in the audience and *agents provocateurs*, but everything was well prepared and the constitution was adopted with enthusiasm. There is one A.M.S. now and it has its Journal. Then I spoke in a hoarse voice and the students cheered endlessly. I consider the A.M.S. more or less as my own child.

SUNDAY, APRIL 18

After my talk yesterday I had to go to bed. I have a deep-seated bronchitis and I am completely voiceless. So I am sick and I am enjoying all the privileges accorded by society to the sick man. I need not go to Boston Thursday. I can call off all my lectures. I need not write letters. Nor must I answer telephone calls. Swell. So I am going to have a vacation after all.

MONDAY, APRIL 19

Cold and pouring rain. A stamp show at the Peal Museum. I used to collect stamps as a boy. Why? Because I was longing to see foreign countries. Later I travelled and therefore stopped collecting. Now I collect the stamps of the countries in which I live. It interests me to see what seems worthy of being represented or commemorated at a given time. Why does the U.S. glorify its army and navy just now? Stamps are one quite significant aspect of the history of civilization of a given country.

SUNDAY, APRIL 25

Seminar on the incidence of tuberculosis and venereal diseases in the various social classes. There can be no doubt that the fight against disease today is primarily a fight against poverty and for better living conditions.

It was a coincidence that a Chinese doctor came to see me today. China is the best illustration for this thesis and the Chinese doctor agreed with me that socialism is the only possible solution of the medical problem also. At least in large countries. Small countries like Denmark may improve conditions through co-operation.

WEDNESDAY, APRIL 28

Dictating the whole day, first five pages of the book, then ten letters, then the address I made at the student conference. Fortunately I kept my notes. My two secretaries are working very hard.

A faculty meeting, then a dinner at home with mint juleps. The mint julep is the greatest drink I know. You drink it slowly, your nose buried in the leaves, and suddenly it opens up your mind and even dull people become talkative and witty. FRIDAY, APRIL 30

The first of May: gigantic parades on Red Square, the Place de la République, in hundreds and hundreds of cities; in Baltimore: nothing. It is incredible how backward the labor movement is here. I remember the parades of my childhood days in Zurich so well. There I first became aware of the fact that there is such a thing as organized labor. They used to assemble in front of our apartment on the Utoquai, and they marched for hours with brass bands and posters demanding the eight-hour day. SATURDAY, MAY 1

Atlantic City
I got up early and worked feverishly on my paper for many hours. Meeting of the American Association of the History of Medicine over which I had to preside. Many papers, some good, some poor. The society must be reorganized from the bottom. The way it is now it cannot live and cannot die. I will try to make it a worthwhile organization, a real factor in American medicine. MONDAY, MAY 3

Washington
I have to give a radio talk in Washington in the studio of the National Broadcasting Company. Once and never again! Nothing is more unpleasant than broadcasting in America. You have to talk down to the people. I was addressing the Parent and Teacher Association and I had been warned that the intellectual level of the audience would be that of 14-year-old children. I had written a very simple story but it was still considered much too highbrow. MAY, 19

New York
Early in New York. Breakfast at the station. Then the boat. Sailing on the *Queen Mary* at 11:00 a.m. WEDNESDAY, JUNE 9

Paris
First visit to the Exposition. Very few pavilions are finished and it will take a long time before the whole exhibition will be completed. The Swiss pavilion is decidedly shabby and does not give an adequate idea of the country's activities. The textile and the watch industries are well represented but that's about all. Belgium on the other hand has a superb exhibit, very representative and artistically arranged. The explanation for the greater wealth is given by the Congo pavilion. The exploitation of colonies pays—at least it did. TUESDAY, JUNE 15

My beloved Quartier Latin, the Luxembourg, the familiar shops. Students on the Boulevard St. Michel, the usual international crowd;

and in the court yard of the Faculté de Médecine boys and girls are discussing their exams.

The Exposition: the two largest pavilions, facing each other—Germany and the USSR, eagle and swastica on one side, a worker and a *kolkhoznika* in steel with hammer and sickle and the red flag on the other side. Two worlds facing each other: capitalism in its fascist phase and socialism—two worlds which sooner or later will clash—are clashing already in Spain. WEDNESDAY, JUNE 16

Kastanienbaum

From Basle to Kastanienbaum with sixteen pieces of luggage. A glorious day, sunny and warm. And what a beautiful region and so utterly peaceful. How good it would be to forget the world and its troubles. But it is impossible. SATURDAY, JULY 3

The lake, swimming, fishing (successfully!). I should go back to work soon but I decide to wait for one more week. After all, I deserve a full month's vacation; and it is so pleasant to loaf. Soon the galley proofs of my book will pour in and I will be more than busy. So let's take it easy for one more week. SUNDAY, JULY 4

I have subscribed to four newspapers: the conservative *Basler Nachrichten,* the liberal *National Zeitung,* the radical *Oeuvre* and the socialist *Ce soir.* It is incredible how different the reporting is and it is impossible to form an opinion without reading several papers. Unfortunately the *Humanité* is forbidden in Switzerland and in general the communist party has been suppressed. MONDAY, JULY 5

I must improve my English. I have reached the point where I can express myself without difficulty but not well enough. I became strongly aware of my deficiencies when I wrote the book. It is essential not to remain stationary but to develop constantly and to have more words available all the time. I am doing now what I did once before: I am reading a few pages of Aldous Huxley *(The Olive Tree)* every day, analyzing every sentence and making notes of every expression and construction that I would not have used. THURSDAY, JULY 8

Four Baltimore girls, classmates of Erica, came for supper and we all had a jolly good time. They made me realize how much attached to America I am. America is my field of action today, and already I am looking forward to returning in the fall. I think it would be very difficult for me to readjust myself to Europe.

I spent most of the day planning next academic year's *plan rabot* [plan of work], and closely connected with it, the plan of my History of Medicine. I think I will have to write it in four volumes instead of three as I originally planned. It is easier to group the material in four volumes. But it will take eight years to complete the task, a long time.

THURSDAY, JULY 22

Einsiedeln
Erica and I went to Einsiedeln to see the mystery play that is being given this summer. From Goldau we travelled in a car built in 1878 so that the trip alone was a historic experience. In Einsiedeln we stayed in the Hotel Pfau, an old-fashioned house, well kept and where the food and the Johannisberger are excellent. Meals are served on a terrace in front of the monastery. We of course went to see the church, rather cheap baroque inside while the façade is splendid, sober and most impressive. In front of the church the play was given at night: Calderon's *Das Grosse Welttheater* acted by "Das Volk von Einsiedeln." The play is orthodox Catholic with all the cruelty of the Catholic Church, but the performance, the music, the choir—all this in these beautiful surroundings— were superb. This is living theatre like—on the other side—the revolutionary theatre.

THURSDAY, JULY 29

We went on a pilgrimage to the birth-place of Paracelsus on the Sihl, near the Teufelsbrücke. It is an inn now, as it was at the time of Paracelsus, but the building, of course, is new. The Kronenwirtin, the present owner of the place, has two sons in California. I took her portrait and will send her copies for the sons. Years ago, it must have been in 1920 or 1921, I was here with Sudhoff. Dear old Sudhoff. I am still very much attached to him and regret that he never writes. He probably resents that I left Leipzig and that I did not become a Nazi as he did.

FRIDAY, JULY 30

Kastanienbaum
My cousin Bruno is a great cook and I have the ambition to become one. He is my teacher and from him I learned to make the *canard à l'orange* which was so successful in America. Today we spent the whole morning in the kitchen and made *poulet de la Mère Fillou*—a great dish.

TUESDAY, AUGUST 3

I finished *Le Débâcle* and found it by far the greatest of Zola's books I had read. Not a *roman à thèse* but a gigantic fresco, a most powerful picture of pathetic events. It is a masterpiece and will live for ever. Such a book recreates history better than any history book. SATURDAY, AUGUST 4

Paris
An unforgettable evening: Gorky's *Vragi* given by the Moscow Art Theatre. A performance that was perfect in every respect. Not only Kachalov and Tarassova, all the actors down to the smallest part were perfect. I could follow very well and understood much more than last

126

year. This evening was worth the whole trip and I only regret that I could not see the other plays. TUESDAY, AUGUST 24

I am not a pacifist. I think peace is more important than pacifism. I disagree with Aldous Huxley and believe that we have to fight to make peace possible. The point is that we must know what causes are worth being defended and what not. In 1917 Americans went to war to make the world safe for democracy. What was the mistake? The mistake was that people did not take the trouble to analyze the situation. Therefore they did not recognize the imperialist character of the war. They were driven by propaganda slogans and actually fought for J. P. Morgan's investments. They did not know what economic conditions make real democracy possible. SUNDAY, AUGUST 29

The "Berengaria"
Paris—Cherbourg—*Berengaria*. In Cherbourg I gave the porter 50 francs which was very much indeed, more than he ever gets. He was not satisfied but begged for more in a most impudent way. Such fellows do a tremendous harm to the prestige of the Front Populaire. Tourists who after having been in Italy and Germany meet with such an experience will draw the conclusion that the French worker is demoralized. Some are, why? Capitalism breeds parasites—the enormous legions of all the people who live from tips, from what the rich are willing to give voluntarily. They lose their dignity and once they are used to begging they begin to cheat. Everybody is a sucker to them. The worker must be given dignity and pride first of all. WEDNESDAY, SEPTEMBER 22

Baltimore
This is the beginning of the new academic year. There will be eight months of work without interruption, but I feel very rested and I am eager to begin. After all, it is much more comfortable to work here with two good secretaries and all facilities at hand than in the country or in hotel rooms.
I begin the day with an hour of Russian, reading *Pravda*. At 11:00 a.m. I am in the Institute and dictate the ten daily letters. I wish to devote the afternoons to research, preparing the first volume of my History of Medicine. MONDAY, OCTOBER 4

I am sticking to my programme: so far I have refused fifteen lecture invitations ranging from Vermont to New Orleans. People will come to learn that it is not quite so easy to get me to talk.
Many visitors, mostly students who come for advice on all kinds of problems. FRIDAY, OCTOBER 8

First current events talk. This is a new experiment. I thought I would like to discuss with the students new developments in the field of social medicine, state medicine, medical economics, and similar subjects. It will oblige me to keep in very close touch with such developments and to take a definite stand.

I expected only a small group, my more intimate students, the left wing, but the seminar room was overflowing and we shall have to move to the lecture hall.   WEDNESDAY, OCTOBER 13

I received forty copies of the American edition of my Soviet book today. So it is out. The official day of publication is tomorrow, I believe. The book has a pleasant appearance and I am very glad that I need not read it. I think I know it by heart. Now I am ready to be insulted by the conservative press. I think I can stand it.   THURSDAY, OCTOBER 28

I was very much upset today. The British edition of my book came and I discovered that the index had been omitted without which the book is almost worthless. I immediately cabled to Gollancz and I received an answer in the evening with apologies and explanations. The accident had happened only in a few advanced copies while the bulk of the edition was safe.

Sidney Webb wrote a foreword in which he explained why he found my book better than other books on the same subject. Webb made two criticisms, both perfectly justified: 1) the style, 2) the introduction. There is no doubt that the book is written in an atrocious style, a kind of primitive baby-talk. Norton found that it reads as if it had been written by a native, but the American natives cannot write either. What depresses me is that I was a stylist as long as I wrote German—and now Germany is closed to me and I have to write English which always will be a foreign language to me because I learned it too late. As to the introduction, it decidedly is too long and Webb is probably right that a mere summary of Marxism does not mean much.   MONDAY, NOVEMBER 8

Yesterday at 5:00 I gave my current events talk and this morning at breakfast I found all I had said in the newspaper. I was furious. It is incredible that reporters dare to come to your classes. I do not make statements that I cannot defend publicly, but in a public meeting I would phrase them differently. When I speak to students I like to call a skunk a skunk. First I thought of asking the President to protest against this intrusion of the press into classes of the University. Then, after consulting with Larkey[34] and a few others, I decided to let things go. After all...   THURSDAY, NOVEMBER 18

McDaniel[35] wrote me a very nice letter. He was reading my book and got scared for me. He thought it was a tactical error. That may be correct

[34]Sanford V. Larkey, Librarian of the Welch Medical Library.
[35]Walton B. McDaniel II, then Librarian of the College of Physicians of Philadelphia.

but I am not a strategist. I am a professor which means a *Bekenner*. I have to say what I consider the truth. I always have no matter what the consequences were. It would be so simple to glorify the existing conditions, but I have never been ambitious. I do not care for honors or recognition or anything of the kind. I know my line and I am going to stick to it. SUNDAY, NOVEMBER 21

San and Jerry Larkey came for Thanksgiving dinner and I did all the cooking. The dinner was carefully prepared days in advance and was a great success. The chief course had to be a turkey, but what I cooked was a *dinde truffé* which was delicious. I sent greetings to my master across the sea, "le grand Bruno."

It was much fun and gave me a real day of rest. THURSDAY, NOVEMBER 25

I received an invitation to give a talk on Russian medicine at the Mexican Embassy. I accepted because I am interested in Mexico. This is one more country where medicine cannot succeed until it has been socialized. The population is too poor to be able to purchase medical service. I wished I could survey the conditions and help in building up a public service after the Russian pattern.

All my life has been spent in studying medical conditions past and present, in interpreting them, commenting upon them and criticizing them. The dream of my life is to be able to act for once, to put my experiences into practice, actually to build socialism. It probably will never be realized but I am still hopeful. I am not so old after all and events are developing rapidly.

The Chinese Students' Club invited me for a tea to meet Professor Hu Shih, Dean of the National University of Peiping and leader of the Chinese renaissance. He is the man who wrote such a delightful introduction to the Chinese edition of my *Man and Medicine* and I was most anxious to meet him. He spoke very tactfully on the Far Eastern situation. SUNDAY, NOVEMBER 27

Canby Robinson[36] burst into my office and asked me if I wished to go to China. When? Right away. How long? Oh, about half a year. The China Board of the Rockefeller Foundation had appropriated funds to send me over as a visiting professor. Well, I'd be delighted to go but not without some preparation. I told Canby that I would have to know about a year in advance so as to plan the year accordingly. The war would not daunt me, on the contrary, it would be a most interesting time to be there. WEDNESDAY, DECEMBER 8

[36]G. Canby Robinson, (1878-1960), former Dean of the School of Medicine at Washington University and at Vanderbilt, who was then Lecturer on Preventive Medicine at Johns Hopkins University. In 1935 he had been visiting Professor of Medicine at Peiping Union Medical College.

Christmas. A beautiful tree, spring weather and nice gifts. The high spot: records of the Bach *Violin Concerto in E Major,* a superb piece of music.   FRIDAY, DECEMBER 24

1938

Baltimore

The greatest problem in the organization of research is to find a system that would allow the scholar to do his work. Under the present system the scholar who succeeds becomes an administrator and can do research only at night after a long day spent on trifles. It is hard even to keep one's standards. The present situation is stupid and something must be done about it.   TUESDAY, JANUARY 4

A medical fraternity invited me to address them and to discuss my book with them. It was an easy task. A queer institution these fraternities. They don't admit Jews so that the Jewish students, the most intelligent and alert group, are totally isolated. I do not think that more than one student (he was from Minnesota) in this particular fraternity had read my book.   WEDNESDAY, JANUARY 5

New York

A queer day. Castiglioni was in New York. He is on a West Indies cruise. He met me at the station and we had a luncheon with a few other people on the *Saturnia.* So I was in Italy all of a sudden, in fascist Italy where the people greet you by lifting their arm. It was a queer sensation and it was a relief to see the Empire State Building through the window. But the luncheon was delicious. Castiglioni is fed up with the regime and made the cruise to get out of the country for a whole month.   FRIDAY, JANUARY 7

Alan Gregg[37] was in my office for three hours and we talked and talked. He is a devoted friend of our Institute and I have no doubt that he will do for us whatever he can. He wants to get $15,000 for us for ten years. This would remove a disturbing element of uncertainty. And it is just the time that I need to complete my work. It is pretty liberal, after all, that the Foundation supports me in spite of my radical attitude. I do not hesitate to accept the money. It is nothing but social justice that this money should serve the ends for which I am fighting.   MONDAY, JANUARY 10

Lunch in Homewood with Gaetano Salvemini. He is an anti-fascist exile, now professor at Harvard, a fascinating personality. He began

[37]Alan Gregg (1890-1957), Director of Medical Sciences, Rockefeller Foundation.

his career as a Marxian historian, has somewhat modified his views now but is still aware of economic factors. After lunch he met the history seminar and we discussed basic problems of historiography. In the evening he spoke to the Foreign Policy Association and was opposed by Sir Willmott Lewis, the Washington correspondent of *The Times* who defended the British point of view in the traditional way.

WEDNESDAY, JANUARY 19

I am reading Borgese's new book on fascism, *Goliath*. It is brilliantly written, a violent attack on the line of Demosthenes. I do not agree with many of his interpretations. To him history is made through the passion of individuals. He discards economic interpretations. Nevertheless it is an entrancing book. THURSDAY, JANUARY 20

New York

Golden Boy by Clifford Odets at the Belasco. Odets could have become one of the most significant playwrights of our day if he had kept his social consciousness. *Waiting for Lefty,* his first play, was his best. This one is weak, cleverly done of course, because he masters the technique, but the characters are conventional. It will make a good average film and that is all. The acting naturally was good. THURSDAY, JANUARY 27

I dictated from 9:00 a.m. to 3:00 p.m. In the evening I wrote a few more pages and the paper was finished. Is it good? I don't know. Is it acceptable to the *Yale Review*?[38] We'll see. I took a very strong stand on recommending a complete system of state medicine. There is no chance in the world of having such a system adopted in America at the present time but it is good to have a definite goal in mind and I do not know of any other solution of our problem.

I received an invitation from Yale University to deliver three lectures next year on the Terry Foundation. The honorarium offered is $1,250. It is very tempting particularly as we need a new car. But there is a difficulty namely that the lectures have to be on some aspect of Science and Religion. And religion is certainly not my field. Joseph Needham gave the lectures a few years ago and he is supposed to be a Marxist. So it may be possible after all. FRIDAY, FEBRUARY 5

I read somewhere that it is important to own things without possessing them. That's just it. I own the treasures of the Louvre, the Uffizi, or the Metropolitan without possessing them. For a long time I thought I had to possess the books I read and now I enjoy library books just as much. I have a big library and where is it? Stored in Basel. Property is a burden. The less we possess the freer we are. I want to possess a copy of my own works for reference. I want to keep my manu-

[38]The paper was published with the title "Socialized Medicine" in the March 1938 issue.

scripts, diaries, and scrap books because they are part of my memory. The rest does not count. The less it is, the better.

I accepted to give the Terry Lectures at Yale and I think I have a good subject, Medicine and Social Welfare with three lectures: 1. The Significance of Disease; 2. The Significance of Health; 3. The Physician's Mission. It will be three months' work but it will be on my line, not a waste of time but preparation for my book. TUESDAY, FEBRUARY 15

Eve Curie has written a beautiful book on her mother. It is unpretentious, warmly written and gives a splendid picture of this great and most lovable woman. At the same time it is a strong indictment of France which is unable to support its scientists properly—not because it is a democracy but because it is a capitalist state.

Hitler is addressing the Reichstag today. Soon we'll hear what he said. It can't be anything good. He is conquering Austria. Who will be the next victim? SUNDAY, FEBRUARY 20

Julius Caesar at Ford's Theater in black shirts, modern costumes, and uniforms. The play is still modern and very much alive: Caesar, the dictator who knows what he wants; Brutus, the liberal, hesitating and finally failing. Good light effects instead of scenery. All in all a good and very impressive performance. MONDAY, FEBRUARY 21

One of those sad days when everything goes wrong and you wished you were thousands of miles away. The Russian trip seems to be off. We cannot get any answer from Moscow. Cannon, in Boston, writes that he had reports according to which Kammisky, Gurevich, and Bronner had been shot. I hope it is not true. If it is, conditions must indeed be very critical. The Narkomzdrav[39] seems to be disorganized. For months the papers have not reported any progress in the public health field. I don't want to force the trip. I can't beg for the privilege to help the Soviets. WEDNESDAY, FEBRUARY 23

If there is a crisis in Russia it of course does not mean that socialism does not work. It means that the Russians are unable to make it work and that we will have to do a better job. But it would be a pity—the first large-scale experiment. In 1935 and 1936 the conditions were so extraordinarily good. I am still hopeful, but cannot help being depressed at times. THURSDAY, FEBRUARY 24

John Dos Passos and his wife came with Horsley Gantt.[40] I think I have read all the books of Dos Passos and I have a great admiration for him. His novels give the whole social history of America since the

---

[39]People's Commissariat of Health.
[40]W. Horsley Gantt, a student of Pavlov from 1925 to 1929, who established the Pavlovian Laboratory at Johns Hopkins Medical School.

war. To meet him was not a disappointment. He is a modest and quiet person and has a great deal of charm. Physically he reminds me of Duhamel but, thank God, his writing is different.   FRIDAY, FEBRUARY 25

Parran, the Surgeon-General, gave a lecture on "A Forward Look at National Health"—carefully worded but progressive. In his position, watched by newspaper people, he obviously cannot say openly what he has in his mind, but it was easy to guess that he is aiming at some kind of services. It was a pleasure to listen to him.   TUESDAY, MARCH 1

Edward H. Hume, our Noguchi lecturer[41], arrived today. He talked on the Far Eastern situation to the Cosmopolitan Club. He talks exceedingly well. His oratory is half ecclesiastical, half Chinese and reminds me very much of Ko. His approach is purely spiritual and he does not recognize any economic problems but he tries to be fair to the communists. He gave many interesting sidelights particularly on life in Japan. The audience was half American, half Oriental.   SATURDAY, MARCH 5

The end of Austria! The Reich has annexed it. German troops are pouring in. What for? To impress the population or to prepare an attack on Czechoslovakia? The people of Vienna are delirious. Why? They like shows and Nazi showmanship has intoxicated them. Workers are beaten up, Jews are persecuted, and Hitler is living an unforgettable day entering in triumph into the city in which he suffered such deep humiliations. The British government is perplexed as it did not realize that all these events are the direct and logical result of its policy.   MONDAY, MARCH 14

The Spanish front seems to be breaking down. New and completely motorized Italian troops and German aircraft are pushing toward the Mediterranean. The situation seems hopeless. The Second World War is on, has been for a long time. Manchuria lost, Ethiopia lost, Austria lost, China and Spain being conquered. And nobody to stop fascism. And it could have been stopped long ago if France, England, and the United States had stood together. They did not because their ruling classes were afraid of communism and preferred fascism to any change in the economic system.   TUESDAY, MARCH 15

I could not possibly have a more interesting life. And what makes it so fascinating and worthwhile is my permanent contact with young people. My position and my work—scientific and political—brings me in touch with endless young people. They respect me, listen to me, and I can influence their lives, can help them and sometimes direct them in their development.   SUNDAY, MARCH 27

[41]A lecture series at the Institute had been named in memory of Hideyo Noguchi (1876-1928).

I am 47 years old today. If I have ten more years of good health I can finish my work. But I shall have to change my mode of living. This winter was perfectly awful. I slaved day and night and achieved nothing. And now on the eve of Graduate Week[42] I am dog-tired. Next year I will stay at home every morning and write from 9 to 1. In the afternoon I will attend to routine work of the Institute and devote the evenings to research. Few outside lectures and no new committees.

THURSDAY, APRIL 7

The historical concert that we are planning attracts much attention. The newspapers mentioned it and I am receiving piles of letters. Two broadcasting companies want us on the air. The public does not care for Graduate Week but the concert seems to have popular appeal.

FRIDAY, APRIL 8

Next winter I will write the first volume of my History and it just occurs to me that I have never seen Egypt. This is a terrible gap. How can I put color into the narrative if I have not experienced the atmosphere of the country, if I have not seen the Nile, the desert, the pyramids? The difficulty is that it seems impossible to travel during the summer so that I would need a leave of absence. I'll see what can be done about it.

MONDAY, APRIL 11

Great meeting in Hurd Hall to commemorate John Billings[43] who did more to launch our Hospital and School than anybody else, including Welch. We had five speakers on the programme (elaborately printed), a formal dinner preceding the meeting. But in spite of all publicity we had a meager audience of hardly 200 people. No students, very few young doctors. In other words Billings is forgotten. Why? I tried to explain it in my preface to the memorial number of the *Bulletin*. Great achievements are not enough to keep the memory of a man alive. His character and the personality are just as important.

TUESDAY, APRIL 12

Graduate Week has created quite a sensation in our medical center and everybody is congratulating me. It certainly was a complete success and has created many new friends for the Institute and the University at large.

MONDAY, APRIL 25

[42]The First Graduate Week in Medical History was held at the Institute from April 18 to 23, 1938, and was attended by thirty-three persons from sixteen states and Canada. The programme included seminars on teaching and research in the field. Sigerist gave a lecture on Music in Medicine which was followed by a concert featuring music that had been composed for a medical purpose or was related to medical personages.

[43]See above, p. 95.

134

Atlantic City

Real summer weather and the sea is so beautiful that you overlook the horrors of the board walk.

Meeting of the American Association of the History of Medicine. Twelve papers, some quite good, others poor. But most important was that the new Constitution was adopted unanimously in a few minutes' time. The people voted without knowing what they were voting for. I was elected secretary, Larkey treasurer. Now it is up to me to reorganize the Association and to make it a success. I am most optimistic—otherwise I would not have accepted.   MONDAY, MAY 2

Baltimore

Stupid evening at the Baltimore Art Museum. The new Jacobs wing was inaugurated. Too many people had been invited so that most of them could not sit and that it was impossible to see a single picture. We ran away as soon as we could. The speakers were old stuffed shirts and the only joke of the evening was when they—all of them sworn enemies of Roosevelt—had to admit that the new wing would never have been built if there had not been a W.P.A.   FRIDAY, MAY 6

Slept ten hours. Still have a temperature but can keep it down with aspirin—have to because I must prepare a lecture for tomorrow on Naturalism in Science. I worked hard till 2:00 a.m. but learned a great deal. It is a fascinating period. Taine, Renan, Zola, they all had such a strong influence on the foundation of my intellect. And the Paris of my childhood was still the Paris of materialism. And I love France. *Je suis français de coeur et d'esprit et je le resterai toujours.* SUNDAY, MAY 15

Downtown for a Re-entry Permit. I am tired of these formalities and I am seriously thinking of applying for citizenship. My future is in America and I want to take an active part in the political life of the country.

Naturalism and the Theatre: Chekhov's *Uncle Vanya,* remarkably well performed. I prefer this play to *The Sea Gull.* It is not quite so hysterical.   TUESDAY, MAY 17

A new invitation: the Messenger Lectures at Cornell for 1940-41, six lectures, two weeks in the University, $1,500, but a book. It seems that I have reached the point where all the big (in American speech: the high-priced) lectureships come to you. I am inclined to accept not on account of the money or the honor, but because I like the idea of spending some time in another university, living its life. The chief point, however, is to select a subject that will serve my great book. This, however, should not be difficult.   WEDNESDAY, MAY 18

For the first time in years France was energetic, banged the fist on the table and declared that she would go to war if Hitler invaded Czecho-

135

slovakia. This is the only language that Hitler understands and as a result he immediately withdrew. He is not ready yet for the final test so the tension is lessened but there is still plenty of dynamite in Europe.

SUNDAY, MAY 22

Another visitor, from Zurich. This is the second Swiss doctor who came over this year with the idea of emigrating. Why? Because in Europe there is no future for the children. The war is inevitable and no matter who wins, the result will be chaos and barbarism. Eight more days and we'll be gone.

WEDNESDAY, MAY 25

I began writing a new paper on Haller for a Swiss publication. It is quite unfamiliar to write in German but I notice that I still master German much better than English. I have a richer vocabulary and I know where the grammatic rules can be broken and where not so that my style is much more personal than in English.

MONDAY, MAY 30

We sailed on the *Statendam*.

FRIDAY, JUNE 3

New York

Landing in New York. The *Queen Mary* carried 2,112 passengers, 300 more than she can accomodate. They slept in the hospital, the gymnasium, in lounges, everywhere. Now that the immediate war danger is over 40 passengers stay on board to sail back to Europe. In Cherbourg the harbor was mined and our tender almost touched the mines. Until the last minute we did not know whether the *Queen Mary* would sail or not. It seems that the American government requested the British government to let her sail. Soon the news of the Munich Conference came (by radio) and the betrayal of Czechoslovakia was complete.

MONDAY, OCTOBER 3

Baltimore

I am agreeably surprised to find that public opinion in America is unanimous in condemning Chamberlain. People here, of course, are far from the battlefield and do not feel menaced. It is not they who would have to go to war. But the fact that they are far away makes them see much clearer. They recognize the real issue namely that the whole affair is nothing but one more episode in the world offensive of fascism, the liquidation of the small democracies, the beginning of the end of the British Empire. Never was Germany more unpopular than now.

TUESDAY, OCTOBER 4

Four lawyers, associates of the Attorney General, came to consult me. They are after the A.M.A., and nothing could please me more. They want to stop the terrorism of the A.M.A. and to protect the Washington Group Health Association, or rather to protect the people's liberties. I have a

136

tremendous admiration for the present administration. They have a difficult task, handicapped as they are by the capitalist system, but they certainly do whatever can be done under the circumstances. I may have to be a witness before a grand jury in the matter, which I do not particularly like, but if it helps the cause I'll do it.   FRIDAY, OCTOBER 7

I have an invitation to be the South African Universities' Visiting Lecturer for 1939. This means twenty-five lectures in eight universities and colleges from August 1 to November. The invitation came from the University of Witwatersrand in Johannesburg. For several years Gilman[44] and other friends have wanted me to come over. The allowance is very generous, travelling expenses First Class and 350 pounds, which will cover other expenses largely. I am thrilled at the idea of seeing a new country. All these journeys help me to gather material for my Sociology of Medicine.   SATURDAY, OCTOBER 8

The evening paper had an AP dispatch stating that Karl Sudhoff had died. Diepgen[45] told me in Amsterdam that he was very sick and that he would not live to see his eighty-fifth birthday. I am terribly sorry. I was very much attached to him. I loved him like a father. He was so kind when I first wrote him during the war and when I first went to see him in 1919. He brought me to Leipzig and I do not know what my career would have been without him. He had very few real students and he concentrated all his affection on me. Then I left Leipzig and conditions changed in Germany. I wrote him regularly but he never answered. He probably resented my political views.   FRIDAY, OCTOBER 14

When a European is sick he suffers patiently and keeps going and doing his work as long as he possibly can. When an American is taken ill he feels offended. He immediately lies down, calls a doctor or several doctors. The American way is probably the better one.

SATURDAY, OCTOBER 15

The Bach Club began a series of Beethoven chamber music concerts with the Budapest String Quartet. Particularly beautiful was *Opus 59, No. 1*. Cadoa Hall was full of friends, students, colleagues. It is very pleasant to live in a city where there is such a friendly atmosphere.

MONDAY, OCTOBER 17

In today's current events talk I discussed the attitude of the A.M.A. towards the National Health Conference. I tried to be fair towards the A.M.A. It is a stupid, reactionary body, but why is it so? I think that the explanation is that as long as the tasks were purely medical (education, hospitals, etc.), the A.M.A. could do an excellent job, but now

"See earlier footnote, p. 95.
"Paul Diepgen, Professor of the History of Medicine at Berlin.

that the problem to solve is a social problem the physicians find themselves utterly incompetent. The initiative was therefore taken by others, the A.M.A. found itself in the background and became an oppositionary force.   WEDNESDAY, OCTOBER 19

We had a terrible shock in the Institute today. The official announcement of Sudhoff's death came, addressed not to me, his most intimate disciple, but to the Institute. It announced that Pg. (Parteigenosse) Karl Sudhoff had died. So the rumor was true. He who was an old liberal, a democrat at the time of the Kaiser, a follower of the Volkspartei during the days of the Republic, he who before 1933 loathed the Nazis finally officially joined. It is hard to believe and very depressing. What were his motives? Vanity, the desire to be one of them at the top, patriotism, or just senility? Who knows? Now I understand why he did not write me anymore. He was ashamed. THURSDAY, OCTOBER 20

That marvelous feeling of being on an American train. You relax, time does not count, you have hours ahead of you. A cocktail in the lounge car, a good dinner, not rushed as in European diners, but leisurely, served by kindly colored waiters—and then a pipe and a book in the observation car. And this one is a new car built in exquisite style by an excellent interior decorator. Then early to bed, a good soft bed in which you can stretch yourself until you fall a sleep. SATURDAY, OCTOBER 22

The "Spirit of St. Louis"

I am on the *Spirit of St. Louis* that left Baltimore yesterday at 6:05 p.m. My first trip of the season and I do enjoy it. I have two lectures to give at the University of Missouri but they are easy so that I need not worry about them. The Mississippi, broad, majestic, St. Louis, another train, full of public health people en route to a meeting in Kansas City. Mexico is my station, yes, Mexico! Professor Curtis expects me, drives me to Columbia through endless plains, but not monotonous, trees, and a cloudless sky. Hotel Tiger! Convention of the Missouri State Association of Retail Grocers.   SUNDAY, OCTOBER 23

Jefferson City

In Jefferson City I saw the murals of Benton—very impressive. The condensed history of the state, the true history, with its heroism and barbarity. At last an American artist—and a most powerful one—has discovered his homeland instead of painting the Luxembourg and Seine, *à la* Cézanne, Renoir, or Rousseau.   TUESDAY, OCTOBER 25

Baltimore

I cannot prepare lectures unless I am under terrific pressure. Some of my best lectures were prepared in a New York hotel room a few hours before I delivered them. Of course it's agony you go through, a regular

138

ordeal, but it is incredible how the mind sparkles under such conditions. I prefer my other way of thinking matters through, when I can write four pages a day, slowly, giving my thought definite formulation. But this is different. You cannot prepare a talk in writing or it is no longer a talk and will invariably be dull.

At any rate I am under pressure now. For weeks I had insuperable inhibitions towards my Yale lectures but now they have to be written—and they are written. In the last few weeks I collected materials. Tuesday I prepared the first lecture. Saturday I stayed at home the whole day and at midnight the second lecture was finished. And today at midnight I had the third ready. But now it seems to me that the first has been rather poorly prepared.   SATURDAY, OCTOBER 29

New Haven

I think the lectures were quite successful. I kept my audience to the last lecture. Personally I was uneasy because what I said was not new to me. I have not done much research recently and I am reproaching myself all the time. What I need is a whole year devoted to research, without any lectures.

I went to New York, took a baronial suite, did not see anybody, did not talk to anybody, but sat in a chair and took it easy, read and made a detailed programme for the following weeks.

Leisurely dinner in a French restaurant then a theatre: *Danton's Death* produced by Orson Wells. It was very good, but the play had been cut down so much that it lost a great deal. Reinhardt's production that I once saw in Zurich was far superior.   FRIDAY, NOVEMBER 4

Bridgeport

I must give one more Terry Lecture in Bridgeport to the Evening Community Forum. Terry was from Bridgeport and required that the lecturer repeat one lecture in his home town. It was an interesting experience. The city is an industrial center, therefore red, but the doctors are ultra-conservative. They gave me a dinner and looked at me with great suspicion. The minister of the United Church acted as host. The lecture followed a regular service with hymns, prayers, blessings, offerings. A typical petty bourgeois audience. The protestant church cannot grip the masses. When the money that had been collected was brought to the altar, everybody rose, paying tribute to god Mammon (I know that charity is a Christian virtue, but still). I gave the three lectures in one. When I was through there were many questions—and the doctors had disapproved tactfully. They must have been shocked. Back to New York on a late train.   SUNDAY, NOVEMBER 6

Baltimore

The interns of the various hospitals have organized a Baltimore chapter of the Intern Council of America. Six of them met for the first time two weeks ago. They were convinced of the timeliness and even necessity of such an organization, but were quite scared about what they had done. How would the step be received? How would it affect their careers? They met again today—twelve of them—and invited me to join and address them, to give them courage. I did it with pleasure. I talked to them on how medicine is becoming a social institution and on what I think about unionization. And I recollected the early history of the Council in New York which I had helped when everybody else was fighting it. Should I ever leave America there is one thing I would leave behind me: organized students and organized interns. Not that I did the work but I think I can take the credit that I acted as a ferment in the process.

TUESDAY, NOVEMBER 8

There was so much mail today that I had not the time to read it at the Institute but took it home. It was perfectly sickening: nothing but invitations to lecture or to write articles. People take me for a slot-machine: you press a button and the machine spits out a lecture, or article, or statement. I cannot understand why people are so crazy about lectures. I never attend a lecture unless I have to. I prefer to read books. You sit in a more comfortable chair, you can smoke a pipe, can make notes, check the author. But when you read you have to think, when you listen to a lecture the other fellow thinks for you. I suppose that's why.

SATURDAY, NOVEMBER 12

There is not much to thank for. Hitler is persecuting the Jews in the most savage way. Mussolini imitates him. Daladier persecutes the French working class, signs a non-aggression pact with Germany which everyone knows to be a farce. Chamberlain is still in power, and the future of Europe is darker than ever. And yet we can be grateful for being alive, for breathing the air and seeing the sky. And we can be thankful for being in America, the one country in the world where you can lead a decent human life. And so we celebrated the day and invited the Temkins and Edelsteins[46] for an exquisite dinner that I had cooked.

THURSDAY, NOVEMBER 24

I just read Granville Hicks' biography of John Reed with much pleasure. His life reminds me of my own in many respects. (We belong after all to the same generation.) Before the war he was a poet and I a scholar, and I cared just as little for the labor movement as he did. I wore a bracelet, dressed with care, and felt very superior as a member of the intelligentsia. Then came the war that we both experienced as observers, and the great awakening. And we both saw that nothing but socialism could save the world. What a terrible place America must have been in 1919 and 1920.

SUNDAY, NOVEMBER 27

---

[46]Temkin and Edelstein were staff members at the Institute.

140

I intend to apply for American citizenship. For various reasons. First, I feel greatly handicapped in my work by being a foreigner. I am taking an active part in the life of this country and I would talk much more freely if I were a citizen. Then here is the future of the children that must be considered. And finally I have the impression that there is growing animosity against foreigners which is bound to increase as more refugees come in. I am a citizen of the world and I don't care what kind of passport I have, but since we are living here and since there is no future for us in Europe it is better to take the step.   SUNDAY, DECEMBER 4

The A.M.A., three constituent societies, and 21 individual members have been indicted by a federal grand jury of conspiracy in violation of the Sherman Anti-Trust Act. It is well deserved but a disgrace to the medical profession. What a shame to be accused of dirty business practices. I hope that it will stir the rank and file and make them realize that their leaders are stupid and rotten. I brought the matter before my forum.   WEDNESDAY, DECEMBER 21

I do not know how to escape reporters. They hound me day and night. I found that the only way to get rid of them was to grant them interviews, but I hate publicity. All I want is to be left in peace so that I can do my work. But wherever I go a reporter crosses my path and asks silly questions. A few days ago a photographer came to do my portrait in color for the magazine *Time* and today a *Sun* reporter was in my office for a whole hour. It's hopeless!   THURSDAY, DECEMBER 22

A superb Toscanini concert, perfect in every respect. *Oberon's Overture,* Beethoven's *Third* and some Wagner that even I enjoyed. We cannot complain. We have excellent music in Baltimore. What we miss is an opera and a repertory theatre.
Toscanini was received enthusiastically not only because he is a great artist but because he is one of the few who has shown great courage in opposing fascist barbarism.   TUESDAY, DECEMBER 27

1939

THE VISIT TO SOUTH AFRICA

Baltimore

The past year was extremely success-
ful as far as the Institute and my general studies were concerned. The
Soviet trip was a great success, and the Yugoslavian trip a most interesting
experience. My reputation has grown. I have many enemies but many
friends and very loyal friends particularly in the younger generation. So
far I had no troubles in spite of my radical views. The University respects
me and needs the credit and publicity that the Institute brings to it. As
long as the Roosevelt administration is in power I do not expect trouble
from outside either.

But I wrote very little in the past year and what I wrote was not
important. I sincerely hope that this year, in spite of the terrific pressure
under which I live, I may be able to begin my great work, the one that
really counts—the History and Sociology. The trip to South Africa and
Egypt will give me new material, and all in all, I hope that things will go
on as in the past.   SUNDAY, JANUARY 1

A splendid meeting for Spain. An English M.P., Dr. Edith Summer-
skill, member of the Labour party, elected in opposition to Chamberlain,
was here, a charming woman. We gave her a dinner and had the meeting
at the Pythian Hall. She gave an excellent talk, stirred the people and
moved them with the result that almost $400 was contributed for the
"Children's Cities" in Spain. I spoke and my students presented me
with a beautiful bronze bust of Delores Ibarrúri, la Passionaria, Spain's
great woman who pronounced the words: "It is better to die on your feet
than to live on your knees." Nothing could have touched me more than this
token of sympathy from the students, and I shall treasure the bust and
feel inspired by it as long as I live. My whole life is devoted to the students.
They are the future—the better future—that I am trying to prepare. I often
regret that I cannot devote more time to the students, that I am indulging in so many other activities. I am a scholar by nature and
wished I could live a retired life devoted to research and writing. But in
times like these, the scientist has the duty to take sides and to enter the
struggle. The students have demonstrated by their gift that they understand and appreciate my attitude and I feel most grateful and encouraged.
                                                        WEDNESDAY, JANUARY 4

1939

Whenever I am introduced to an audience like the one yesterday I am introduced as an authority on social medicine. Nothing could please me more. I know, of course, that I am an amateur in the field but sometimes I feel that the amateur has a part to play in the world. He often has more imagination and less inhibition than the specialist who is inclined to think along traditional lines, and who, being aware of difficulties, often lacks courage. Semashko[47] and Stampar were amateurs and so was Dr. Welch. And how many amateur soldiers (like Colonel Modestoa in Spain) have defeated academically trained generals. Imagination and courage—that's what's needed.   SUNDAY, JANUARY 8

So much is being said and written in America about methods of higher education. Elaborate tests are devised to find "first rate" students, to breed geniuses. It all impresses me as being utterly futile. I do not think that I am a poor teacher judging from the reaction of my students and yet my method of teaching is the most primitive there is. It consists merely in thinking aloud and working in public thereby giving the students a chance to watch me while I think and to help me in my work. This should inspire the students or challenge them. I never try to give the students facts that they can find in any book. What they must be taught is where you can find facts and how they must be approached and interpreted—in other words: methods of working. The actual work they have to do themselves. This "thinking aloud," of course, must be prepared carefully. It must be clear, logical thinking that can serve as an example.   MONDAY, JANUARY 9

Today's current events discussion was devoted to Chile. I worked on the subject yesterday until 2:00 a.m. and the whole morning today and I am full of it. Chile has most progressive social legislation, and the medical work they are doing is superb. Already I see that after South Africa my next trip will be to Chile and Mexico. And it is time to brush up my Spanish.   WEDNESDAY, JANUARY 11

I wrote an article for the New York *Daily News*. It is a lousy sheet but they are running a series on the present medical situation and so far they had nobody to recommend compulsory health insurance. So I felt I had to do it. I think the European mistakes can all be avoided once two principles are accepted:
1. That the premiums must not be used to finance the present type of medical service, but to finance health centers, that is, to promote group medicine;
2. That the unlimited free choice of physician must be given up.
                                    MONDAY, JANUARY 16

[47]Nikolai Alexandrovich Semashko, first People's Commissar of Health of the USSR, later Director of the Medical History Institute in the Academy of Medical Sciences, Moscow.

Today the President read a message to Congress recommending the National Health Program which includes compulsory health insurance. Today or tomorrow the *Daily News* in New York publishes an article of mine recommending compulsory health insurance, and Friday *Time* magazine with a million readers is writing me up. So I am in good company. I am afraid that the government scheme will repeat European mistakes, but in a capitalist democracy every policy is a compromise. People will learn from the mistakes they make and will gradually improve the scheme. At any rate the first step is taken—and this is what counts.

MONDAY, JANUARY 23

Wagner's music to me is primarily a childhood reminiscence. You experience it as you experience measles or chicken-pox. It is unavoidable. And when I now hear Flagstad sing *Lohengrin* or *Walküre* I find myself back in the Stadttheater in Zurich where I spent so many inspiring evenings.

WEDNESDAY, FEBRUARY 1

I had to feed a publicity man who works for several pharmaceutical firms. He tells me that each one of these firms spends about $200,000 annually for publicity. The wastage of capitalism. His grand idea now is to have big paintings made illustrating the work of the pioneers of American medicine. One is already finished on Beaumont, by a spectacular, fashionable, second-rate painter! And now he wants Osler treating a child. It must be a child on account of the human interest.

THURSDAY, FEBRUARY 2

Delightful evening in Washington, dinner at the home of Surgeon-General Parran with Paul de Kruif[48] and his wife. Dynamic discussion on public health problems. De Kruif is preparing a new book on unemployment: *The Right to Work*. He makes a good remark: "If you take a microtome and make cuts through Americans and look at them with the microscope you will find in every cell a little dollar sign." MONDAY, FEBRUARY, 6

Senator Pepper has introduced a bill on health insurance in Congress. It is an interesting document. Some provisions are very good. People with higher incomes are admitted on a voluntary basis. But there are other provisions that may wreck the scheme. What scares me most is that the bill takes all the objections of medical organizations into account and gives the physician too much power. The doctors, however, will not hesitate to sabotage the scheme and the result will be the same mess as in Europe. WEDNESDAY, FEBRUARY 8

I spent the whole evening studying my family history. My father had it compiled in 1896 from the archives in Schaffhausen.

[48]Paul de Kruif, noted writer on medical subjects, especially his *Microbe Hunters*.

144

I have the history from 1545 on—400 years. It is the typical history of an artisan's family, good sound city stock: seven generations of butchers, three generations of tanners, my grandfather a wine dealer, my father in bigger business, and I the first member who entered a learned profession. No wealth but no poverty—respected citizens, no mental diseases so far as I can see. But no longevity. From the eighteenth century on death dates are given and in the last six generations there are no old men (with the exception of the grandfather): 64, 53, 63, 45, 70, 42. I wish I knew the causes of death. It is an unexciting but typical history.

FRIDAY, FEBRUARY 10

The reorganization of the American Association of the History of Medicine is proceeding beautifully. We are getting new members all the time. The local groups are joining one after another. New local societies are being organized, one in Oklahoma, one in Indiana. It is a joy to watch these developments and to feel that you are responsible for them. First I developed the Institute and made it the national research center, and now I am developing the national Association. In five years medical history will be firmly established in the United States.

TUESDAY, FEBRUARY 21

I have thirteen more weeks before sailing and from now on I am on a very strict schedule. I still have a book to write and endless papers and articles. I'll do my best. At any rate I have my reservations for May 31 (and on the *Normandie,* my favorite boat). So I have a date to look forward to. From then on I'll be a normal human being again, sleeping eight hours a night, eating three meals a day and working leisurely, instead of being a slave. (I'm afraid I do not dislike being a labor slave provided it does not last too long.) I certainly have a most interesting life.

MONDAY, FEBRUARY 27

I begin to have plans for next winter. Every year I endeavor to develop some new scheme. Last year my organizational work was concentrated on the Institute and I built up the institution of Graduate Week. It is firmly established now and all we have to do is to maintain the high standard and to avoid developing a routine.

This year I concentrated on the reorganization of the American Association of the History of Medicine and so far the work has been very successful. By the end of the year the Association should be in good shape and functioning. It will still need a good deal of pushing but the main work will be done. So I'll be free for something new.

The plans are still hazy but I am going to work them out during the summer—I am thinking of an Institute for International Studies in the Organization of Medicine, or whatever it might be called. Something like Grotjahn's[49] seminar in Berlin. My first plan was to develop a

[49] Alfred Grotjahn (1869-1931) occupied the first chair of Social Hygiene at the Medical Faculty of the University of Berlin.

sociological section of our Institute which would have been the logical thing to do. But quite apart from funds there are great difficulties. So I am thinking of an Institute that would be independent of the Hopkins, financed possibly on public funds—an old house in the neighborhood, an associate, a secretary, a library, collections, all on a minimum budget. It would be open to Hopkins students but also to workers. I would give a seminar and gather a group of young enthusiasts. And so a nucleus would be formed to develop and carry out a vigorous, progressive public health policy. Why not? Grotjahn has demonstrated what can be done with little money.   THURSDAY, MARCH 2

I am working on a new paper: Science and the Greek Tradition, for a symposium at the Art Museum. I have a thesis that I would like to develop, namely that until the Renaissance science and the Greek tradition were one but from then on there are two parallel developments: one, scientific which is materialistic and quantitative in approach, and one which is qualitative, spiritualistic, tending to establish systems and therefore following the Greek tradition. This can be traced down to our days where there is—in fascist countries—a neo-hippocratic and neo-paracelsic movement.
                                                      SUNDAY, MARCH 12

I am on a new "revised" schedule for the next eleven weeks. I must weekly:
  1. write thirty pages of my book
  2. dictate twenty pages of papers
  3. dictate a minimum of sixty letters, in addition, of course, to teaching, editorial work, committee work, my graduate course, the Association of the History of Medicine, the Citizens' Health Committee, and endless other routine occupations. But it can be done and must be done, that's all.
                                                      MONDAY, MARCH 13

Very tired, a beginning cold, pouring rain. I stay at home and cook— my own birthday dinner: *petites marmites,* lobster creole, Bratwürste. Owens[50] came, the Pearls[51], Mrs. Nohowel, and my old teacher and friend Oskar Baudisch. And at midnight I entered my forty-ninth year.
                                                      THURSDAY, APRIL 6

No denying it: I shall be fifty soon, half a century old. In spite of hard work I am still in pretty good shape and I only hope to live long enough to be able to write my six-volume book so as to sum up my experience. I work very hard and lead a most unhygienic life, but I have not the excitements of a statesman or a big business man or a surgeon. The daily contact with young students keeps me young and so does my

[50]Hamilton Owens, editor of the *Baltimore Sun.*
[51]Raymond Pearl (1879-1940), Professor of Biology, Johns Hopkins University.

travelling. If you stay always in the same place you soon develop a routine and necessarily get old. It was my good fortune to avoid this. I always had to conquer new countries and new groups. First it was Switzerland, then Germany, then the United States, then the USSR, and now South Africa, South America, and who next? This necessarily prevents you from getting rusty. FRIDAY, APRIL 7

The beginning of the celebration of the fiftieth anniversary of the Hospital. Mobs have come from all over the country and speeches are held by the dozen. And everybody seems bored. I think it is time to change the style of such celebrations. THURSDAY, MAY 4

I have a vertical programme this week and the whole day was devoted to dictating the Annual Report on the activities of the Institute. It was quite a good year and there is plenty to report. I did not write as much as I intended (still, fourteen papers) because I had to devote much time fighting for the National Health Program. The issue is so vitally important for the people that I feel obliged to sacrifice much of my research and to throw in my entire personality. WEDNESDAY, MAY 24

Meeting of the first All-Maryland Health Conference. The afternoon session was splendid. Delegates of the labor unions, of the farm bureau, and a Negro doctor spoke. Their arguments were excellent and there was much enthusiasm. The evening session was rotten. The delegate of the medical chirurgical faculty spoke, the usual reactionary stuff (attacking me), and then a number of stuffed shirts presented official views. At the end I was asked to talk and I brought the meeting back to the atmosphere of the afternoon. Great ovation. SATURDAY, MAY 27

Second day of the Health Conference. I. S. Falk was brilliant, spoke on and for health insurance, had all the facts and figures on hand and could refute all contrary arguments easily. Embittered discussion. The three delegates of the A.M.A. faced the almost unanimous opposition of the 350 delegates from 120 organizations. It was the doctors against the people. The doctors as the enemies of the people. A shocking performance, result of the policy of the A.M.A. And, of course, a mere repetition of what happened in other countries. SUNDAY, MAY 28

The "Normandie"

For the first time I find it difficult to leave America. Or rather until now I felt that going to Europe was going home and that America was my working place. Now I feel that I am rooted in America, that my work is needed and I am going "abroad." Of course I am looking forward to six months of travelling, to a new experience, a new country, and to a period of quiet work and planning. But I am a little sad and the many telegrams I received showed me that I have the affection of devoted friends.

147 WEDNESDAY, MAY 31

I must try to restore my health during the summer and this will not be easy. I am not sick but I am not well or at least not normal. First of all my sleep mechanism has gone to pieces in the last few months. I am often awake until five or six in the morning and sleep only two or three hours at night. As a result I am tired during the day and go to sleep as soon as the tension lessens. In Kastanienbaum I must undergo a regular treatment:

1. cut down smoking
2. no hard liquor of any kind
3. no coffee
4. reduce weight to 165
5. decongest liver by drinking Carlsbad water
6. sleep eight hours in twenty-four
7. very regular life

And next winter I must have my nose and throat treated. SATURDAY, JUNE 3

Paris

We had just time to get up. The French coast was in sight. At 1:30 p.m. we landed. It was hot, a real summer day. Cherry trees full of ripe fruit. Rich green meadows. The Seine, always the Seine. Monet. Maupassant. Such a small river. So full of great reminiscences. The small river of a great city. Abdullah cigarettes, one very poor. All of a sudden: Tour Eiffel, fifty years old. So it's Paris. MONDAY, JUNE 5

Ondine by Giraudoux at the Athénée with Louis Jouvet and Madeleine Ozeray, an exquisite play exquisitely staged and acted. The old story of Undine but with Giraudoux and Madeleine Ozeray. This evening revives an old plan in me: to edit and translate and comment upon the treatise of Paracelsus. Why? I don't know. I intended to do it in Leipzig years ago but dropped the plan. I may do it now for 1941. The subject fascinates me. There is so much poetry in it and I have no idea what Paracelsus meant when he wrote the little book. THURSDAY, JUNE 8

Basle

Basle has a new and beautiful university building and great celebrations are being held. We watched a big parade this morning: the students, the local and federal authorities, delegates from all over the country and at the end the faculty in brand new gowns. A few observations:

1. The entire city participates in such an event. The schools are closed, the children are all in the streets with flowers. The population considers the university its own and treasured possession. This would be very different in America.

2. The parade was poorly staged and the people marched in a sloppy way. In other words there was nothing military in it. And this is good.

3. There was hardly any applause when the President of the Republic, the federal councillors and the army chiefs passed. Does it mean that they are unpopular? I don't think so. The explanation is rather that the

148

population is very sober and unenthusiastic. And this is not so bad either.   SATURDAY, JUNE 10

We visited the new university building today. It is in excellent style, modern with some old elements cleverly used. The furniture is very good too. It strikes me that there are no individual offices for the professors and no seminar rooms, nothing but lecture halls, large, medium and small: the professor at his desk, the students squeezed in uncomfortable school benches. They apparently do not know the charm of teaching while sitting informally with the students around a table.[52] SUNDAY, JUNE 11

Kastanienbaum

With Nora to Kastanienbaum. Here we are again in this delightful spot. It is the sixth year and I am quite at home. Everything has its place and it is a pleasure to unpack the luggage. Everybody knows you and is kind: the people at the delicatessen store in Lucerne who know what I like better than I do, the people at the post office, Herr Brückenwart who brings the trunks. There is snow still on the Pilatus and other mountains but what do I care about the weather. What matters is that we are here.
                                                                THURSDAY, JUNE 15

It is only now that I realize how run down I was. The tension is gone and I feel that my carcass is beginning to be old and worn. I must recover before I leave for South Africa and I am doing my best by leading a very sober and regular life. I have not done any work in the last few weeks.

It is cold and we had to heat the furnace, but the place is, nevertheless, enchanting, so perfectly quiet and peaceful. How I wish I could spend several months here.

Toscanini must have been attracted by the place also. He is spending the summer in a chalet not far from us.   SUNDAY, JUNE 18

The weather is glorious and we decided to go to Zurich to see the National Exposition. It is extraordinarily well done, in excellent taste, on both shores of the lake. I saw the exhibit of 1914 in Berne which was very unimpressive. Now it is different. Hitler has succeeded in arousing wild patriotic feelings in Switzerland and the Exposition has become a symbol of Swiss independence and national unity. To go to the Exposition has become a pilgrimage. Every school sends the children, every firm its employees. And there could not be a better cross section through the activities of the country.   THURSDAY, JUNE 29

[52]The new building, called the *Kollegiengebäude,* contains only lecture halls and the university administration. The seminar rooms and institutes remained in separate buildings.—[Ed.].

Like all European countries Switzerland is preparing for war. People who once were found unfit for military service are re-examined and if fit for anything will have to serve in auxiliary services. The population is invited to buy gas masks and whoever can efford it is urged to buy food supplies for two months. In case of war food stores would be closed and only indigents would be supplied until the distribution of food could be organized. Most people bought supplies but ate them up when war did not break out.   TUESDAY, JULY 11

And so the last day came. It was all too short—four weeks. How I wish I could have had one more month in Kastanienbaum. And during those four weeks I had so much work. Why can I not have a vacation like other people? And now travelling again. I am not sure that I am looking forward to it. But everything is set and there is no choice.

SUNDAY, JULY 16

London—The "Arundel Castle"
One of those days that move along automatically. All you have to do is to follow the stream.

Packing, breakfast, luggage off, boat train at Waterloo Station, leaving 11:15 a.m., Southampton, the docks, the ship, mail from family and Institute, God save the King, and off we go.

Complete relaxation. Thirteen days on a swimming island. Nice outside single cabin, not very large but comfortable. Early to bed with a Penguin Parade and a night of long dreamless sleep.   THURSDAY, JULY 20

We saw land this morning, bare islands of the Madeiras. And then at 2:00 p.m. we arrived in Funchal. Dozens of small boats with brown people selling beautiful embroideries for little money. We had four hours time, enough to make the classic excursion on shore. Ox-carts to the station, then by cog-wheel railway to the top of a mountain of 3,300 feet. The vegetation is incredibly rich: palm trees, banana trees, eucalyptus, enormous blue hydrangias, fuchsia, and many other strong-scented flowers. Beautiful view on city and port. Then down the slope on tobog- gans, two men running along with braking or pulling, a rough ride, but I was comfortable between two old English ladies. At 6:00 p.m. we left. Five Portuguese battleships were in the harbor.

Early to bed running a slight temperature.   SUNDAY, JULY 23

Awful night. It was very windy and as my cabin is close to the water the porthole had to be closed. It was suffocating but I felt well again in the morning and on the veranda it was nicely cool. We passed the Canary Islands. I always thought of them as being flat but they are not. On the contrary. Tenerife is a high mountain.   MONDAY, JULY 24

The heat and dampness are increasing steadily and the nights are now very hot also. Heavy clouds, and the sea looks like lead. All grey in grey. The English people on board are amazing. In spite of all the heat they indulge in the most violent exercise.

So far I haven't been at all excited about the South African tour. Am I getting old and less enterprising? I think it is rather because I resent having had only four weeks in Kastanienbaum where I felt so happy. But today while studying the *South Africa Year Book and Guide* I began to feel excited and made plans to fly to Bulawayo and have a look at the ruins of Great Zumbabwe. They are most puzzling. I do not know yet how much extra travelling my funds will permit, but this will be the only opportunity in my life to visit these regions.

At 11:24 this morning we crossed the Equator and now we are sailing in the Southern hemisphere. It is nice and cool still but the cabins are very warm. The water is 85° and my cabin is very close to it.

Interesting that the English people despise the Dutch. Dr. W., the ship's doctor, said that he considered them an inferior race! And a Dr. C., a chemical engineer, who has lived for twenty years in S.A. and seems to know everybody, said that he considers every Dutchman a liar until proved to the contrary, which happens very rarely. No wonder that the Dutch are kicking.   FRIDAY, JULY 28

We are getting closer and I am reminded of 1931 when I first sailed to America, not knowing what I was going to find. My task in America was at the same time easier and more difficult; easier because I was under the protection of Dr. Welch, and more difficult because I had not lectured in English before. Now I am more mature, I know the language well enough, but what does medical history mean to South Africa? And my social views, will they not shock the people? I am not afraid of Johannesburg where I know people who have seen me in Baltimore and where my publications are known. But I am somewhat apprehensive of Capetown. At any rate I shall do my best. And then, of course, there is the fascinating research task: to obtain as full as possible information about the country.   SUNDAY, JULY 30

I received a radiogram from the Registrar of the University of Capetown saying that he will meet me tomorrow at 8:30. So I know that I am expected and that arrangements must have been made for me. I wish I could live on the campus close to students. I would like to come to know many of them to find out what their problems are, whether they are the same as in America.

I wonder when my lectures will begin. I hope they give me a few days so that I can readjust myself to the new environment but I may have to start soon. At any rate the course in Capetown is the easier of the two. Well, it will be a new experience, and if I can continue my writing the time will not be lost.   WEDNESDAY, AUGUST 2

Capetown

Docked at 7:30. Immigration and customs people very courteous. No trouble of any kind. First impression: an enchanting city, the bay on one side, steep rocks, Table Mountain and various peaks on the other. Oriental character of streets. Kaffirs and Indians.   THURSDAY, AUGUST 3

My first university lecture. It was on the Middle Ages, not an ideal subject, but I was in good form and it was a success. The lecture hall holds about 150 and was packed full. And although I spoke for one and a half hours the audience remained very attentive and was very appreciative. I think the next lectures will be easy. My reputation as a lecturer is established.   THURSDAY, AUGUST 10

Pouring rain the whole day but at least it is not too cold. I am here in the worst possible season.

The sore spot in medical education seems to be pre-medical education. Students enter medical school after completion of secondary school (just as in England) and as many secondary schools are rather poor, many students have no culture whatever. Formerly doctors had to study abroad and came home with a European background. In ten years the doctors here will be technically well prepared but quite uneducated. This is where medical history comes in and has an important function to fulfil.

SUNDAY, AUGUST 13

Sun again and another drive to Unizenberg on False Bay and to the Red Mountain from where the view on Simonstown, the Bay, and the Hottentots Holland Mountains, east of the Bay, is most beautiful.

I spent the morning at the Medical Library and found a lot of interesting material on local medical and health conditions in the *South African Medical Journal*. The profession here is infinitely more liberal than in America. It openly advocates national health insurance and I found an article written by the president of a local branch, Louis Wagner, all in favor of a complete system of state medicine.

FRIDAY, AUGUST 18

Drive to Langa, the native reserve, with Jack Simon. About 5,000 natives live there. The government built the houses. The natives pay 10 shillings a month for one room for one individual, 15 shillings if two live in the room. Unmarried men live 24 in one room. Washhouse, communal fire place. Very poor hospital. The whole reserve is not good, but could be much worse. What I miss: nurseries, kindergartens, clubs, libraries, a theatre, a choir, a band. No effort is made to raise the cultural level of the people and for good reasons. Many interviews. Again impressed by the excellent qualities of the Bantu. In spite of long oppression he has not degenerated.   SATURDAY, SEPTEMBER 2

A beautiful day. Drive towards the sea. The meadows are covered with flowers, endless varieties of daisies, and exotic plants that I had never seen before. Ostriches. Picnic in midst of flowers. It is spring. Tea in Malmesbury and there we got the news that England had declared war on Germany at noon. So it is to be war. England no doubt was ready to sell out, but the price Hitler asked was too high. And so the Nazi regime must be destroyed and replaced by a sound conservative government with which the City can deal. These must be England's war aims.

SUNDAY, SEPTEMBER 3

Still no action on the Western front. In the meantime Germany is pushing forward in Poland, not a lightning attack, but a slow systematic and crushing advance. Upper Silesia is conquered, Warsaw threatened. The plan must be to finish Poland and then to turn West, possibly with the help of Mussolini and Franco. Then the critical moment will come for Switzerland. I hope the family will be out by that time. England and France will face a very difficult task unless they can attack now while Germany is engaged in the East or unless Germany breaks down internally.

WEDNESDAY, SEPTEMBER 6

After a long night's sleep I woke up in the Karroo. Desolation. Desert or rather steppe. Grazing land for sheep. But the monotony is impressive. Like the sea. Mountains, *tafelberge*. And a magnificent sunset with purple and violent colors, like the sea. Spent the day in meditation about the world at large, and my personal affairs in particular. The family in Switzerland, I in the Karroo. When shall we come together again? There is no point in my going to Europe, as long as Switzerland is not invaded. This is not my war but just another imperialist war. Our time will come later. We had better prepare for it. I shall go back to America directly when I am through with my lectures.

THURSDAY, SEPTEMBER 7

Most interesting day. Drive to Alice, to Fort Hare, the S.A. native college, a drive of almost two hours over mountains through cactus, aloe trees, and bush. And natives all along the road, in blankets, the men dignified, the girls smiling charmingly. I begin to be infatuated by Africa. I love the Bantus. I must make an effort not to romanticize them and to retain a realistic approach. The College, faculty (mostly white), and students, all natives. Intelligent faces, eager eyes. I talked to them on public health. The place has a promising beginning but it stinks of religion. How much better such work could be done under socialist leadership. Lovedale Hospital for natives and school for the training of native nurses is very primitive. Three doctors for 185 beds, poor equipment, not scientific medicine.

SATURDAY, SEPTEMBER 9

Another most interesting day. Dr. Ella Britten took me to the native

153

location and we spent the whole afternoon there. The place is bad enough but better than Langa. The natives live not in tenements but in individual huts. A new type of house with 3 rooms is quite good. Rent: 4 shillings a week. There are other horrible huts built of oil cans. There the natives pay rent for the ground and build their huts themselves. Infant mortality 250, but 400 if the second year is included. A relatively prosperous family: he earns 16 shillings a week, she 4 shillings through washing. She had seven children, three of which died. They live in two rooms, keep them clean and tidy. Dr. Britten runs a daily child clinic with a native nurse. Schools including high school and industrial school (weaving etc.). A community hall with library. A beer house, run by the city council for profit, is a seat of prostitution. MONDAY, SEPTEMBER 11

I intended to sleep late but at 6:30 somebody knocked at my door. It was the maid bringing that God-damned bloody early tea. And yet I had told her that I did not want her confounded tea. It is hopeless. I drank the tea and was wide awake. I am resigned now and shall swallow tea without protest whenever I am supposed to do it, even if it is at 3:00 a.m.

Quiet day. Morning tea at the University with the faculty, a bunch of politicians. Bloemfontein is a big village with some nice buildings and dried up gardens. A settlement in the veldt.

Wrote letters and planned. Johannesburg will be very strenuous. fourteen lectures but fortunately most of them are the same as in Capetown. Evening in the movies. An English film, not bad but conventional. WEDNESDAY, SEPTEMBER 13

The antagonism between British and Dutch is nothing but the antagonism between the Chamber of Mines and the feudal landowners. The Chamber of Mines obviously stands for British imperialism. The landowners whose economy has many pre-capitalist elements are attracted not by the monopoly capitalism of Nazism but by its medieval aspects.

Somebody said to me: "There is more race prejudice in your Southern states than here." My answer: "Yes, because you have not liberated your slaves yet. Wait until they are emancipated and begin to compete freely with you. You'll have more prejudice than we."

Morning in the Zoo. The famous "Liger," a crossing between lion and tiger. Most interesting afternoon in the native location with Miss Oppenheim. THURSDAY, SEPTEMBER 14

At 2:30 the Gillmans came and told me that the Soviet army was marching into Poland. I almost collapsed. What does it mean? I don't know. We'll have to wait for news. SUNDAY, SEPTEMBER 17

I understand the Russian move now. It is a move not with but against Germany. The USSR cannot run the risk of having the German army on

154

its borders, knowing Hitler's aspirations on the Ukraine. By marching into Poland the Red Army saves the Ukrainian and White Russian minority from destruction by Germany. And besides the Red Army must be mobilized and ready to march into Germany in case revolution breaks out before England can crush it. Poland collapsed in two weeks not only on account of the superiority of the German army but because the Polish state was rotten all through. You cannot expect the oppressed Polish peasant to fight with enthusiasm for the preservation of a regime that he loathes.   MONDAY, SEPTEMBER 18

The University would like me to make a survey of the health situation of the whole continent of Africa. It is a most tempting task and I would love to undertake it some day.   TUESDAY, SEPTEMBER 19

Called on Mr. B. and Miss J. at the Municipal Native Affairs Department. They control first of all native housing, the locations. B. said that native wages could not be increased because otherwise the native would work shorter periods—which is bunk. Miss J. is Oxford movement. I hate the missionary spirit toward the native. The missionary no doubt does a lot, but he always expects the native to do something in exchange: to sing Christian hymns, to dress in European clothes. Much as the missionary may do he cannot make the native forget that the white men took away his land and now makes him pay taxes.   WEDNESDAY, SEPTEMBER 20

At Orenstein's office at 9:00 a.m. I interviewed him about the health work in mines. It is very scientific and I am making a careful study of it. I want to use it for propaganda in America because it is a splendid demonstration of the fact that health work pays. Otherwise the hard-boiled mine owners would not have such a programme. We then visited the compound and hospital and sewage system. It is all very good indeed.

Dinner with the Graduate Association which is chiefly responsible for bringing me here. Then my lecture on Post-graduate Medical Education. I was handicapped by a bad cold.   THURSDAY, SEPTEMBER 21

Visit to the General Hospital. The European section is good. The system of financing is very complicated, the unfortunate heritage of England. The non-European section is a scandal. It is crowded. In the children's ward there are two children in every bed, large children and infants in the same room. The superintendent made the profound remark: "There is no point in building new wards, they would be just as crowded. Besides, the natives come chiefly because the food is so good." To me they looked sick enough.

In the evening my first public lecture on Egypt and Babylonia, much better than yesterday.   FRIDAY, SEPTEMBER 22

Dr. Wulf Sachs took me to Pretoria to see the mental hospital. It has about 1,700 patients with eight physicians. The white patients have nice pavilions, the natives merely a yard. Conditions as they existed in Europe before Pinel. Lunch with Sachs at his home. In the afternoon in Orlando, the native location. Went to see John, the hero of *Black Hamlet*, Maggie his fat wife, children, patients. Photos. John is an Uganga, a medicine man. He threw the bones for me. The whole show was interesting but disappointing. He told me nothing but obvious matters.

SATURDAY, SEPTEMBER 23

Klerksdorp

Yesterday after dinner we went underground, about 3,000 feet. The main shafts are broad, well lit, and well ventilated. I asked them how many fatal accidents they had. "Only one in two years," the answer. This seemed incredible. "Does that include native workers?" "Oh no, one was killed only yesterday. The other day seven were killed in one accident. But we lost only one white worker." This morning we saw the compound and the workers staged a dance in our honor.   SUNDAY, OCTOBER 1

Kruger National Park

My physicians prescribed a short vacation for my complete recovery from septic tonsillitis and I went with the Gillmans to the Game Reserve. We left at 6:00 a.m., drove to Springs, Witbank, Middelburg, Lydenburg, to Pilgrim's Rest where we had a rest and lunch. Then to Grashop where we saw the Pinnacle, over the mountain pass down to the reserve. It was late afternoon but we saw game: wildebeest, a most ridiculous animal with too big a head, zebras, bucks, and a jackal. We camped in the rest home of Pretorius in a Kaffir-style hut. It is a most comfortable camp with showers and bathrooms. Phyllis Gillman prepared an excellent supper and at 9:30 p.m. the lights were turned out. I enjoy such an excursion more than I can tell.   FRIDAY, OCTOBER 13

A great day again—driving about 200 miles through the Reserve. Again we saw many animals: five lions. One of them was only 17 feet from the car. Hippopotamus, baboons, warthogs. We did not see giraffes and were rather disappointed about it. I take many pictures, cinema and Leica. This game reserve is a unique institution.   SATURDAY, OCTOBER 14

Telegram from Glyn Thomas announcing that the Senate and Council of the University have conferred upon me the honorary degree of Doctor of Literature. I am extremely pleased. Honorary degrees, after all, are the highest recognition of a professor's work. It is moreover the external expression of the success of my lecture tour and it creates a bond with a University to which I am very much attached. I am really delighted.

TUESDAY, OCTOBER 31

156

My forty-ninth and I hope last public appearence in South Africa. Adler in Krugersdorp had invited about fifty people to his house, all civic leaders and I spoke on Group Health Insurance as introduction to a long discussion. This ends my lecture tour. I think it has done some good. It has given self-confidence to the progressives and food for reflection to the others. The country is ready for socialized services and my visit may accelerate the process.   SATURDAY, NOVEMBER 18

Port Elizabeth

Beautiful drive from East London to Port Elizabeth, about 200 miles. The Ciskei has a character of its own, a landscape that is particularly dear to me. It was here, driving to Fort Hare, that I first felt myself in Africa and first came under the spell of the dark continent. I feel that some day I shall come back. I want to see more, more natives under different regimes. I want to survey the health situation of the whole continent south of the Sahara. I love the black man. He is good and intelligent. He needs education and liberation. Once set free he will create good artistic values and contribute his share to civilization. I have no doubt of it.   SUNDAY, DECEMBER 3

The snake park where hundreds of cobras, puff adders, and other horrible serpents are kept. Their venom is extracted at regular intervals and sent to Grasset who makes a serum from it. A native keeper plays with them. A Swiss family from Solothurn watching them. We talk and our thoughts are in Europe.   MONDAY, DECEMBER 4

The "City of New York"

The last day in South Africa. The sun shines gloriously, but the southeaster spoils everything. This wind is a real curse that prevents you from enjoying the beauty of the city. The Gillmans came to say good-bye. They are very loyal friends. At noon I went to the harbor. Visitors are not admitted but with pull you can obtain a pass. We had lunch on board and got a drink as soon as the custom officers had left. The harbor is frightfully congested, ships from all over the world, neutrals in bright colors. British boats in grey or fantastically camouflaged. At 7:00 p.m. we left, rolling under the southeaster.   TUESDAY, DECEMBER 12

Three weeks cut off from the rest of the world. I'm glad it's so long. I need a rest and a break between two periods. The last four months were so full of experiences, events, and also emotions. And the war on—the second imperialist war—that's what it is. It may and probably will change all our lives.

I shall lead a regular life on board, establish a healthy routine. I want to do some writing, four pages a day, and I have plenty of books to read. And first of all I must quiet down, get a perfect balance.   WEDNESDAY, DECEMBER 13

Good news: the *Admiral Scheer*, the German pocket battleship raider in the Southern Atlantic, has been found and attacked by a British man o'war. It took refuge in Montevideo but must leave in 24 hours. H.M.S. *Ajax* is watching it. This makes our trip safer.

I began writing my graduation address. I like the idea of recalling the figures of some of my teachers, and today, while I wrote about Beust, I remembered vividly those early days in Zurich. The beginnings were difficult because coming from Paris I was different from other boys. I could not speak German properly and was dressed differently. I also was afraid of bathing in the lake. I could not swim properly and boys would come and push my head under the water. I was not the fighting type. I am aggressive enough now but I always hated fist-fights. Today still I hate the sight of boys struggling out of school, pushing and beating each other.   THURSDAY, DECEMBER 14

The paper is progressing very nicely. It is great fun writing a kind of autobiographic sketch. If I get old enough, or rather if I ever succeed in finishing my History and Sociology, I shall consider an autobiography. I have seen much in my life, many countries and many people. But I have no idea how such a book could be written. In the present paper I have a thesis: I want to demonstrate with my own career and the personalities of some of my teachers what university education should be and what it is not—neither in America nor in South Africa.
                                                    SATURDAY, DECEMBER 16

I shall have a difficult position in America, explaining my attitude towards the war and so I must try to clarify my thought.

At the present moment the war is an imperialist war, the clash between British and Nazi imperialism. The British and French governments supported Hitler as long as they possibly could because their real enemy is their own working class and the USSR. They were hopeful that Hitler would turn East and establish an empire that would not interfere with their own interests and that he would ultimately come into conflict with the USSR which would weaken them both. Then Hitler invaded Poland. Why? It was the way of least resistance. He probably thought that the non-aggression pact with the USSR would deter Britain. He probably had to go to war to save his regime in view of great economic difficulties.   SUNDAY, DECEMBER 17

I began a new piece of work, a translation of Paracelsus, *De Nymphis, Sylphis, Pygmalis, Salamandris;* I may publish it as a little book with an essay and illustrations for the four hundredth anniversary of his death. It will have little to do with medicine, but will be a study in comparative literature and art. The translation is by no means easy but

I enjoy the work greatly. I often get tired of politics and "socialized medicine" and wished I could devote more time to pure historical research.

WEDNESDAY, DECEMBER 27

Port of Spain, Trinidad

Yesterday night we saw the first light houses, the first sign of land after fifteen days. This morning I got up at 5:30 as we were sailing between Tobago and Trinidad and soon after 8 we went on shore. The city, Port of Spain, is a typical colonial city with a mixed population in which Indians and Negroes dominate. Many Chinese. It is a splendid feeling to be in a country where there is no color bar but compulsory education for all, where colored people have high positions and do very well and where there is a strong labor movement. Beautiful gardens with orchids.

The vegetation of the hills and valleys around the city is enchanting, a typical island that reminds me of Hawaii but more tropical still. Bamboo groves, palm trees of all kinds, cocoa, coffee, sugar cane, citrus fruit, pineapples. The island is rich, not only fruits but oil wells and a pitch lake.

At 3 we went back to the boat and heard that we were sailing not to New York but to Boston instead. General consternation and bitter feelings against the company that treats its passengers like cargo.

THURSDAY, DECEMBER 28

And so the year has come to an end. The war, long expected, long delayed, is on and soon will be an open war against the USSR and socialism.

In a few days I shall be at home and back at the Institute, after seven months of travelling. I have enough of it. I can hardly wait to see the family again. But I am afraid of the Institute, of the terrific amount of work, of stupid administrative work that is expecting me. It is getting so much more every year that I do not know where this will end, and how I shall escape. I wish I could live in Kastanienbaum and write my six volumes in peace.

SUNDAY, DECEMBER 31

1940-44

THE WAR YEARS IN AMERICA

The war period placed a heavy burden on Sigerist, both physically and morally. He felt acutely the separation from Europe, for his summers abroad had not just been pleasure trips, but constituted an important renewing of spiritual contacts. Now the ghastly loss of life brought on by the war, the destruction of cultural monuments, and the wastage and stupidity of an armed conflict were a never-ending cause for worry. The manpower shortage also placed many additional burdens on an already crowded schedule, but Sigerist never refused any extra work, feeling that the war had to be fought at home just as much as on the battlefields. An ardent anti-fascist, he did not underestimate the nature of the conflict. His health was seriously affected by the strain that anxiety and long working-hours placed upon him.

During these years the diaries were kept more irregularly than before and in some he used French, his maternal language.

In 1940, the gap from June to October is explained by a two-month car trip through the United States which he took with his family and about which he wrote eighteen articles on various public health problems for the newspaper PM. French was used for most of the diary entries.

The 1941 diary, also kept in French, stops abruptly with October 8. No mention is made of Pearl Harbor or the American entry into the war. The summer was spent in a charming cottage in the Adirondacks on the shores of Lake George. At first Sigerist considered it a poor substitute for a European sojourn, but he soon came to like the scenery and the simplicity of the little wooden house. (I remember sharing the open tower-room with a family of flying squirrels.) The kitchen with only a kerosene stove stimulated his culinary imagination to produce excellent daily meals.

In 1942 the same cottage was rented for the summer. No diary was kept until October and then he wrote in English again. The diary for 1943 shows Sigerist's involvement in the war effort and the terrific pressure of work which this entailed.

In 1944 the diary ends on October 24. Sigerist wrote about his November trip to India in a report to the President of Johns Hopkins, and in the official report of the Bhore Commission.

160

1940

N EW YEAR. Writing letters. The *The "City of New York"*
boat is rolling heavily and I am in a pessimistic mood. I am afraid of
America, of the atmosphere that I may find and of the burden of work that
crushes you. I am a European and shall remain one. I play with the idea of
going back some day either for action in a world of revolution or to disap-
pear in seclusion and to work in peace.

A storm develops. The ship rolls and rocks. Captain's dinner with
most people seasick.   MONDAY, JANUARY 1

Baltimore

Yesterday night I gave an interview to the press, mostly about my
South African experiences. At the end I mentioned briefly the war situation. And now the morning papers came out with head lines: "Dr.
Sigerist defends Russian invasion of Finland. Dr. Sigerist okays Russian
aggression." What I had said was completely distorted. I did not defend
aggression but tried to understand the Russian motives for it. A storm
broke loose. Everybody attacks me. The country is perfectly hysterical.
The New Deal is dead. Whatever England does is perfect.

                                                    FRIDAY, JANUARY 5

The storm goes on. Both the evening and morning papers came out
with editorials attacking me in a disgusting way. The lesson: a
newspaper man can never be your friend. He will betray you whenever the
policy of the paper requires it.

America has become the most intolerant country in the world. No dis-
senting view is tolerated. You are not yet jailed for being unorthodox but
boycotted and spit at.   SATURDAY, JANUARY 6

For the first time we will not be able to go to Switzerland this year.
Although I have spent most of my life abroad, yet I have gone to
Switzerland every single year.

The plans for this year are to buy a new car with the money refunded
by the shipping company—it should be $800—and to spend July and
August travelling through the continent. It should be a great experience,
particularly for the children who have never seen the West.

                                                    MONDAY, JANUARY 8

Again I am violently attacked in the newspapers, this time by a Hopkins
man. I think it is a shame to attack one another within the family. I
would never do it. The article is stupid. It reasons that since Russia has
invaded Finland, health insurance cannot be any good in America.
Nevertheless it upsets me. I wrote a letter to the editor, worked two hours
on it clarifying my position. But then I did not send it. MONDAY, JANUARY 15

Last night I could not sleep and I thought. I devised a plan. I think of retiring from the University next year. 1941 would be a good time for such a step. I shall be fifty years old and shall have been ten years in America and twenty years in academic teaching. My chief motive is that I refuse to give up my research and want to write my six volume book. It was a serious sacrifice to devote so much time to improving the people's health and what I got for it was hatred. I have enough. I'm through. I have no money, of course, but it is quite possible that the Rockefeller Foundation would give me a fellowship. In war-ridden Europe I would have more peace than here.   TUESDAY, JANUARY 16

I began an English translation of Arnald de Villanova's little treatise on wine. It is not a very easy German, and I am glad that the Latin text is available. It is infinitely clearer. Schuman in New York wants to publish it with a facsimile of the first German printed edition.[53] At the same time I want to publish a little study about the content of the book and the use of medicinal wines, tracing the development from antiquity to vermouth and cocktails. It is quite interesting.

Went to New York for a Town Hall broadcast. I strongly dislike broadcasting; it is most time-consuming. You have to write a manuscript, have to travel to the place, waste an evening, and you are fortunate if you get your expenses paid. There were three on the programme: Dr. Townsend representing the A.M.A., Winslow[54], and I. I was very weak being greatly handicapped by the many recent attacks. Winslow was brilliant, full of fire, and Townsend had a hell of a time. It is always the same story: when the A.M.A. must face the people it is invariably booed.

                              THURSDAY, JANUARY 18

I have a good press. Because my radio talk was spineless everybody is satisfied with it. And yet there are people who expect me not to retire but to act. A trade-union man from Washington came to see me. He tells me that the federal employees want compulsory health insurance. Can I help them? What can I do, handicapped, muzzled as I am. It's an awful situation. And next week I must start my teaching and won't be able to say what I think!   SATURDAY, JANUARY 20

And so I am writing in French for a change. Why? Useless to analyze the reasons, at least just now. After all, French is my mother tongue. I am coming back to it. I feel more European than ever in this period of crisis. One can live a whole lifetime in the States and never become an

[53]Henry Schuman (1899-1962), rare medical book dealer and publisher of books on the history of medicine and science. *The Earliest Printed Book on Wine,* by Arnald of Villanova, was published in 1943.

[54]Charles-Edward Amory Winslow (1877-1957), Anna M. R. Lauder Professor of Public Health, Yale Medical School from 1915 to 1945; Director of the John B. Pierce Laboratory of Hygiene, 1932-47.

American. One is reminded that one's roots are in Europe when Europe is in flames, and when the future is so uncertain.   SUNDAY, JANUARY 21

The State Planning Commission of the State of Maryland has organized a committee (to which I belong) to study medical services. Today we met for the first time. I am delighted. If we had not had that famous Conference of last May nothing would have happened. But the success of that Conference has forced the physicians to act. This is a great step forward. The President was forced to admit that not everything was perfect in Maryland. I have no intention of taking an active part in the work of the committee. I will remain an observer, but I am very satisfied that my efforts led to something.   TUESDAY, JANUARY 23

I think much about the future. I really have enough of this country which is the most conservative country in the world. A friend said to me today: America is progressive in its mechanical toys, but its philosophy is very reactionary. That's very true. Here Europe is regarded as a cadaver. That's a mistake. Since 1911 Europe has been going through a very serious crisis, but it will be reborn, regenerated, and rejuvenated. Europe's creative strength is infinitely greater than America's.
MONDAY, JANUARY 29

I spent an hour with Dr. Freeman and I told him of my intention to retire from the University. I told him about my lassitude, about the profound disgust I have for the shameful methods used by the physicians in attacking me. I have enough of this country; I will never adapt myself; I have only one desire: to return to Switzerland, to hide in a village and to work, to write my book. I offered my services to the Swiss Legation in case the country needs doctors, and I would be happy to wear their uniform once again.

Freeman is a true friend. He listened patiently and advised me to stay quiet but not to leave. Well, we'll see. At any rate it relieved me to talk to him.   THURSDAY, FEBRUARY 1

In April I will give a big lecture on my African trip and at the same time exhibit about a hundred of my photographs. I am already working on it and I have some pictures that are really beautiful.
SUNDAY, FEBRUARY 11

York, Pa.
I am simply disgusted. I have just given a lecture on the organization of medical services to the Medical Society of York in Pennsylvania. I am so intimidated that without being reactionary I was very weak. I confined myself to discussing the historical aspects of the problem. I was applauded, and one of the local big wigs gave a big speech in which he said that we were above all a Christian nation striving to follow the maxims

of Christ, and in this way all medical problems would be solved. The general idea of the discussion was that the county of York has no medical problems and that all the inhabitants, rich or poor, receive all the necessary care. And to think that York is an industrial county with a large mining population! It was simply scandalous. I congratulated these imbeciles, went back to the hotel, but I felt sick enough to vomit.

At noon I took the train back to Baltimore and I worked like crazy trying to forget this defeat.　　　　　　　　　　SATURDAY, FEBRUARY 17

Baltimore

I took up my Spanish studies again. One of my next trips will be to Mexico and South America. I studied the language formerly in Zurich, before my first trip to Spain, but I have forgotten much. At any rate it is an easy language. I am studying the grammar and analyzing a Spanish book by Azorin. If I could continue for a year I could easily give lectures in Spanish.　　　　　　　　　　MONDAY, FEBRUARY 19

It is very curious: instead of retreating to write my book I am embroiled in a new project. Last evening Kingsley Roberts[55] told me that plans were being made in New York to organize a new medical school which would accept talented young people, whether men or women, Jews, Negroes, or Aryans. Suddenly it occurred to me that this would be a unique opportunity to organize a completely new kind of school, a school which prepares not the physician of the past, but of the future—the social physician. And so for two nights I worked on a plan for this new school. I have no idea if this will interest the people involved. I don't even know who they are. But who knows, perhaps they are intelligent people who have a certain amount of imagination and want to try something new. It is in any case a unique opportunity and I shall not fail to get in touch with them and submit my idea.　　　　WEDNESDAY, FEBRUARY 21

I think a great deal about the new school of medicine, of the complete reorganization and reorientation of medical education. What an excellent job could be done—to create a new spirit, a spirit of cooperation. The social doctor practicing social medicine—the medicine of tomorrow. It is more than probable that nothing will be done. The men who have the power to act, generally have no imagination. And in America, a terribly conservative country, all the institutions have a tendency to become standardized, and consequently rigid. Some day I will publish my programme.　　　　　　　　　　SATURDAY, FEBRUARY 24

Palm Sunday, in Europe a spring holiday. One has guests for lunch and goes to the country to see if there are any flowers. Usually one

[55]Kingsley Roberts (1893-1947), medical economist. He was Medical Director of the Bureau of Cooperative Medicine, New York, 1936-41; Executive Director of the Medical Administration Service, 1941-47.

finds none, only old tin cans. Spring does not begin in the country but in the center of cities. There one can find Parma violets, carnations, and narcissus.

Here it is a grey day, a day of work. Yesterday there was snow still and freezing. Today it is a little warmer but spring seems far off still.

SUNDAY, MARCH 17

We gave a reception after a concert of the Bach Club. Musicians and scholars. A very international group: Americans, Austrians, Germans, Hungarians, Russians, Syrians, Italians, and Swiss. All languages were spoken and the conversation never stopped. Baltimore's only charm is that it has foreigners, for the native Baltimoreans are impossible. Dr. Welch told me one day, "In New York you are asked how much money you have, the Bostonians want to know what your university titles are, and in Baltimore you are asked who your grandfather was." Very correct and acute.

WEDNESDAY, MARCH 20

Easter Sunday. For the devout Christian it is a great holiday, the resurrection of Christ. For us, who do not believe in the dogmas of the Church, the holiday has lost its meaning. We celebrate it because of tradition, with eggs and rabbits, pagan elements, but we are moved. The festival is more a childhood remembrance, and above all a tradition. We have not yet learned to replace Christian festivals by new, civic holidays. Christianity was careful to replace pagan festivals with its own festivals. This is an example to follow. Festivals are necessary, but what is particularly necessary is to develop a sense of community.

SUNDAY, MARCH 24

Sometimes one has moments of inspiration and feels in a creative mood. Tonight I was preparing my course on the history of social medicine, and began thinking of the future of the Institute and of the courses I was going to announce for next winter. I always intended to develop a section of medical sociology at the Institute, to form a group of students similar to those in the seminars of Grotjahn in Berlin. I made a beginning that was not bad, but I have come to a point where I must be able to develop this idea, or stop altogether. Now I have neither the money, nor the assistants, nor even a room for my archives and for study. So I will withdraw into myself, continue my research in social medicine, and publish without bothering with any students. Let the Institute of Preventive Medicine take over. I will only give two courses, an introduction to medicine to Homewood students, and one hour a week at the Medical School where I will discuss the problems of history and sociology which interest me at the moment.

And in thinking about my courses I made a plan for a new edition of my *Man and Medicine*. This will be a summary of my medical philosophy.

MONDAY, MARCH 25

New York

At the Museum of Modern Art there is an exhibit of Italian paintings, a remarkable collection loaned by the Italian government. A huge crowd, jostling against each other. I observe the people, all these women, young girls, a few men for it is Saturday. What are they thinking? They seem ecstatic, but their expression is identical before a Botticelli Venus, Raphael's "Madonna of the Chair," or Guercino's "Cul de Diana" which does not even make them smile (it makes me think of Verlaine). Are they really moved or are they simply looking if the catalogue is correct? Perhaps they count to ten before each picture. I don't think that this exhibit has influenced their lives.

I spend the day by myself. Complete retreat. "You are damned lonely, aren't you? Of course I am," but I forget to add that it is good to be by oneself once in a while. I read and rest, and suddenly it is midnight and it is my birthday. I have completed my forty-ninth year—almost a half century. I have a bottle of cognac with me and drink a glass to my own health.   SATURDAY, APRIL 6

Washington

An escapade. I wanted to escape, and since I received an invitation for the chamber music festival in Washington, I accepted. Here I am for two and half days, far from my study. That's how I love concerts—not at night after an exhausting day of work, but in the morning or in the afternoon when one is rested. And the first concert is marvellous: classical and modern, some Bach, some Beethoven, and then the moderns, Loeffler, Malipiero, and Pizzetti.   APRIL 12

Baltimore

People are really funny here. I gave my lecture on South Africa. I painted a rather somber picture: extreme misery, diseases, exploitation, etc., and afterwards people, especially ladies, congratulated me saying: "What a wonderful country it must be!" I showed some photos and a film, and played some native music. The exhibit was very successful. The mental mechanism is very simple and very American: you retouch whatever is disagreable and remember only the pleasant things. The hall was jammed full and it seems that my popularity has not suffered.
                                                              MONDAY, APRIL 22

This morning my secretary called: "The Institute is a madhouse. Stay away as long as you can." It really was a madhouse. People throw themselves at you and squeeze you like a lemon. First it was a photographer with his lamps who took my portrait; and then visitors; then my course; Dr. Hume's course. But at night I worked and wrote eight pages.   TUESDAY, APRIL 30

A letter from E. L. She writes that a new play is being given in New York called *Medicine Show*. At a certain moment an actor cries: "What we need now are men like Dr. Sigerist of Hopkins and Peters of Yale. That's what we need." It's a strange sensation to realize that each night my name is spoken publicly on a New York stage.   THURSDAY, MAY 2

Alarming news: Germany has invaded Holland, Belgium and Luxembourg. It was to be expected, but it is always a shock when it does happen. We are thinking especially of our families in Switzerland who find themselves threatened from one day to the next, although I don't believe that Switzerland is in any immediate danger. Germany is looking for bases from which to attack England. But the day Italy enters the war, the situation will change.   FRIDAY, MAY 10

I heard a Toscanini concert in Washington: the *Egmont Overture,* Brahms' *First Symphony*. How beautiful the concert was. The voice of Germany, the other, the real Germany. It is so difficult to reconcile the two things: music and cannons. The same individuals who perhaps yesterday were profoundly moved while listening to a concert, today fly planes which are destroying half of Europe. It is difficult to understand.   TUESDAY, MAY 14

Twenty-one German divisions at the Swiss border. Switzerland has mobilized every man up to sixty years of age, and has distributed forty cartridges to every civilian who owns a rifle.

I did not sleep all night and am dreadfully excited. Switzerland can be attacked at any minute. It is unbearable to be here in America and not to be able to act. In 1914 I detested uniforms. Now I would be happy to wear one. My mother and sister live two minutes from the station and airport in Basle, and this idea is a torture. At midnight I couldn't stand it any longer and sent a telegram. And at ten in the morning I received an answer. My mother is in Flims, but where is my sister?

It seems that the German advance has been stopped at the Meuse, but will it last? I have little hope.

I am working furiously. It is the only way to forget for a few hours.   WEDNESDAY, MAY 15

Last year I was getting ready to leave with Nora. We were looking forward to seeing Paris again, Jouvet's theatre, the good little restaurants, the Luxembourg. And then it was Kastanienbaum. How far away all that seems. And when will we see Europe again, and what kind of a Europe? I cannot imagine vacations in America. A study trip, yes, but a vacation? Yet all my colleagues have bungalows where they rest very well. Yes, but this is their country, whereas I am a stranger and right now strangers are regarded with suspicion.   WEDNESDAY, MAY 29

New York

Ralph Ingersoll just founded a new daily, *PM* which will be a liberal paper. The public health section interests me very much because it is defending the National Programme. Ingersoll is interested in my summer's trip through the States and would like me to send regular reports of all the medical observations I might make while travelling. I accept gladly, and will take the trip as a journalist.   WEDNESDAY, JUNE 19

Wrote an article on spas in America. An analysis of the reasons spas have not been developed until now.

I am translating a lecture by J. P. Frank from the Latin, "De populorum miseria: morborum genitrice" from 1790. It is beautiful and powerful. And today, 150 years later, misery is still the prime cause of disease.   FRIDAY, OCTOBER 18

Ithaca

I am in Ithaca, at Cornell University. I live in a students' house, the Telluride Association, where I have a beautiful room with a large desk and two windows facing the park. It is cold already but the trees still have some of their leaves. And it is so peaceful. I hear a student playing Bach and Mozart. At dinner we speak of Tolstoy and Chekhov. For a moment one forgets the catastrophe in Europe. I hope to write some good pages.   TUESRAY, OCTOBER 29

I read *Tragédie en France* by André Maurois. The book is interesting because it was lived, but as an analysis of the situation the book is very weak, and superficial. Either he does not see the problems, or refuses to discuss them in order not to damage France. It is obvious that Daladier and Reynaud played a role, and their mistresses also. But to understand the *débâcle* one has to go back into history, and analyze the economic and social causes. Maurois is a good and very cultivated bourgeois, but not a historian.   THURSDAY, OCTOBER 31

A grey and sad day, terribly sad. It is raining and cold. Soon it will be winter. I write my four pages a day: on the misery of the peasants in the eighteenth century. And today? Misery, war, hatred, and destruction everywhere. Tomorrow the elections. A President will be elected who will lead the people of the United States into butchery. And why? To preserve the old system at all costs.   MONDAY, NOVEMBER 4

The professor of musicology, Kinkeldey, gave a big dinner—very good and excellent wines. The guests were all professors. I wonder what life is like in such a university. For the students it must be very pleasant, but for the professors? 7,000 students, and many of them are just children who came not to learn something but to have a good time. I prefer my university which resembles a European university.   TUESDAY, NOVEMBER 5

I have developed a new technique for my lectures. I begin with some general or philosophic remarks which immediately create a certain atmosphere. People arrive still busy with their own affairs, thinking about all sorts of things. My introductory remarks prepare them for the lecture. I have developed this technique consistently at Cornell. It is somewhat like the function of a prayer at the beginning of a service.

TUESDAY, NOVEMBER 12

Baltimore

I had some pleasant times this year. First of all the beautiful trip across the States which will remain unforgettable. And the three peaceful weeks in Cornell with the students. And then, yes really, the day of my operation. I shall never forget the feeling of profound peace as I experienced it that morning. I had not had any morphine, but I was calm as never before, and when I went to sleep I was in perfect harmony with the world.

THURSDAY, NOVEMBER 14

Yesterday morning Basle was bombed by British pilots who probably thought they were over Mannheim. The British were never good in geography. The bombs fell very near my sister's house. We sent a telegram immediately and fortunately the reply was good.

WEDNESDAY, DECEMBER 18

1941

A new year has begun. Where shall we be next year? In the war? A poisoned atmosphere? America mobilizing all its resources to make reaction triumph? Who knows? In any case the year will not be amusing, and all one can do now is to work. I am in a creative period. One book in press, two others and an article in preparation. I must hurry, for by 1942 I must be free—free to begin my big work, the History and Sociology of Medicine. That will be the final period.

WEDNESDAY, JANUARY 1

New York

I again had a very warm reception in New York. The Academy of Medicine gave me a dinner, and afterwards I gave a lecture on Paracelsus. The Academy printed a very beautiful programme illustrated with the portrait by Hirschvogel of 1538. The lecture was much applauded: I had to sign a whole stack of programmes and felt like a movie actor.

The lecture was much work, for basically I detest Paracelsus' mysticism, I prefer Descartes.

THURSDAY, JANUARY 23

The Swiss Legation phoned asking whether I would take part in a neutral commission which is to inspect prisoner of war camps in Canada. A treaty was signed in 1929 regarding the treatment of prisoners of war, and the Swiss government is in charge of supervising its application and at the same time is arranging for an exchange of sick prisoners. The Legation is having difficulties finding doctors of Swiss nationality and that's why they asked me. I accepted immediately, at least in principle. Before accepting definitely I must have more precise information. Of course I would be happy to serve the Swiss government. It would also be a very interesting experience.   TUESDAY, FEBRUARY 18

Commemoration Day! The University in great gala—I in my red robe. Dykstra gave the official address. He is President of the University of Wisconsin and director of army recruitment—a strange combination. His talk is patriotic: America represents the only true democracy, and Europe (excepting England) savage barbarism. Everybody is very satisfied and goes to have lunch with the president at Homewood.

SATURDAY, FEBRUARY 22

My article on the new medical school has some interesting repercussions. The department of public health in Ohio asked me for 15 copies. The students in Chicago want to make it a subject for study. Robert S. Lynd, Columbia's famous sociologist, wants to discuss it with his students. Winslow wrote me a very flattering letter. The article is read and discussed.   FRIDAY, FEBRUARY 28

J. S. came to tell me of his difficulties in Greenbelt. It's a sad story but very instructive. Three young doctors, full of enthusiasm and idealism, organized a medical cooperative in a splendid way and everything went well. Unfortunately the cooperative has a poor administrative council which meddles into everything. And now there are intrigues and factions which complicate everything. They want to fire J. S. and it's quite possible that the whole organization will go to pieces. This case shows very clearly that the weak point of the cooperative system lies in the administration, in the control of the organization by willing but incompetent people.   TUESDAY, MARCH 4

It's a terrible week. I again had to abandon writing my book. I am preparing a lecture on the evolution of dental art and continuing my work on the laudanum of Paracelsus. I have to edit a bibliography of Paracelsus' works, to prepare an exhibit, and then the annual meeting of the Association of the History of Medicine. And everything at once. Also I sleep badly and my nose is worse than ever.   FRIDAY, APRIL 4

Today I finished the scrapbook of my South African trip. It was an immense task, for the book has 264 of my own photos, but it is a

170

beautiful souvenir—an illustrated history of my trip, day by day. And together with my photographs I have the programmes of my lectures, newspaper clippings, maps, etc.

And now I am going to make an album of my last year's American trip.   SATURDAY, APRIL 5

I am completing my fiftieth year. I have been married for 25 years, a professor for 20 years, and 10 years in the United States. I do not feel old, but of course I am no longer young. I would like to choose a new nose. Mine is not worth much. I have some rheumatism in my arms. My arterial tension does not bother me, but my circulatory system is beginning to wear out. Well, I hope to last until I have completed my big work. And that's already something in this day and age when millions of young people are stupidly killed.   SUNDAY, APRIL 6

Yesterday we celebrated my birthday. 37 people, my best friends, came for a Swiss dinner. The children in Swiss costumes, *Bratwürste, Pâtés,* gruyère cheese, etc. We played charades and it was very gay.

Tonight my assistants invited me for a wonderful dinner. They know that I still appreciate good food.   MONDAY, APRIL 7

I am really disgusted. My publisher advertises my book as "highly readable and entertaining." That's an insult, and means that every idiot can read it without thinking and will find the book amusing. I did what I could to write a serious book. I tried to develop a thesis as strongly as possible. If the result is an amusing book, it is a miserable result. I will never again give a book to this publisher.

WEDNESDAY, APRIL 30

Lillian Hellman[56] has a house one hour from New York and yesterday we went to have dinner with her. She was dressed all in white, a flowing robe, bare legs, sandals. She looked Greek, and yet she is a very modern woman. I have a great admiration for her. She has an extraordinary psychological flair and yet is very modest, almost timid. Very refined dinner with excellent wines and conversation like fireworks. Sometimes life is very good.   SATURDAY, MAY 17

I have an idea: I should take a three weeks' cure at a spa, perhaps at Saratoga Springs, in September. There I could have the rheumatism in my right arm treated, could have inhalations for my nose, and could treat my heart and kidney. During three weeks I would not smoke, nor touch any alcoholic beverages. I could sleep, take walks, and lose ten pounds. After that I would be rejuvenated and ready for the work of the winter. It's an excellent idea and the question is only whether I have enough money.   FRIDAY, MAY 23

[56]Lillian Hellman, noted American playwright.

A professor is a man who professes what he on the basis of his expert studies considers the truth.

In doing it he always runs the risk of breaking his neck. To him this is an occupational hazard.   SATURDAY, JUNE 21

Bailey Cottage, Bolton Landing, N.Y.
We are well settled for two months, and the place is charming. Lake George is a mountain lake with forests reaching to the shores. The bungalow is very comfortable and I have a beautiful room to myself which serves as a study and bedroom. I am free. And the essential is to be away from Baltimore where it is impossible to work in peace, where I am interrupted every minute. Here I hope to accomplish a lot.   WEDNESDAY, JULY 2

Ingersoll came and now I know what he wanted, quite simply to invite me to accompany him to Moscow. He is leaving Tuesday, in three days. "Around the World in Eighty Days," and by plane. San Francisco, the Hawaiian Islands, Central Asia, Moscow. Four weeks in Moscow. From there he hopes to fly in a British military plane to London. And return via Lisbon. He has never been to the Soviet Union, does not know the language, does not know what to do, and would like me to accompany him. There! It's a shock! It was too sudden. I would have had to leave immediately to put my passport in order. Two years ago I would not have hesitated, but now I feel old. I no longer have the courage to make sudden decisions. I want to write my books in peace, in the country if possible, with a cat at my feet. It's heart-breaking, a real loss. Never again will I have the opportunity to see the world at a critical moment in its history.   SATURDAY, JULY 5

Gradually I am recovering from the shock of Ingersoll's visit. It pours all day long. I take up my work again where I had left it. This week I want to finish the translation of the nymphs of Paracelsus. This will not change the world, but it's amusing. And the nymphs are charming girls.

Tonight I began working on my abandoned book—the economic questions of medicine. It seems to me that I have forgotten everything and I don't know yet how it will go.   MONDAY, JULY 7

The only way I have to rest and distract myself from my work is by driving a car. While driving you have to pay attention and cannot think. You see new landscapes and all this is a marvellous relaxation. After a car excursion you feel tired and completely relaxed. The only trouble is that three of us drive, and in order to be fair only one-third of the mileage is left to me.   TUESDAY, JULY 8

For the first time I am certain that Hitler will be defeated. He has committed a serious psychological mistake. He will bleed to death in the USSR and I think that in England and here the imperialist interests are stronger than the class interest. A victory of industrial Germany would present a serious danger to the trade of the Anglo-Saxon countries, and one seems determined to defeat Hitler and then turn against the Soviets after the victory. Yesterday the United States occupied Iceland and is seriously preparing for war.   WEDNESDAY, JULY 9

I am working day and night and my only recreation is photography and cooking. I will make a photographic study of the region and of our life in this region. I already made a plan which I want to follow as much as possible.

And cooking—that's my passion. I cook one or two meals every day for the family and I've already cooked some good dishes. I think of my cooking teacher, Bruno, who is now in Brussels and cannot be very happy.   FRIDAY, JULY 25

I write five pages a day. Just now it is the introduction to Paracelsus' treaty on nymphs, etc. I never feel better than when I'm writing. Creative work gives me real pleasure. The subject is very interesting. Unfortunately I don't have the time, nor at present the facilities, to make a complete study of the history of nymphs from antiquity to the Renaissance, but I hope to do it some day.   SATURDAY, JULY 26

I have a little wooden room which serves as my study and bedroom. It's very simple. Instead of a desk I have a table. One corner of the room, hidden by a curtain, serves as closet. I have my papers in an old chest of drawers. It's even primitive. We have a bathtub but no hot water. But it's just in such an environment that I can work best, that I have my best ideas, and perhaps that I am happiest.   MONDAY, JULY 28

Today is the six hundred and fiftieth anniversary of the founding of the Swiss Republic. Switzerland is celebrating at a very serious moment. By a miracle the country has escaped the war, but the danger of an attack still exists. And there is another danger—the slow infiltration of fascist ideas. Everyone realizes that a new order will have to be established in Europe, but what sort? I have no doubt that in case of invasion the country will defend itself to the last man and woman, but is Switzerland strong enough to resist the poison which enters by little doses from Germany. Let's hope that Hitler will be defeated and that his regime will collapse before it's too late.

We also celebrate this great day. Baudisch,[57] who was in Switzerland for nine years, spends the day with us, and I cook a good dinner. We drink a bottle of champagne and sing some Swiss songs, just a few, not too many, for we are all close to tears. Nostalgia is a national disease and two years have passed, two long years that we have not been in Switzerland.   FRIDAY, AUGUST 1

[57]Oscar Baudisch, a family friend, who was working as chemist at Saratoga Springs.

We again made a beautiful excursion into the Adirondack mountains. It's wild but not terrifying like the rocks, snow, and ice of the Alps. It is more like virgin forest. I thought of the Indians who inhabited these forests, of bears, and of snakes. Now everything is peaceful and New York State takes excellent care of this region.

We continued to Lake Placid and Lake Saranac where we visited the Trudeau sanatorium, the first of its kind in the United States. A very impressive statue of Trudeau—a good head, intelligent and sympathetic. We saw also a cottage painted red, built in 1884, which was the beginning of the sanatorium.

And finally we drove home via Tupper Lake and other lakes.

Trudeau did not invent the open-air cure for treating tuberculosis. The treatment was used before his time in Germany and Switzerland. And even in the United States a German doctor living in Baltimore, a Dr. Seitzman, treated tuberculosis before 1884 according to this method. He is little known because he did not persevere, whereas Trudeau introduced this method once and for all. And then there is also the human element. Trudeau himself was affected by the disease, while Seitzman was not. This tragic element is very important in history. It's like the Semmelweis-Holmes affair. TUESDAY, AUGUST 5

Roosevelt and Churchill held a meeting in the open ocean and announced an eight-point programme of war aims. It's a pitiful document, infinitely weaker than Wilson's fourteen points. Peace won't be concluded by these men of yesterday. FRIDAY, AUGUST 15

We have a summer theatre in Bolton Landing and today the whole company came for tea. They are very young, and very nice. Almost all have no job for the winter. A career in the theatre is very difficult in America where there are no repertory theatres. FRIDAY, AUGUST 22

Leningrad is in great danger. The Germans are approaching from all sides, but two million men, women, and children are prepared to protect Lenin's city with their bodies. Every house is a fortress, the factories are working day and night. A triple garrison defends the city: the Red Army, the People's Army hastily put together from workers and intellectuals, and finally the population, the old people, the women and children. Voroshilov made a moving proclamation. Everyone is ready. Under these conditions I don't think that the Germans will assault the city. The price will be too high. The Germans will have to kill a million inhabitants and will lose at least as many. The fall is rapidly approaching and soon it will be winter with snow and long nights.

The hatred in the whole world towards the Germans will be simply terrifying. The day will come when one idea will dominate every country—kill the Germans. Guilty and innocent will be massacred. SATURDAY, AUGUST 23

I received a letter announcing that Queens University at Kingston, Ontario, wants to give me a Doctor of Laws *honoris causa* at the university's centenary in October. What a great pleasure! I'm neither vain nor ambitious; all I want is to be left in peace to work, but it is a great satisfaction to know that my work has been appreciated and recognized.

WEDNESDAY, AUGUST 27

Saratoga Springs

Erica and Nora accompany me to Saratoga Springs and help me find a room. At two o'clock I have an appointment with the doctor. Dr. Carl R. Comstock is a charming person and makes a very good impression as physician. He examined me at length, and put me on a regime which is quite general until the laboratory results will allow a more exact diagnosis.

TUESDAY, SEPTEMBER 2

Yesterday I began my cure, I continued today, and will continue for another 21 days!

At 7:45: half a glass of hot water with 2-3 spoons of Oxy-cristine. Guaranteed results.

8:30: breakfast in bed: orange juice, a soft-boiled egg, a cup of black coffee, no bread.

10:00: at the Washington Bath House:
1. complete massage
2. mineral bath: 10 minutes
3. rest: 45 minutes. The doctor's assistant takes my arterial tension.

12:00: 1-2 glasses of Saratoga Geyser

1:00 lunch: fruit, vegetables, lean meat

2:00: rest of one to two hours

4:00: one hour walk at first, two hours later

6:00: 1-2 glasses of Saratoga Geyser

7:00: dinner, same as lunch

10:00: to bed

With each meal a capsule of vitamin B complex. Next week I'll begin my nasal inhalations. No alcoholic beverages, no tobacco, one cup of coffee a day only. The regime is very strict but that's just what I needed.

Only now do I feel how tired I was. I sleep constantly, and it seems to be the first time in years that I'm getting a good rest. The massage is good and the baths very agreeable; I'm covered with gas bubbles and on getting out I am pink and feel very relaxed. My arterial tension reacts very favorably. I have also lost several pounds. Usually I weigh at least 165, yesterday only 159½.

THURSDAY, SEPTEMBER 4

A paradox: for a professor I have a very good appointment, but I have no money to spend whatsoever. One makes always the same error: one lives on too high a standard. With $10,000 one should live on a standard of $5,000 and one would be rich. Well, we can't complain. I can let my children study and that's essential. FRIDAY, SEPTEMBER 19

Dr. Comstock examined me and the result is very satisfactory. In three weeks I lost eleven pounds, reduced my arterial tension considerably, feel rested, and at night can even breathe without benzedrine. My heart is certainly not quite normal, and has not been for some time, but with a little care I can live long enough to be able to finish my work—that is the six volumes. Finances permitting I will take such a cure every year before the winter. The results are not only physical but also psychological. During three weeks without work one has time to think and to slow down the tempo of life. I will work much this winter—the plan is made—but I'll try not to become enervated. I must distinguish between what is important and what isn't. What counts is creative work and not the time wasted in giving lectures.

At 9 in the evening I arrived in New York. I gave myself 24 hours of complete liberty, that is, I ate whatever tempted me. What I missed most during my cure was bread—*il dono più dolce di Dio*.

WEDNESDAY, SEPTEMBER 24

1942

Baltimore

It is two months since I returned from Saratoga Springs and I have not done a thing. I have written a short article for *Soviet Russia Today* and that is all. It's a hopeless situation. Of course I have not been idle and that's just the trouble. I have been too busy to do any real work. What I did so far was:

1. Take charge of the Welch Library, put it in good shape, win the full confidence and cooperation of the personnel and develop plans for the future.

2. Keep the Institute in excellent shape. Launch the courses very successfully, particularly the one on Sociology.

3. Develop a very promising plan for volumes XIII and XIV of the *Bulletin*, along new lines.

4. Develop a plan for an American Russian Medical Society. Thus the time was not wasted, yet what counts is my research and writing and I simply must find my way back to it. Time is precious.

SATURDAY, NOVEMBER 14

The problem in these days of war is how to survive them. We older people are not going to be killed on the battlefields but we have good chances of being killed by overwork. Last year I finally adopted a mode of living adapted to my health condition and felt extremely well. This is all gone. I suffer from lack of sleep and in spite of working 14 hours a day achieve very little. THURSDAY, NOVEMBER 19

I cook a big Thanksgiving Dinner, probably the last elaborate dinner for the duration. It is getting terribly complicated to obtain the necessary ingredients and already I had to use much *ersatz*. THURSDAY, NOVEMBER 26

A hobby is a blessing because it always gives you something to look forward to. I am fortunate in having three hobbies: 1. photography, my chief hobby that I use in building up scrapbooks; 2. cooking that I cannot practice often but last August I cooked two meals a day for four weeks—and enjoyed it; 3. my tea collection of which I make good use three to four times a day. Sunday morning I devote to my hobbies after a huge breakfast. SUNDAY, NOVEMBER 29

I did something perfectly foolish. I am terribly behind in my work. The dietetics paper is overdue, so are the spa papers, the Arnald introduction, not to speak of the South African study. Instead of attending to the most urgent, tonight I started working on a new book for which there is no hurry at all, namely a publication of documents from the Jacobs Collection. The only excuse is that I was so terribly tired that I just could not write. All I could do was study and transcribe a Boerhaave Latin document. Thus the night was not quite lost. MONDAY, NOVEMBER 30

Back to Baltimore in a blizzard, in a crowded train, the steam out of order. Why do American soldiers not sing? The car was full of them, soldiers, sailors and marines. In Europe they would sing, there would be a regular singing contest between the groups. Here they were quiet and gloomy. They had been on furlough, were rejoining their troops and an uncertain future. But in Europe they would sing just to overcome the gloom. And in the USSR they would not only sing but sing beautifully in four voices. One reason why they don't sing may be that there is little marching in a modern, mechanized army. Still, the Russians and Germans do sing. SUNDAY, DECEMBER 13

The Beveridge Report has come. Macmillan issued a first American printing of 50,000 copies. It is undoubtedly the most interesting document that has come from the war. I ordered eight copies of it for the Institute and Library. As a prominent British Conservative put it—it is the cheapest insurance against revolution. It is a typical Conservative document, the attempt to save the existing mode of production by bribing the people into a feeling of social security. I intend to write a series of articles "From Bismarck to Beveridge" in which I will give a historical and sociological analysis of the conditions which, in the various countries, led to social security legislation. The Beveridge plan is probably the last of its kind; the next step will be socialization.

SUNDAY, DECEMBER 20

My Indian student, Kamala Gosh, turned up all of a sudden. Her's is an amazing story. She was sailing in a convoy from Scotland to India, had a terrific storm in the Atlantic that scattered the convoy in all directions and seriously damaged the boat whereupon they went to a Canadian port for repairs. She took advantage of the opportunity for a ten-day trip to the States.

She was three weeks in Britain and her report is interesting. The whole country looks like a depressed area—houses out of repair, people badly dressed, etc. Civilian services like telegraph have completely collapsed. Food situation is under control, diet adequate for everybody but queues for everything you want to buy. Many people distrust Churchill but there is nobody to replace him. America is as unpopular in England as England is in the States. American soldiers are disliked because they have so much more money to spend than English soldiers.

I spent almost the whole day in the kitchen preparing a cold buffet for tonight. The Institute came and we had a very pleasant evening.

THURSDAY, DECEMBER 31

1943

Baltimore

Wrote twenty-one pages—a record—and finished the Arnald.[58] I think I hit the right tone. It is scholarly in the beginning and ends in the light vein which should be about correct for this kind of book. It was a great pleasure writing it. There is nothing I like more than philological work and it is my bad luck that I have not more time for it. Circumstances have driven me into so many other fields but I always wish I could go back to pure philology. SATURDAY, JANUARY 2

Began a new paper, an editorial with which I intend to open the new volume of the *Bulletin*. I call it "On the Threshhold of Another Year of War." I am in a creative mood and must take advantage of it. I want the *Bulletin* to have a strong personal note such as Virchow's *Archiv* had in its high days, and I cannot begin a new year without addressing my audience personally. The work proceeded so well that I kept going until 2:00 a.m. I have so much on my chest that I must get rid of it. MONDAY, JANUARY 4

Began my work as Chief Consultant to the Board of Economic Warfare in Washington. I arranged with them that I would come every Saturday.

[58]Arnald of Villanova,*The Earliest Printed Book on Wine* (New York: Schuman, 1943).

It suits them well and is very convenient to me in that it permits me to carry on with my University work. The job promises to be extremely interesting. The task is still somewhat hazy but seems to have great possibilities. Long conference with Dr. Rosenberg and Miss Abbott. Then I had to read a large confidential dossier on Spain. Certain facts appear clearly from such a variety of documents: that the Franco government (like all fascist governments) is corrupt through and through; that there is a shortage of food, but of course the rich can get everything on the black market while the poor are starving; that transportation has collapsed. This all explains why Germany has not yet marched in.

I feel that my work is well organized now for the duration. I have five desks: one in the Library, two at the Institute for administration and research, one at home and one in Washington. I work quite regularly from 9:15 a.m. to 1:00 a.m. with a break from 6:00 to 8:00 p.m., weekdays and Sundays, moving from one desk to another. Thus I hope to accomplish a lot and all I need is sufficient health. But just now I feel splendid. SATURDAY, JANUARY 16

Roosevelt and Churchill met in Casablanca. Of course nobody knows what the result of the conference has been, except that no allied war council has been established. The President's flight to Africa has a highly dramatic element that must impress the people, but I think it is a mistake for the head of a government to leave the country in a period of emergency. Wilson lost his power the moment he left the White House. Stalin is strong as long as he stays in the Kremlin. The head of a government is much more than an individual—he is a symbol. Zeus was a powerful god as long as he resided on Mt. Olympus but became very human whenever he stepped down. TUESDAY, JANUARY 26

The Board of Economic Warfare pays me $22.22 for every day I work there, and I have just decided to turn over the money to the University. The University supports me by paying me a salary and the work I do for the BEW I do on University time. It therefore would not be fair to accept any compensation. I consider my work with the BEW a sacrifice that I am bringing joyfully in order to help the United States win the war. In times like these everybody should be expected to work twice as long and twice as hard without extra remuneration. There is no sacrifice when you are paid for the work you do, when war becomes a period of boom. The men on the battlefields sacrifice not only money but their lives and we should be ashamed to accept extra money for extra work. I run the Welch Medical Library, a $7,500 job, without any remuneration and that is the way it should be. TUESDAY, FEBRUARY 2

Yesterday I had a very successful day in New York. I helped organize the American Russian Medical Society or whatever it may be called ultimately. Abraham Stone had called a meeting, about twenty people to his home, and we discussed matters from 7:30 to 1:30. The meeting was very well prepared so that there was hardly any opposition but on the contrary great enthusiasm. I shall be editor of the new journal—a new job but an interesting one. The whole affair is very timely. The interest in Soviet medicine is tremendous and the ignorance abysmal. I should think that the journal will be very welcome to the authorities here; it will help the war effort. Of course I had great hesitations to overcome before accepting the job because I already had such a full load. But I really do not know who else could do it because the editor must have the following qualifications. He must: 1. be very familiar with Soviet medicine; 2. have a good standing in American medicine; 3. be *persona grata* in Moscow; 4. have good medical connections in the USSR; 5. know Russian; 6. have editorial experience.   FRIDAY, FEBRUARY 5

I suppose I prostituted myself today, one more evidence that prostitution is primarily due to economic causes.

An advertising agent of the J. Walter Thompson Co. came, a big firm, 500 employees. They handle the publicity of Pan American Airways and want statements on the post-war world, not more than 450 words, ads for *Time* magazine. They pay, of course, $300 or more, and I had to accept it in order to pay my taxes. It's awful. I am in good company. So far the contributors have been John Dewey, Hu Shi, the Archbishop of Canterbury, the president of Yale, Masaryk, etc., but it is humiliating nevertheless. The more work I have, the less money I get. That is normal because there never has been any relation between my work and my income.   FRIDAY, FEBRUARY 26

Greatly upset because I received news that my old friend, W. F., had committed suicide. He was in France, had found refuge in the Pyrénées where he was living miserably with his wife and daughter in a small village. The Gestapo was after him. For years we tried to get him a visa. We succeeded finally but it was too late. The Germans had invaded the unoccupied zone, were massing troops in the Pyrénées. He felt trapped and had no other escape. I think he acted correctly. It is better to die from your own hand than by the tortures of the Gestapo. And he probably thought that his wife, being Aryan, would find it easier to get to America without him. It is terrible nevertheless. I must say I expected this end because his situation was hopeless.   TUESDAY, MARCH 16

Wrote a statement for the Pan American Airways—the prostitution statement. But I am reconciled with it. After all, if there has to be advertising it is better to propagate the ideas of certain people than to have girlie gags. I stuck to my line, tried to write forcefully in the manifesto style. I suppose they will "edit" it and spoil it, but at least I wrote as I felt.   THURSDAY, MARCH 18

Heard a beautiful joke: Why is the USSR doing so well in this war? Because it is the only country that is not afraid of bolshevism.

There is much truth in this joke. The fear of the possibility of socio-economic change is undoubtedly stifling the war effort in many countries.

FRIDAY, MARCH 26

52 years old. I do not feel my age. As a matter of fact, I still feel much more at home with my students than with my colleagues. Now that I am so busy I do not see anybody outside my students and my immediate co-workers and I could not wish for anything better. I am in a creative phase and only hope my health will not fail me. Kidneys and heart are not too good and with the three jobs I have I cannot be very gentle to them, but I hope I can go on for some more time. There is so much to be done.

WEDNESDAY, APRIL 7

Martha Eliot, head of the Children's Bureau in Washington, came for a long talk. She and the Secretary of Labor Perkins think that plans should be made now for the organization of medical care after the war, and that at the moment there is no independent agency or group doing the work. They both think of calling a small group for informal discussions and if it can agree on a plan they will appoint a technical staff to work out the details. Then when the moment comes the plan would be brought before the people.

This is the most encouraging talk I have had in a long time. It really is a great country. Things may look dark at times, and then all of a sudden people of wisdom and courage step forward and there is hope again. And such nice people who do great things not fanatically but with a smile. I was not sure how Martha Eliot spells her name and looking up *Who's Who* I found that we were born the same day, April 7, 1891. No wonder that the plans of medical care we have in mind are almost identical.

WEDNESDAY, APRIL 14

Spent most of the night figuring out what my exact financial status was. Made a semi-annual balance and a new budget for the next half year, just as governments do in times of crisis, and crisis it is for us salaried people. Taxes, insurance, and rent absorb half of the income and the purchasing power of the rest has dropped considerably. In normal years I could make almost $1,000 additional income through lectures and from publisher's royalties. In the last six months I made exactly $34.43! The richest colleges like Vassar and Sarah Lawrence don't pay a cent for lectures. At best they pay expenses, that is railroad fare, but every such lecture costs you money. For my work in Washington I get $5.00 for expenses per day which does not cover them. For my work as librarian or as editor of the new journal I do not get one cent, yet every new job increases your professional expenses. I am editor of two journals and devote a lot of time to them, yet I cannot afford to have them bound at the end of the year. I must make some money to increase my operating balance and I decided to sell my Haller collection. It is bitter because it is the result of 25 years of collecting and every volume has its history. It is, moreover, one more tie with Switzerland that will be separated but it cannot be helped. Besides, one should not be attached to objects.

WEDNESDAY, APRIL 21

The second quarter has begun and today I began a new course. It was announced as "The Historical Foundations of the Present World Conflict." Our young students feel that they are in the midst of a gigantic historical process that they do not quite understand. They want to know and are looking for help, and I think it is the duty of the academic teacher to help them. I have no ready-made answers, but I am trying to understand the world also and together, through frank discussion, we may clarify our thought. I intended to hold the course in the seminar room, but so many came that we had to move into the lecture hall.

TUESDAY, APRIL 27

Kamala Gosh, one of my closest and dearest students, a real friend, is in all probability dead. I received a letter from Oxford telling me that the ship on which she was sailing was lost and that she has been reported as missing. I am terribly upset and very sad. There is still a faint chance that she may have been picked up but I hardly have any hope. Since she was sailing on an American ship I shall move heaven and earth to find out. Such a brave and lovely woman. It cannot be true!

WEDNESDAY, MAY 26

I had my citizenship examination today. Chesney and Schultz were my witnesses. It was easy and pleasant. American officials are infinitely more agreeable to deal with than European ones. They are correct but human and basically friendly. They have not that superior attitude of the European (including the Swiss) petty official. I was well prepared and everything went off very well. And now I hope early in September to be a citizen of this great country to which I feel so deeply attached.

THURSDAY, JUNE 3

Princeton

Demoralizing visit at the Institute for Advanced Studies. It was demoralizing because it showed what a life devoted to research can be. It must be marvelous to be able to work in daytime without being exhausted, to ponder over a problem, to write a book or a paper leisurely and not in a rush. Well, it will never be my lot.

SATURDAY, JUNE 12

New York

Long talk with Alan Gregg at the Rockefeller Foundation. I like him very much. He is honest, sincere, eager and relatively unspoiled by his foundation work. He really means to be helpful. Just now he is planning to launch a Medical Council realizing that the A.M.A. alone does not represent medicine in its present complexity—an excellent plan and very timely.

In the evening, testimonial dinner for Lebedenko [59] at the Pennsylvania, a huge affair, 500 people, music, many speeches. I was chairman and the dinner went off very well except that the programme as usual was too long. It was the official launching of the American Soviet Medical Society in Manhattan.   FRIDAY, JUNE 18

All my papers are finished and in print but I am in such a tension that I cannot stop. At one o'clock when my tea was ready I was desperately looking for a manuscript because for five months lunch to me had been manuscript work. At night I had an enormous amount of work waiting but at eleven I simply could not resist the temptation any longer and I began writing a new paper on the spelling of proper names. I wrote twelve pages until 3:30 a.m., a perfectly foolish affair.

Today the tension continued and I cleaned up the Library, the Institute, and the *Review*. It is high time for me to get away otherwise I would devise plans for the reorganization not only of the Library and Institute, but of the Medical School, the University, and the City of Baltimore,

FRIDAY, JULY 23

Ithaca

I am conducting a one week's workshop on Medicine and Health in a summer course called "Intensive Study of Contemporary Russian Civilization."

The course is thrilling. It is the first time that regular instruction on the Soviet Union is given in an American university. The impulse came from the Rockefeller Foundation which is contributing one-half of the cost. There are about 75 very eager students.   MONDAY, JULY 26

Bolton Landing

Travelling by bus is pleasant and democratic. You sit very comfortably, can read or sleep, and you talk with your fellow-passengers. Ithaca to Syracuse, from Greece to Italy, from Ulysses to Archimedes.

This really is a fine country. At the station in Syracuse was a train with Italian prisoners of war, heavily guarded. They were comfortable in coaches, every man had a seat—while I sat on my bag until Albany. On the platform were many soldiers and sailors. As soon as they noticed the captives they brought them cigarettes, had kind words and jokes for them, and the guards had no objection. There is no hatred, and a sense of fair play and decency pervades all actions. That is the way it should be.

[59]Vladimir V. Lebedenko, Professor of Neurosurgery at the First Moscow Medical Institute. During World War II he was in the U.S. as official representative of the Russian Red Cross and Red Crescent.

Of course if we had been invaded, it would probably be a different story.   SATURDAY, JULY 31

It just occurs to me that my work has never received any official recognition in the United States. I was given honorary degrees in Spain, South Africa, and Canada, but never from an American, *id est* U.S., university. I think this is perfectly normal. At home you are taken for granted. Besides, being a liberal who recognized the significance of the USSR before other people, I cannot be popular with university presidents. What difference does it make?   THURSDAY, AUGUST 5

Leona Baumgartner[60] has written an excellent article on Klebs[61] for my July number of the *Bulletin* with very characteristic abstracts from his letters. They all belong to the Osler school of *historia amabilis*. They "had a good time" studying history. Their subjects were limited and never offensive. My history is anything but *amabilis*, but is meant to be stirring, to drive people to action.   FRIDAY, AUGUST 20

Baltimore

I am in a dark mood—I don't know why—and my phantasies run along the following line: the war has wrecked my life. For thirty years I have been preparing two books—a History and a Sociology of Medicine. When the time came to write them, I was made an administrator. I have ten hours of administrative and general academic work every day. I still manage to put in 5-6 hours of research and writing, but what can you do in so little time? I am publishing a lot, but it's all small stuff, odds and ends, of no importance whatsoever. After the war I'll be used up and will have lost so much in health that I will never be able to do any decent work again.   SATURDAY, SEPTEMBER 11

Today at 3:45 p.m. I became a citizen of the United States of America. Judge Chesnut was in the chair and the ceremony was very dignified. It is a great country and the longer I am here the more I love it. I love its vastness, its courage, its informal way of doing great things. It really is a free country: here we have been living as aliens during a terrible war and have not been molested once! How different it would have been in any European country, including Switzerland. I have, of course, been critical of many aspects of America, but it is my job as a professor and scholar to

---

[60]Leona Baumgartner, Commissioner of Health of the New York City Health Department 1954-62; at present Assistant Administrator of the Agency for International Development in Washington.

[61]Arnold Klebs, a close friend of Osler, Welch and Cushing, spent the greater part of his life in Switzerland where he amassed an extensive medical history library and devoted himself to historical studies. His library now forms part of the Historical Library of Yale Medical School.

be critical, and I am critical because I love the country and want it to be still better and greater. The fact that I was permitted to be critical shows how free the country is.   MONDAY, SEPTEMBER 13

I had a letter from Harvard. A committee is planning a reorganization of medical education. A year ago I was asked for reprints of my paper on medical education for distribution to the members of the committee and now they would like to have a conference with me and to have me present my views on the subject. I will do it and I am delighted to see my paper had these repercussions. I wrote it just for the purpose of stimulating thought and discussion.   MONDAY, SEPTEMBER 20

No work done today but celebrated a great deal: a birthday, then the first number of the *American Review of Soviet Medicine*. It came by plane and looks fine. The plan was conceived in 1938. It took five years and a world war to have it materialize, but here it is, a constructive step out of chaos. The July number of the *Bulletin* came also today, finally the October number of the Welch *Bulletin*. And so we had a very good lunch at Miller's with oysters, lobsters, and plenty of cocktails. FRIDAY, OCTOBER 15

A miserable week and I am in miserable health. The last two nights I slept only three hours and I am under constant terrific pressure. Everybody wants something, everybody hammers at me and there is no escape.

The most depressing thought is to know that my research career is ended. Even if the war should end soon and if I got rid of the library, I would be used up, unable to give a synthesis, good only for little odds and ends.   THURSDAY, NOVEMBER 4

This morning I was called before the Civil Service Commission to answer questions. It was the usual charges: activities in so-called communist front organizations, and articles written for the *New Masses*, others for *Soviet Russia Today*, etc. I must say that the investigation was extremely fair, impartial and benevolent, but it is significant nevertheless that one is incriminated for having been opposed to fascism. I did not hesitate to say that I was proud to have served on the Bureau for Medical Aid to Spain, and that I would do it again. Well, I think this is a good opportunity to resign from the Board of Economic Warfare. The work I did there was a great sacrifice and if I am not entirely welcome I do not see why I should burden myself with it.   MONDAY, NOVEMBER 15

I am so bitter and keep telling myself what a miserable life I have. This is perfectly stupid because millions of people are really suffering and I am not. I am just tired and worn out. Still, I must do something, must try to have something to look forward to. I took my scrapbook up again and will make a few more photos.   FRIDAY, NOVEMBER 26

Washington

In Washington for a meeting of the Medical Advisory Council of the Medical Research Institute of the UAW-CIO. It was pleasant and worthwhile. The old public health gang was there. What pleased me most was that everybody congratulated me on my students. Wherever they are, they are doing extremely well. They represent a new type of doctor.

FRIDAY, DECEMBER 3

1944

Interesting day in Washington at the Senate Office with Senators Wagner and Murray, and Congressman Dingell. The two senators make a very good impression. Dingell is a staunch liberal also, but cannot talk without making speeches. A meeting had been called to launch an organization in support of the bill on health insurance. There were a few doctors, and representatives of the CIO, AFL, Farmers' Union, etc., and I am sure that a strong organization will result. We shall probably lose but at least not without a fight. SATURDAY, FEBRUARY 5

New York

Two years ago I had promised to give a lecture on "Music in Medicine" to the Bach Club of New York and today I had to pay my debt. It was quite an enjoyable evening. It began with a dinner at the National Arts Club, then came the lecture in a packed full room. The music was very good: Yella Pessl played her large harpsichord, a singer fresh from Juilliard sang very well and we had a violinist and cellist in addition. I brought the usual stories—tarantism, St. Sebastian, etc., and two old ladies walked out when I quoted Casanova on syphilis. Good audience— Elizabeth Schuman, Mrs. Damrosch, Emil Ludwig. Reception after the lecture, ending up in a night club. MONDAY, FEBRUARY 28

I am bloody mad—as B. used to say. I had a row with C. not the first, and always about the same question. His attitude is: to hell with the University, with research, with culture. Let's drop everything and win the war. My position is: let's win the war and win the peace by preserving our cultural life, by intensifying our research and rejuvenating the University. I have enough of Hopkins and for the first time I am thinking seriously of looking for another job, for a research position. I am really tired of being an administrator and in a new position I might even be able to write my History and Sociology. If a change has to be done it should be made soon while I am at the height of my reputation, not later when I will be decrepit. WEDNESDAY, MARCH 15

186

Emil Ludwig came. He intends to write a piece against Freud pointing out that he has become a danger to America and is responsible for the widespread "inferiority complex."   MONDAY, MARCH 27

To me Debussy has an incredible charm. I just heard the *Quartet*, songs, and *L'Après-midi d'un faune*. He always makes me think of the Luxembourg Garden, of the silvery mist of Paris, of a young woman, tall, blonde, and sad. Aglavaine et Sélysette, Mélisande, all the ethereal women of Maeterlinck—who is still alive. Forêt de Saint Germain, old parks, the water covered with green algae. He is not spring but autumn, when the leaves are falling slowly, uncertain where they should touch the soil.   SATURDAY, APRIL 8

The C.C.F.[62] has just won a smashing victory in Saskatchewan, 43 of 52 seats. The first time that a socialist party has full control of a Canadian province. Now there is a possibility of organizing medical services in a sensible way. They want me to advise them and I feel very tempted to do some field work for a change.   FRIDAY, JUNE 16

Journal Club. It is very depressing to see how many miserable books are published in the field of medical history. We had three such books in succession: Ricci's gynaecology, Leonardo's surgery, and now Gordon's *Romance* (the word makes me sick) *of Medicine*. It is a sad comment on my work that after twelve years of my activity people still dare publish such books and find respectable publishers for them. I only hope that our reviews will discourage the publishers.   TUESDAY, JUNE 20

Seminar on health education, physical culture, rest, and recreation—in good form. After the class a student came and said: "What the Russians are doing is fine but we could not do it because we are individualists." I felt like saying: "Are you?" Some day I must write an article on the concept of individualism and how it is misinterpreted. To most people individualism is merely the possibility of making much money while otherwise being exactly like their neighbors. Even the rich people are anything but individualists. They are bound by the very rigid code of their class.   THURSDAY, JUNE 22

I have an idea for an amusing paper, American Truffles: A Thanksgiving Fantasia in C minor. It began when I found a letter of Mitchill written in 1812 in which he expressed the view that the truffle might be a native of America. Unfortunately he was wrong. Then I found an eighteenth-century dissertation of an Avignon physician on the truffle. The piece is going to end as a satire on the A.M.A. Such articles add some salt to the *Bulletin* and I think are permissible as long as they have some connection with medical history.   FRIDAY, JUNE 30

[62]Cooperative Commonwealth Federation, now the New Democratic party.

Worked the whole day and finally I became so tense that I dropped everything and began writing the truffle paper. I write these light pieces when I am under greatest pressure. In such a condition I cannot relax in any other way. I cannot read, lie down, or sleep. All I can do is work slowly on such a paper. Then all of a sudden I do relax. It's great fun. What a good life one could have doing research and writing instead of having this deadly office work. What a fool I was ever to accept a chair. Years ago in Switzerland I had a little money and could have lived modestly in the country in some village. But I was ambitious, wanted to be a "professor." What is a professor but a poor wage-slave?

TUESDAY, JULY 4

The last few days I was much depressed — lack of sleep, too much work — but today a telegram came that cheered me up a great deal. The Premier of Saskatchewan, T. C. Douglas, wants to have a survey made of the health needs of the province and wants me to be head of a fact-finding committee. This would be a good opportunity to do some field work and a really constructive job. Besides, good material for the book.

TUESDAY, JULY 20

Last day at the Institute. It is such a good place, the best place in the world for studies in the history of medicine, and it is a real tragedy that the people best qualified in the field are denied the privilege of working in it. How stupid a university can be!

SATURDAY, JULY 22

Lewes, Delaware

We left on the Love Point Ferry at 7:00 a.m. A two-hour boat trip. The harbor section is a fascinating sight, teaming with life, ships from all over the world, in all stages of construction or repair, all in grey or fancifully camouflaged, armed with guns—war. I remember the first ship I saw in war paint. It was five years ago in Port Alfred, South Africa. Five long years of war. Full employment in this harbor. Why can we not have it in peace time?

An eighty-mile drive to Lewes. The car is old but behaved very well. The landscape is rather monotonous, a truck farming region that has suffered from drought. Small towns that seem run down and have little charm.

First impression of Lewes: that it is as hot as Baltimore, but a torrential rain brought relief. The cottage is very comfortable. I have a good study with green as the keynote and—very important—the kitchen is superlative.

TUESDAY, AUGUST 1

I received an exciting letter from the State Department conveying an invitation of the Government of India to assist in a survey of postwar health organization and administration. A committee has been organized in India and the committee has requested that some foreign experts be invited. From the United States they want Dr. Mountain,

188

Assistant Surgeon-General of the Public Health Service, and me. I think the choice is interesting. It shows that liberal forces are involved. Kamala Gosh must have prepared the ground. She always wanted me to visit her country and must have written about it to her friends.

Of course I would love to accept the invitation. India would be another great experience that I could work up in my books.

It is interesting that I have much more influence abroad, particularly in the British Empire, than in the States. The reason is obvious. There is in almost every country—outside the U.S. and some South American republics—a swing to the left. Therefore there is demand for a new kind of medical statesmanship. My books are well known in the British Empire and liberal governments look to me for advice. South Africa, Canada, India. Sooner or later I am sure to get invited to Australia and New Zealand, to Mexico and Chile. I have had endless difficulties and trouble enough but as a student of history I always knew that I was on the right track, that I was preparing for a future that was bound to come.

There is so much work to be done, and I must write my twelve volumes. This would complete and crown my work. If only my health does not fail me.   WEDNESDAY, AUGUST 16

Regina, Saskatchewan

At 7:20 in Regina. The Premier, T. C. Douglas, a young man, and Dr. Sheps at the station. A very nice room at the hotel Saskatchewan. Making contacts. And, of course, the newspaper hounds.

WEDNESDAY, SEPTEMBER 6

Whole day at the office in the legislative building. The C.C.F. is determined to make a demonstration of what a socialist government can do for the people. They find that the health field is best suited because the people are aware of the problem and ready for a plan.

FRIDAY, SEPTEMBER 8

It is most pleasant to deal with this government. They are simple and honest people, idealists with a realistic approach. Everything is very informal and that makes it so pleasant.

Meeting of the Commission in the morning establishing our programme. I have the status of Beveridge, that is, I alone will be responsible for the report and the other members act as technical advisers. In this way we are sure to avoid a minority report.

At 8:00 a.m. we left in two cars for a tour of inspection through the province. First stop was Strasbourg where we held hearings at the town hall. It was a joy to listen to these farmers. A splendid type of men, accustomed to take care of their own affairs. Outstanding a Norwegian, Anderson, who went back to the old country, found that they were doing more for the people's health, came back and launched the mu-

nicipal doctor system. Drive to Wadena through wheat fields. The year
was good and the farmer is prosperous.   WEDNESDAY, SEPTEMBER 13

Trisdale

Hearings the whole day. People came from all over the district, travelling fifty miles and more to present their problems.   FRIDAY, SEPTEMBER 15

A letter from President Bowman who graciously grants me a leave of
absence for the Indian trip under the condition that I do not make any
statement either in India or after my return that could serve any political
interest. This is the freedom of research of a great endowed University. The
Indian health problem obviously is a social, economic, and political
one and if you cannot call the child by its name, then there is little you
can do. I will have to save up my experience for the Sociology and for
the time when I will have left Hopkins.   MONDAY, SEPTEMBER 18

Regina

From Swift Current to Moose Jaw and Regina. This ends the tour
and now the chief work is beginning, the report. The tour was extraordinarily interesting and informative. We could feel the pulse of the
province and I have definite ideas as to what I shall recommend.
SATURDAY, SEPTEMBER 23

Revising the report, editing it, and adding to it. At five minutes past
midnight we were through. I think the report is good. It is realistic and
foresees a gradual socialization of services. It is by no means complete,
but is the best I could do in less than four weeks.   SUNDAY, OCTOBER 1

And now a new assignment begins—India. I was delighted to hear
that John Ryle of Oxford will be there too. The tour outlined for
November sounds most promising. It will lead us through many sections
of India.   SATURDAY, OCTOBER 7

I really am looking forward to the trip. All the reports I have read
so far are perfectly unrealistic. They simply postulate what should be
done according to Western standards (e.g., 300,000 more doctors) but this
cannot be done in India. I wonder if the people want health. It may well
be that they do not mind being sick and dying young. They are very
religious and more concerned about the hereafter. Russia destroyed religion first and then developed health. This is a point that I must study.
FRIDAY, OCTOBER 13

The last day—but is it? My secretary went to Washington to get my
passport at the British Embassy and was told that it was at the State
Department and that I had to get it in person. I have never seen a more
involved, sticky and sickening red tape. Well, I'll go tomorrow but I

feel inclined to tell them all to go to hell. I suppose I shall get away
somehow.   MONDAY, OCTOBER 23

I did get away.   TUESDAY, OCTOBER 24

1945-47

THE END OF THE WAR
AND RETURN TO EUROPE

The summer of 1945 was spent in Ithaca in a beautiful house overlooking Lake Cayuga. The library at Cornell University was at Sigerist's disposal for the writing of the first volume of his History.

In 1946, for the first time since the war, the Sigerist family again spent most of the summer in Switzerland. The diary itself was left in Baltimore, and no entries exist between July 18 and September 28. French was used until July. The few weeks spent in the Ticino, the Italian canton of Switzerland, convinced Sigerist that here was the ideal spot in which to settle once he had detached himself from Baltimore.

During 1947 Sigerist resigned from Johns Hopkins and moved to the house at Pura, Switzerland, where he spent his final years.

1945

M ajor tasks for the coming year:
1. To begin writing the History of Medicine on October 1.
2. To that end, break away from Hopkins if a position can be found anywhere that will give me more time and leisure.
3. If this is not possible begin the book nevertheless by making a superhuman effort.
4. Until October 1 clean up my desk and not begin anything new, refuse lecture invitations and not accept any engagements.

MONDAY, JANUARY 1

At night twelve pages on the report I am writing on my Indian tour for President Bowman. I am addressing it to the President, but through him I am aiming at the State Department because I feel sure that he will turn it in, and I have no other way of reaching the Department.

TUESDAY, JANUARY 2

There is hardly any more stupid variety of *homo sapiens* than the Baltimore socialite who vainly tries to compensate his alcoholic degeneracy with kindness. Dr. Welch could handle them beautifully and managed to mix with them without getting bored. I tried in the beginning but never succeeded. Life is too short to be wasted in such a way.

THURSDAY, JANUARY 4

At last I finished the report on India for the President. It has the length of a good sized paper. He may not read it at all, but it was quite good for me to write a brief summary of my experience while the impressions were still fresh.

TUESDAY, JANUARY 9

An empty day preparing lectures and attending to routine matters.

My major research project this week is to find out how the cost of heating and lighting the building should be divided among the University, represented by the Welch Library, and the Government of the U.S., represented by the Malaria Drug Survey. After weeks of preparation we shall have a conference tomorrow, and it is to be hoped that the combined efforts, knowledge, and skill of a clinician, a chemist, and a historian may lead to a wise solution in which nobody (but the Dean) is interested.

MONDAY, FEBRUARY, 5

In Washington, I don't know why. Well, I had to pay my respects to the Indian Agent General. And besides I wanted to remind them tactfully that the British Empire owes me money that I need to pay my taxes next month. It is not by accident that a socialist government (like that in Saskatchewan) pays you without delay, while a capitalist government refunds our expenses as late as ever possible.

FRIDAY, FEBRUARY, 9

Meeting of the University Advisory Board at which W. gave a report on behalf of the Committee on Organization and Policy of which he is chairman. Late at night it occurred to me that this committee would be the agency to which I could present a report on the reorganization of the Institute. My remaining at Hopkins would have advantages both to the University and to myself. To the University because it would remain the center of medico-historical studies instead of having the center gravitate to some other institution. To me because I could use the excellent facilities of the Institute. I worked during most of the night and throughout the morning, writing a report, outlining a plan which I think is sound, feasible, and timely. It sets a new pattern, separating administration and research. It would make the Institute a division of the Welch Library and me a Research Associate. I would be satisfied with one half of my present salary. $5,000 a year would not be too heavy a price for buying the freedom to engage in creative work. I would be overjoyed if the University accepted the plan and I would start a new life, living hygienically so as to have twelve more years to complete my work. I do not know what the chances are, but I think I have a very good argument.

FRIDAY, FEBRUARY 23

An interesting day. Longcope gave a lunch for Pasteur Valléry-Radot who is on a mission to South America. He was medical director of the Resistance, lived underground for the last two years, and directed the medical services from the basement of the Institut Pasteur. He had many interesting stories to tell: reception of the resistance leaders by De Gaulle, éditions de Minuit, how he found the hiding place of Drieux de la Rochelle but was unable to inform on him, etc. I met also for the first time Julian and Anne Green.[63]

Received a very courteous letter from W. acknowledging the receipt of my memorandum. The letter makes clear, however, that the University will not do anything for me. One has to wait, W. says, until one sees how things develop a few years after the war. At least I know where I stand.

TUESDAY, MARCH 6

I went to see Longcope for a physical examination. He found that my condition was exactly the same as last year. Of course he has not yet the results of the various examinations. So we'll have to wait for a final diagnosis. But there is one result already, namely that he found that I should be relieved of the Library and that he will talk to Chesney and Bowman. This, of course, would mean a great deal.

TUESDAY, APRIL 10

News came in the evening that President Roosevelt has suddenly died of a cerebral hemorrhage. It is a terrible loss, particularly at this crucial moment. He was a great President, one of the last liberals. The mistakes he made were not so much due to him as to the system under which he had to work. He sacrificed Spain in order to save his New Deal, and played with the Pope for the same reason. He was a member of the propertied class but was intelligent enough to see that adjustments had to be made. His death greatly weakens America's position. Truman seems to be an honest man but is a local politician, unprepared for the international scene.

Longcope telephoned. The laboratory reports are not too good. There is no doubt that I have lost ground and that I must do something. I plan to go to Saratoga Springs on July 1, have a three-weeks' treatment, then spend two quiet months somewhere working on volume I.

THURSDAY, APRIL 12

Longcope telephoned and wants me to go to the hospital for a week to have a complete rest and to have a number of tests made. I think it is a good idea.

TUESDAY, APRIL 17

[63]Julian H. Green, the writer, and his sister, Anne.

194

Germany has surrendered unconditionally. There is still some fighting in Prague but it is a question of hours and the war in Europe will have come to an end. Germany is beaten, its industries gone, the cities destroyed. The dream of a *Grossdeutschland* is over, I think once and for all because in the future the formation of large groups will not be along national but along economic lines. The famous German army has been routed twice in one generation.   MONDAY, MAY 7

Saratoga Springs
First day. Bath at one o'clock. Very pleasant sensation to discover the bubbles of gas and a certain smell which is difficult to define. Then an inhalation for my poor desiccated nose.   WEDNESDAY, JUNE 13

A letter from Charles Singer asking me if I would accept a chair in the history of science and the direction of an institute at the University of London. If it had been Oxford, or a chair without an institute, the reply might have been affirmative, very likely even. But London, a big city where one loses so much time, an institute with administrative work, no, it's too late. At present I want to write my books.   MONDAY, JUNE 18

I have not been smoking for almost three months but once in a while I dream that I am smoking, and in these dreams I have the taste of the cigarettes that I used to smoke many years ago. I dreamt, for instance, that I was smoking Virginia Leaf, a cigarette which I used to smoke in Zurich around 1919. And very recently I awoke with the very distinct flavor in my mouth of a Turkish cigarette I had stolen from my father in Montmorency when I was eight or nine years old.   TUESDAY, JULY 3

The last day. The cure is finished and I must say that it was a complete success. For three weeks I did absolutely nothing, and I feel very rested. Now I am ready for the *vita nuova* and for the book.
          WEDNESDAY, JULY 4

Ithaca
A great day. Today, the fifteenth of July, I began my History of Medicine. I have prepared for and spoken of this book for more than twenty years. And finally the day has come. From today on this book will be at the center of all my thoughts and all my actions. I will not think whether my health will permit me to finish the book, but I will act as if I had eight more years to live.   SUNDAY, JULY 15

A great event! The newspapers announce the British election results. Triumph of the Labour party. That's very important. The example of England, a very conservative country, will have great repercussions in all of Europe. It is socialism on the march in England, as in all of Europe. The United States will remain the fortress of reaction. For me, personally, this result is important also. In a socialist England I could play an important part, whereas here I am considered a crackpot. My historical and sociological work has never been appreciated in America, whereas it has been a great deal in the whole British Empire. Of course it is not pleasant to change at my age, but one must think of the future. It is very possible that in a few years it will be impossible to pursue historical studies in America.   THURSDAY, JULY 26

The government announced the atomic bomb, triumph of science. A first bomb was exploded with great success in New Mexico on July 17, and a second destroyed a Japanese city. The government spent $2 billion and employed 127,000 people for several years. Of course it is lucky that we are the first ones to make this discovery. One speaks of nothing but great promises for the future. Personally, I fear for the future. The utilization of atomic energy will accentuate the process which forms the basis of all our values—namely, that technology has developed more rapidly than our sociological organization. Even with our present technology the majority of the world's inhabitants are suffering from famine and misery. So why do we need other sources of energy?

After the war, the government, stimulated by this discovery, will spend great sums to encourage research in the sciences of physics and chemistry, but not a cent for ethical or political science. It is precisely such studies which might prevent another war and prepare for a reasonable peace.   TUESDAY, AUGUST 7

Délire! Pobeda est nasha! [The victory is ours] *Enfin!* Exactly at seven o'clock news came from the White House that Japan had surrendered unconditionally. Five minutes later the town was in a tumult. Everyone was out driving his car, honking their horns. We also took our car and with our neighbors drove to town, yelling, and with our horn giving the sign for victory. A nightmare of six years has come to an end.

All the federal employees have a two-day vacation—they have deserved it—but we are without mail and newspapers, but have the radio. The most important news is that we can have as much gasoline as we want.

40 miles by car—the ration of one week—to Aurora along the lake. Wells College. Coming home we bought some gas without ration card.

"How much do you want?"

"I don't know. Just fill her up!" And we burst out laughing.

                                                          TUESDAY, AUGUST 14

I received a good letter from J. B. S. Haldane[64]. He hopes that I will accept the chair in London. Speaking of the liberty one enjoys in England, he wrote that he never had been molested by the University even

---

[64]John Burdon Sanderson Haldane, Professor of Biometry at London University, 1937-57, and well-known writer on many scientific subjects.

though he was a member of the Executive Committee of the Communist party, even though he wrote a weekly article for the *Daily Worker*, and even though he had recently made thirty speeches during the election campaign. The situation certainly is different from here where President Bowman granted me a leave from the University to visit India on the condition that I make no political statements either in India or in America after my return. This is the beginning of the end of scholastic liberty, and who knows what will follow.

A serious difficulty I have encountered in my book is that it addresses both the historians and the doctors. The first chapter, which discusses problems of historiography, perhaps will seem somewhat simple to the historians, whereas the second chapter, on paleopathology, will seem almost incomprehensible. The doctors, on the other hand, will find the first chapter too complicated and the second too simple.

FRIDAY, AUGUST 31

I have written ten pages and finished my chapter. I reached page 225. I began the book on July 15, and in two months wrote 225 pages plus 75 pages of notes, plus some notes for 16 pages of illustrations and a bibliography. It is more than I had hoped for.

FRIDAY, SEPTEMBER 14

Walter Cannon, the great physiologist of Harvard, died a few days ago, aged 74. I wrote a note about him for the *Review of Soviet Medicine*. He was a perfectly remarkable man, a great scientist and at the same time an impassioned anti-fascist, a rare thing in the United States. We worked together for a long time, on the Committee for Republican Spain, and more recently in the American-Soviet Medical Society.

FRIDAY, OCTOBER 5

Life is good as long as there are sylphs dancing in the moonlight. Massine is in Baltimore with a small group of dancers, and I spent a most enjoyable evening. Anna Istomina is a young Canadian who has become a great ballerina. Every movement, the expression of her face, everything is grace and poesy. Bettina Rosay represents the spirit of gaiety and Rosella Hightower is also a good dancer. The classical ballet is so beautiful, light and unreal, like a dream.   SATURDAY, OCTOBER 6

The German university professors, my former colleagues, have a nerve which exceeds all limits. H. Zeiss, a Nazi, founder of geo-medicine, a type who was probably a spy in Russia, had the nerve to write me a most cordial letter informing me that he and Diepgen would be very happy to see me again and that my presence in Berlin would be most desirable. They have forgiven me for having always been an anti-fascist.

MONDAY, NOVEMBER 19

A good day as I would like to have frequently. I stayed at home and wrote ten pages about primitive medicine. And then I spent the evening with the pianist, Richard Goodman. His wife, Dorothy, sang for me. She has a superb voice, sang some Pergolesi, some Debussy which I adore, Schumann, Strauss. Why are days like these so rare?

THURSDAY, DECEMBER 6

1946

A Baltimore
new year is beginning, a year of peace without peace, in a world filled with fear and suspicion, in a world where millions are suffering from hunger and cold. We are still very privileged in America, but the future is uncertain here also.

My History is begun. This is my chief task, and this year I want to finish volume I and begin volume II.   TUESDAY, JANUARY 1

I heard the *Appassionata*, one of Beethoven's most beautiful sonatas. The sonata always reminds me of the Lévine sisters whom I knew so well before World War I. One studied law at Berlin, the other was a pupil of Schnabel, and the *Appassionata* was her favorite piece. They were Russians from Kiev, daughters of a banker, and spent every summer in Sils-Maria. The war broke out and they probably disappeared in the tempest.   WEDNESDAY, JANUARY 2

Telephone strike, and so an excellent day for work without interruptions. I stayed at home to take advantage, and wrote six pages. If only one could be without a telephone the whole year. For my type of work the telephone is nothing but an annoyance. If one has to write a letter, one thinks beforehand, but one telephones without thinking, from sheer laziness, and each time disturbs the person at the other end of the wire.

SATURDAY, JANUARY 12

To write a diary is to stop an instant every day, to reflect, to think of what one wanted to do and of what one did not do; the effect is very salutary.   SATURDAY, FEBRUARY 16

I was given the first album of Debussy *Préludes* and every morning I begin my day with a prelude. Music before all else. "Votre âme est un paysage choisi"—the Luxembourg Gardens on a spring day! The imperceptible fragrance which floats in the air. And the silvery mist in the evening. The bistros. Young students, boys and girls. Good humor, where is it? An eternal city, without age, reflecting the whole history of France and of Europe.   MONDAY, MARCH 11

I am 55 years old, a half century plus five years and all I want is to have enough years—eight or nine—to be able to finish my History. The whole family is together—Erica came from Washington, Nora from Cornell. I am being spoiled. It is spring, promise of things to come. We make plans for the summer: by plane to Geneva on July 14. And, as a symbol, I write some pages on my book.   SUNDAY, APRIL 7

I began the third section of my book—Egyptian medicine. "Praise to thee, O Nile, that issuest forth from the earth and comest to nourish the dwellers of Egypt..." I am very happy that I visited Egypt in 1944. It was only a few days, but I saw the Nile, the pyramids, the sand of the desert. I breathed the air of Egypt and saw its sky. And now, when writing, I can convey much more color than it would have been possible without my trip.   MONDAY, APRIL 22

Washington

In Washington where the Soviet Embassy gave a reception for Ilya Ehrenburg, Simonov, and another writer, a general, whose name I have forgotten. There are not many guests, and we are *en famille*. I speak French with Ehrenburg who lived for many years in Paris. He looks spent and tired, whereas Simonov is a young man.   SATURDAY, APRIL 27

Baltimore

Twice in my life I lacked courage, and I regret it bitterly. The first time was during the Spanish civil war. I was convinced that the Spanish war was the last chance to prevent a world war. The acceptance of fascist intervention in Spain equalled an acceptance of a world war and the sacrifice of uncountable millions of human beings. I should have done everything to arouse public opinion. I should have gone to Spain to join the Republican ranks, to set an example! If in every country hundreds and millions of individuals in high and respected positions had abandoned everything to show their conviction, then public opinion would have been aroused.

The second time I lacked courage was when I accepted the directorship of the Welch Library. I should have known that these years would destroy both my health and my life's work. I tried to save my life and my work by asking for an assistant, but the Dean and President refused categorically. For them it is simply a question of dollars; for me it was the ruin of 25 years of work. I should have refused, or better still, left the University. I did not do it because in time of war it was so difficult to refuse a service, and it was so much easier to accept.   TUESDAY, MAY 28

I often go to the market, or to the grocer, or the A and P, where I observe people. I see women of all ages, many young women with kids, a few men, old men already retired.

Today I was in town on a glorious day and what struck me particularly were the young girls in bloom, the many young girls employed by the government, banks, shops—salesgirls, secretaries. They are young, fresh, clean, coquettishly dressed, have well groomed hair and manicured nails. They are charming, have only one idea—to get married as soon as possible, like in the movies. They marry the first boy that comes along; he is also a minor employee. Everything goes well the first year; they both work and make enough money. They go out at night and live as they had seen in the movies.

Then the first kid comes. The wife stops her work at the office. Their income is suddenly cut in half just when their expenses increase. The woman becomes the slave of her household. She no longer has time to shave her legs, or take care of her hair and nails; she has not enough money to buy pretty little things, lingerie, dresses, and hats which she could formerly afford. The young girl in flower whom I saw this morning in town has become the woman I see at the grocer, an ill-groomed, tired, impatient woman. This petty bourgeois enslavery is very sad.

TUESDAY, JULY 9

Back home. Home? Back in Baltimore. In my beautiful study that I shall probably lose soon. Confused, with swollen feet, coughing. An Irish cough. The transition is too sudden. Yesterday Paris in all her autumnal glory, the silvery mist in the morning, warm sunshine during the day, the people good-humored, full of jokes, courteous, in spite of the immense difficulties of everyday life, in spite of the gigantic tension that may burst into a revolution at any time.

After a flight of 19 and a half hours—New York. It's too sudden. Two months ago landing in Geneva at 5:00 a.m., a shooting star from a war-shattered, hysterical world into an island of peace, a country that is sane. Confusing months. Coming back. As if the 7 Leipzig and the 14 American years had never existed. Walking into the Café Odéon in Zurich, sitting on the same chair on which I used to sit as a student years ago. Nothing changed but me, and the waiters are no longer Germans but Swiss.

Air transportation is operated not as a business but as a racket, and T.W.A. has the reputation of being the worst of all companies. They sell twice as many tickets as they have seats hoping that they may receive additional planes, machines that never come forth. At the American Express Company in Basle they told me quite openly that the date of my departure would depend on how much I was able and willing to pay at the Paris office of T.W.A. It is profoundly disgusting. The demand is ten times the supply. Conditions must have been similar with the railroads in the beginning. Once you are on board the plane the company takes good care of you and the hostesses are charming.

My friends in Zurich would like me to come back. The government is ready to create a few new chairs and the medical faculty is thinking of establishing a chair of medical history. I have no formal offer yet, but

S. was asked to sound me out. We talked the matter over several times. I really do not know what I should do. The idea of going back to Europe is tempting. Here I am considered a crackpot, because I am writing history instead of making money, and because I like the Russians and do not consider social insurance a form of bolshevism. Working, moreover, is such a terrific struggle here. Every day I have to fight to squeeze out a few hours during which I can do some creative work. Another factor is that the University is changing its character, rapidly becoming some kind of technological institute. I begin to feel a stranger here. I have no ambitions, or rather I have only one desire to be able to write the History, and if possible the Sociology. Hopkins is not a good place for the purpose, at least not for a man in my position. One also has to take into consideration that a few years from now fascism may be going strong in this country, that it may well be impossible to write history without interference. I left Germany in time and perhaps I should leave America in time so as to be able to continue my work.   SATURDAY, SEPTEMBER 28

Why is it that the more science, the more technology a country or nation possesses, the less culture it has? Countries like India and China were and still are deeply cultured and yet science there is on a very low level. In the West the rise of science in the last 50 years was accompanied by a rapid reversal to primitive savagery. I do not know the answer and merely see the phenomena but I think the question should be investigated. I accepted to give a lecture on the natural sciences at Connecticut College in February and may devote it to a discussion of this problem.

It seems that with science, with the mastery of nature, the values change. Plumbing takes the place of culture while plumbing should merely make it easier for us to create cultural values.   SUNDAY, NOVEMBER 3

There is no greater voluptuousness than to take a stiff dose of phenobarbital and to vanish, to fall into a stupor. Until last summer I never took any hypnotics. I used to sleep very well, always having a deficit and rejoicing when I had a chance to sleep. Now I am greedy for hypnotics. Once you have reached that point death has lost much of its sting.   WEDNESDAY, NOVEMBER 6

Every autumn we die a little more. Every year when nature dies we are one year closer to the grave. The leaves are gone and the trees are bare, not all, one ginkgo in our backyard is still holding out. It is not yellow even, but has preserved some of the summer's green. Every morning I step to the window and salute it and feel grateful that it shortens the winter.   FRIDAY, NOVEMBER 8

I am determined by now to leave the University at the end of this academic year and to settle down in a village of the Ticino. I have the choice between the job and the work; either to keep the job and to give up

201

writing my books, or to stick to the task and to give up the chair. I have tried desperately to do both, administrative work and research, but I have no longer the health that this requires. I cannot work past midnight. Of course we will be very poor, but I hope to get a fellowship from the Rockefeller Foundation. With $3,000 a year we could live in a village quite comfortably and after a few years the book should yield a little money.

I have thought of other possibilities such as a chair at the University of Zurich, but there I would have no peace either. I would be considered an "expert on America," would have to advise every Swiss going to the U.S., and welcome every Anglo-American visitor. My only sorrow is to leave the children, but Erica may be willing to come with us if not immediately, then after a while.   TUESDAY, NOVEMBER 12

Kennst Du das Land, wo die Citronen blühn, im dunklen Laub die Gold-Orangen glühn—They bloom in both Italy and California, in both *ein sanfter Wind vom blauen Himmel weht.* Why is it that Italy means so much, is *ein Land der Sehnsucht,* while California is not? It is the past that makes the difference. Italy is the country which for centuries has given untold spiritual values to the world, lavishly, where everything is genuine, while in California everything is faked.   FRIDAY, NOVEMBER 15

After having seen Lillian Hellman's *Another Part of the Forest,* and having reread her *Little Foxes,* both brilliant plays about wicked and morbid people, it is a great relief to read a simple and beautiful book such as Rumer Godden's *Thus Far and No Further,* the diary of half a year that she spent during the war with her two children and three dogs on a tea plantation near Darjeeling. The day by day observations and thoughts of a sensitive woman.   SUNDAY, NOVEMBER 17

If only I can find the right kind of house next summer. I would like an old house with large rooms that have high ceilings. *Auf Säulen ruht sein Dach, es glänzt der Saal, es schimmert das Gemach. Kennst Du es wohl?* I do not care what the plumbing is. And I would like a garden with camellias and mimosas and a lemon tree. It would be the monastery that I would enter and never leave. There I would lead a purely spiritual life, drawing on fifty years' experience, creating without interruption, writing books, papers, articles, reviews, perhaps even poetry. No telephone. The only contact with the outside world would be the mail and occasional visitors, old students, old friends.   MONDAY, NOVEMBER 25

The University is raising funds under the slogan "For Longer Life and Better Living." While most people in this country say that they wish to live long they actually are afraid of life and try to kill time in any possible way. They are frightfully busy, working hard not because they like the work but because they are afraid of the alternative, of the leisure they do not know how to use. They go to the movies because they are sure to forget themselves for two hours. And when they read a book it is a mystery story that will also help to kill some time. I would rather raise funds to devise methods that would help the people to live, that would help them to enjoy life (short or long) and make it meaningful—funds not for science but for the humanities.   TUESDAY, DECEMBER 10

Today I wrote a five-page letter to Alan Gregg of the Rockefeller Foundation telling him what my situation and my plans were and inquiring whether the Foundation would grant me $5,000 a year for three years in support of my work. *Alea iacta est!* Things will be moving now. The next step will be the letter of resignation to the President.
                                        FRIDAY, DECEMBER 27

Three months of complete literary impotence and the worst is that I do not know why. Of course the book is difficult, but not more so than it was in the beginning. Is it the uncertainty about the future, the return to Europe, which is a gamble, of course? Yet I am doing it to save the book. Is it on account of ill health? My health has deteriorated during the year, no doubt, yet I feel comfortable, have no headaches, no subjective symptoms, and I lead a very quiet life. I am restless because I am not writing or am I not writing because I am restless? At any rate I must make a great effort to finish volume I in the next few months. This is the price you pay for freedom.   SUNDAY, DECEMBER 29

1947

Baltimore

I hesitated a long time in what language I should begin this blue book. Emotionally I would prefer French. Italian would be most appropriate since we are going to live in an Italian-speaking country, and Russian would be good practice also. But I decided to write in English because this is the language in which I am writing my book. It probably also is the language that I know best at the moment, having thought and taught in it for the last fifteen years—although I'm not sure.

The coming year should be an eventful one. I hope that it will see the completion of volume I and the beginning of volume II. And, of course, my retirement from academic life, a fresh start, *nel Ticino,* I hope, where I will have time to write and to study. Romain Rolland exerted his greatest influence while he lived at Villeneuve in complete retirement. If only my health does not betray me for a few more years. Then I feel confident that I could achieve something.   WEDNESDAY, JANUARY 1

Busy writing a report for the President on studies in problems of alcohol and alcoholism. He had the silly idea to make me chairman of a committee dealing with the subject. The American liquor industry is making such enormous profits that they are beginning to give money away to suppress alcoholism! Since the University needs money Bowman would like to know how he could get a slice of the cake and I have to suffer for it.   SATURDAY, JANUARY 4

My health is better than it has been in a long time thanks to a new diet that I devised. I had reached the point where I just could not sleep without barbiturates. In other words, something had to be done and I felt that a change of diet would be most appropriate. Just at that moment I found a pamphlet in my library *A Guide to Health*, by Gandhi, the Mahatma, that is full of common sense. He has hypertension also and is now walking from Ahmedabad to Calcutta.

This is my diet:

Breakfast: a large glass of fruit or vegetable juice, nothing else. Lunch: 2 soft-boiled eggs, 2 pieces of toast, a little butter, sometimes a little cheese, an apple or other fruit, tea. Dinner: one evening raw vegetables and fruit, the other evening cooked vegetables and fruit, 1 glass of wine, and after dinner a cup of tea.

I have been on this diet now for almost two weeks; I work better, I sleep well, and feel generally improved. I lose weight which is an advantage also, although my primary purpose is not at all to reduce. What I am after is the disintoxication of the organism, the *Umstimmung*. I am not a vegetarian and will not hesitate to have a good meal with meat from time to time, but as a matter of routine I am sure that a vegetable diet is much better for my condition.   FRIDAY, JANUARY 17

It just occurs to me that one week ago I resigned my chair and that the receipt of my letter was never acknowledged. I know that Bowman was in town last week, but he is busy raising millions and the resignation of a professor obviously is a very minor event. To me it does not make any difference because my determination to leave in June is final.
                                              TUESDAY, JANUARY 21

At last I received a letter from the President, a very kind, very understanding letter. He accepts my resignation and I am much relieved. Now I know where I stand. On the way home I bought flowers and a bottle of champagne to celebrate the beginning of *capitulum ultimum*.
                                             THURSDAY, JANUARY 23

I have at last resumed my old habit of devoting the first period of the day to language studies. I began it when it was about 13 years old. I remember that at that time I used to get up one hour earlier than necessary in order to spend that time in the study of Greek. Then at the

204

age of 15 I began studying Arabic every day. Later it was other languages—Persian, Syriac, Sanskrit, Chinese, Spanish. Now I am translating from Russian for publication in the *Bulletin*. This daily exercise is good mental training and at the same time serves a practical purpose.

MONDAY, FEBRUARY 3

Seminar for beginners at 5:00 p.m. So many students came—about 40—that I had to drop the idea of a seminar and will have to give a lecture course. They know that I am leaving and that these are my last courses. Hence the large attendance. It's a pleasure to give these courses.

George W. Corner formally asked for an appointment and came to invite me to address the Johns Hopkins Medical History Club in the spring. It will be a kind of farewell party. These parties will be a perfect ordeal, like attending your own funeral, but you have to submit to them gracefully for the sake of the Institute and its future. They will also provide an opportunity to tell a few things to a receptive audience. It occurred to me that I might possibly publish these addresses together with a report of the Institute's activities from 1932 to 1947 as a Supplement to the *Bulletin* or in some other way. I am in an unusually good position because I do not want anything anymore.

TUESDAY, FEBRUARY 11

This week was so bad that the less I write about it the better it will be. Oh, it was pleasant enough, with two good seminars, some translation work done, piles of letters dictated, nice visitors from Switzerland, a staff conference, an excellent performance of *Lucia di Lamermoor*, and some good books read. For an ordinary professor this would have been a normal week but what counts with me is the creative work done and that is where I fell down. Why? I really do not know. I had time for some writing but somehow wasted it.

Over the weekend I read a captivating book, Karin Michaelis' autobiography *Little Troll*. Again it was an extremely moving book, like Stefan Zweig's autobiography, because it contained so much of my own life. I suppose all Europeans of my generation have a nostalgia for the world before 1914. It was in many ways a rotten world, one that was doomed, but it was so cultured and we were young at that time. A small country like Denmark had writers of world reputation— Anderson, Jacobsen, Pontoppidan, Herman Bang, Peter Nansen, Georg Brandes, Sophus and Karin Michaelis. Today I could not name a single Danish writer. World War I killed that world, and the period during the two wars was merely an interlude, a breathing spell during which people reminisced. James Joyce and Marcel Proust, the strongest talents of the period, reminisced. The greatest writers here—Dos Passos, Hemingway, Faulkner, Steinbeck—were belated followers of the French naturalist school. A world, and culturally a very gifted one, came to an end in 1914 and the new world has not been born yet. Russia is a beginning, of

205

course, and awakening Asia may be the cradle of a new civilization, but it will take many years before we have a flowering of art and literature such as we had before 1914, and it is the tragedy of my generation that we have to spend our best years in the sterile period between two wars.   SUNDAY, FEBRUARY 16

I just spent three days at Princeton University, attending one of the Bicentennial Conferences, namely the one on "The University and its World Responsibilities." I suppose I was invited on account of my latest book. I spent three days boiling, disagreeing with most that was said and yet I did not speak at all. Since I am leaving the country I did not want to start a row. The conference was mostly a heated discussion between the 100 per cent Americans and the adopted citizens. Our very able spokesman was Borgese. The Americans' view was that Europe is finished, that culture is now an American monopoly, and that it therefore is America's duty to "revive" European culture. We pointed out, whenever we had a chance, that Europe was not "finished," that the creative forces were still tremendous, probably much greater than here, that America was Rome and Europe, Greece. Borgese very appropriately reminded the audience of the well-known letter of Cicero to Atticus! The whole conference, I am sure, left a bitter taste with most of the participants.

In the afternoon of the second day the Institute of Advanced Studies gave a tea at which Albert Einstein was produced. It was announced in advance that Dr. Einstein would be present. The poor man came in spite of a blizzard and was very gracious. You saw that it was an ordeal for him to be looked at like a wild animal and to have to listen to much silly talk. The last time I saw Einstein was about 40 years ago in Zurich. We were students of the Gymnasium and Schinz took me to a meeting of the *Naturforschende Gesellschaft* where Einstein gave one of his early lectures on relativity. We understood but little and yet we felt that what he said was very significant. I still can see the way he looked at that time, dark and slender. Now he is heavy, thick-set, unkempt, pale, and looks rather bored. No wonder, such a tea is a bore for everybody.
                                                                SATURDAY, FEBRUARY 22

I am translating a Russian paper by Rossiski on the study of medical history in the USSR. The nationalism expressed in this paper makes you sick. There seems to be no interest except in Russian subjects. This obviously distorts the view of the historian. Medical history is growing rapidly in breadth, but not in depth. In Latin America new chairs and new societies are founded all the time. In the USSR medical history has been made a required subject in all medical schools. Clubs and societies are founded, and journals are devoting sections to the subject. Yet nine-tenths of all the work produced in this field anywhere in the world is junk, has no value whatsoever. The older I become the more I appreciate Sudhoff and the men of his generation. Sudhoff ended up as a Nazi, yet

206

in his work he was more of an internationalist than most enemies of Nazism. FRIDAY, FEBRUARY 28

Today, I think, I gave one of my best talks. I spoke for two solid hours giving a historical analysis of the social and economic conditions which in Germany led to the enactment of the first social insurance bills. I spoke without effort, logically, and the students seemed to be visibly impressed, particularly when I showed them that history follows a definite pattern in this field. This is my concept of a constructive historical analysis. I only regret that I was not able to write the book that I once planned on the subject. It would undoubtedly have exerted a considerable influence. I never got beyond the first chapter because I had so many other obligations at the time. I will not accept any invitations in 1947 or 1948, not before I have completed volumes I and II. Thereafter I may work out a schedule according to which I will spend ten months on the book and two months lecturing somewhere. We'll see. MONDAY, MARCH 3

Time magazine has an article on my resignation and I must say that it is very fair, very friendly, and almost correct. I am much relieved and very glad because this will convey the news to many people who did not have it yet. It will also stop, I hope, silly rumors that have been heard. SATURDAY, MARCH 8

I thought of the possibility of writing an autobiography some day. I have lived through an interesting period of the world's history and it would be tempting to attempt to recreate this world. But I feel very strongly that nobody should undertake to write such a book unless he can do it in an original way. The autobiographies recently published of Finney, Barns, Young, Freeman, are frightfully conventional and dull. I thought of writing such a book in free associations, the way you reminisce without chronology, or rather without strict chronology. The first chapter would be "Childhood in France," and I would try to recreate the Paris of the 1890's the way a little boy experienced it. Of course it's no easy job. If only I had a few more years. There is so much to be done. SUNDAY, MARCH 9

Exciting news. My mother writes that they found a house in the Ticino that might be very suitable for us. It is in Pura, close to Ponte Tresa, an ideal location. It is in the countryside, removed from the tourist traffic, yet can be reached from Lugano by train in 25 minutes. And the lake is very lovely at that point. The house has seven rooms, rather small considering that it is a workshop, residence, and institute in one, but I could manage. And there are three acres of garden and vineyard, enough to have twelve cats.

I am so tired of living in rented houses with the constant threat of being thrown out. Pleasant as our present house was I never felt that it was home. It was a tent in which we lived for a while and for many years I never asked for more than a tent. Now it's different. I am at journey's end and once settled I don't want to move any more.   SATURDAY, MARCH 29

If *nomina sunt omina* the name of our potential house certainly is a good omen. A telegram just informed us that its name was Casa Serena. Could there be a better name for the house of a philosopher? Could I wish anything better than serenity? And Pura, the name of the village, also sounds so beautiful.

Casa Serena
Pura, Ticino

What an address!

It is Easter Sunday, 80°, spring at last, and my birthday is celebrated in advance. Both children are here. Nora on a short vacation, Erica for good.   SUNDAY, APRIL 6

56 years old! The fortress is battered but still holding. At the end of the seminar the students presented me with a bottle of rare cognac, milk for an old man.   MONDAY, APRIL 7

Hopkins tea in the Welch Library, the first since the war. Many new faces, young people. The first such tea I attended was in 1931. Dr. Welch was the host, and what a delightful host. He knew everything and everybody worshiped him. President Ames, staunch old liberal, was there. The climate has changed and I am glad that I am leaving the University. I no longer feel at home in it. I wonder what makes the climate of such a place? Tradition probably and a few strong personalities who embody this tradition. The Hopkins people are mere shadows of their masters, a poor second generation! And faculty members like myself are outsiders, foreigners, who were honored guests as long as the Welchs who had called us were alive. Now it is all different and Hopkins is losing its character and standing very rapidly. Something new may emerge from the ruins, an efficient technological institute, but it won't be what Hopkins stood for.   SUNDAY, APRIL 13

Today I began the series of farewell dinners and addresses. The Hamilton Street Club, my old Club that I had deserted during the war, gave me a very delightful party and I spoke for an hour. I was glad to have an opportunity to tell my old friends why I had not resumed my membership and why I was leaving Baltimore and the University. I gave them the history of my two books and they seemed very interested.   THURSDAY, MAY 1

Today I spoke at the School of Hygiene, at the weekly luncheon of the Department of Parasitology. My subject was the same as yesterday but condensed to half an hour. The members of the staff listen with wide-open

208

mouths and Professor C. at the end pointed out that my talk should be a great lesson to them because it showed how one can work planfully for many years and, furthermore, that the work is more important than the position. To young people at the beginning of their career it must seem strange to see a professor give up the best chair and the best department and a salary of $10,000 to live in a village in the wilderness on $3,000, just because the work requires it. FRIDAY, MAY 2

I have not written a line for weeks, busy with many testimonial dinners and parties. Here a mere list:

May 9: Big banquet in New York with 300 people, very moving.
May 10: Meeting with old students in New York.
May 14: Valedictory address in Hurd Hall, followed by a dinner of the Johns Hopkins Medical History Club in the Welch Library.
May 15: In New York for a farewell lunch for Castiglioni at the Academy.
May 17: Eighty students at home for a farewell cocktail party.
May 19: My seminar (about 40 students and wives) gave me a splendid Chinese banquet at the China Inn.
May 20: Dinner at Amy Greif's.
May 23: Reception in New York at the home of Lincoln Shuster, attended by the American-Soviet Medical Society.
May 25-26: Annual meeting of the American Association of the History of Medicine at Cleveland. Symposium of the Institute.

It was all very touching and very exhausting. My colleagues seem genuinely sorry that I am leaving. As long as I was here I was taken for granted and criticized and often antagonized. Now many realize how much I did for them. TUESDAY, MAY 27

The City Department of Public Welfare gave me a farewell luncheon that was very moving. Judge Waxter spoke, and Miss Lazarus, his right hand, and they presented me with a book that I much appreciated. I answered telling them why I had always felt very close to them, because I always thought that we were working towards the same end, endeavoring to keep our fellow-men adjusted to their environment or to readjust them if necessary. All I had done for the Department was give them a few lectures, but they were so nice because they liked my general attitude and philosophy. TUESDAY, JUNE 3

My suite at the Institute looks awful. The books are being packed, the pictures taken from the wall; everything is grey in grey. The sooner we can leave the better—to make a fresh start, and resume work on the book. But we just heard that our flight has been postponed from June 22 to June 24. THURSDAY, JUNE 5

A week of packing and a terrific heat; the atmosphere is leaden and work rather difficult. I am at the Stafford Hotel for ten days, ending up where I started fifteen years ago. Yesterday I turned my car over to Nora. What I will need in Pura is a donkey rather than a car.

THURSDAY, JUNE 12

A week went by, a week of farewell. I cooked several dinners in the houses of friends. Endless work at the Institute, and yesterday the staff gave us a final farewell dinner at the Hamilton Street Club. It was a great party which turned out to be a great success. It was a sad event and everybody felt like crying. And so there was only one alternative, to be very merry. Larkey set the pace and we laughed, sang, danced, had plenty of drinks. Gino and I sang *canzoni Ticinesi,* we yodeled at general request. It was real *Galgenhumor* but everybody will remember the evening with much pleasure.

To Washington from where we are flying.   SATURDAY, JUNE 21

Washington

Today I am beginning a new chapter of my life and a new routine. Now that I am a free lance and have no academic responsibilities I find it very important to establish a strict working discipline. At Pura, once I am settled, it will not be difficult to work planfully but I do not want to waste these in-between weeks. Another point is that lecturing forces you to keep up to date with subjects that are not those of your research. Now that I am no longer teaching I will keep up to date by reviewing many books.   SUNDAY, JUNE 22

No flying today, perhaps tomorrow, maybe. Military air transportation functioned very well during the war, but civilian air service is still in its early beginnings. Not enough machines nor personnel. It is probably impossible to operate an efficient service and make a profit at this stage.

Eisenhower has just been appointed president of Columbia University. A general by all means! I suppose Hopkins will invite McArthur when Bowman retires, and soon our universities will be turned into military academies.   WEDNESDAY, JUNE 25

Long day of waiting. At last at 10:40 p.m. we flew off.   FRIDAY, JUNE 27

Basel

My last day as a Hopkins professor. From tomorrow on I will be on the faculty of Yale University. It's all very strange.

I am glad to be here because America had become unbearable with an atmosphere of suspicion, hatred, intolerance, with a corrupt press poisoning public opinion steadily, with generals in key positions and a policy of cynical dollar imperialism. I have no doubt that the government is preparing a purge of the universities. A book dealer in Washington

210

informed me (through a friend) that he had sold a copy of my Soviet book for $10 (!) to—the Department of Justice (read FBI). Sometime next fall or winter the Rankin Committee will clamp down on the universities and force them to dismiss all their liberal professors. I say on purpose liberal because they are the real target. The number of communists on American faculties in infinitesimal. This coming purge is probably also the reason why a well-informed man such as President Bowman accepted my resignation with such alacrity and refused to be a sponsor of my New York dinner.

I did not leave America in order to escape. I left in order to be able to write my books and made the decision before the situation had become so acute. When it did become critical I actually thought of reconsidering my plans, of staying on, waiting for the challenge to come and of becoming the spokesman for the persecuted left-wing professors. The chief reason why I discarded such a course was my poor health, an illness that makes you nervous, excitable, irritable, tire very quickly— poor qualifications when you have to fight in the political arena. The alternative was to write my books and to write articles, to carry on the fight with the pen, to continue my teachings through my books. I will keep out of local politics entirely, will try to be *au-dessus de la mêlée,* working to the best of my ability for the preparation of a better world.

MONDAY, JUNE 30

Pura, Casa Serena

We moved into the house today. At home at last. Here I will live and work, and die when the time comes. The house is charming, just right, not too big and not too small, and the view is superb. I placed my desk so that I am looking north, not east. On the east side the view is overwhelming and you feel like being on top of a high tower. This I find disturbing and disquieting, not conducive to meditation. Looking north I see a fig tree, vineyards, mulberry trees and in the distance the village of Neggio.

JULY 19

I have two palm trees, *Phoenix dactylifera* I think. They are stiff but belong to the south, with camellias. *Fern im Süd die Palmen rauschen.* I remember so well the first palm trees I saw as a child, at Nervi in the hotel garden. Mine are much smaller of course, one is about my size and the other looks as if it had been transplanted from a drawing room. But every living being has been small once and palm trees grow slowly.

SATURDAY, JULY 26

Everybody wants me to go to Lausanne for the International Congress of the History of Science. Why should I go? It is so much more pleasant to be here. And why should I interrupt my work? I am through with these international vanity fairs where there is a lot of talking and no action. And I do not care to see the old guard. If I could go unseen as an

211

observer it might be fun, but this is impossible. As a charter member and vice-president of the Academy I would be elected to committees and this is just what I am trying to escape. No, I will indulge in the luxury of skipping all meetings for the time being. My writings will prevent my being forgotten. TUESDAY, SEPTEMBER 2

We are hit by the drought and very seriously. The garden is drying up, the flowers are fading and yesterday we had to gather all our grapes in a great hurry because they were drying up also. Mr. Sciolli very kindly offered to press them for us and today he reported that we might expect 50 quarts of wine and some *grappa*, which sounds very good.

SUNDAY, SEPTEMBER 21

I am writing a review of Duhamel's *Paroles de médecin*, and as a matter of preparation I was reading his *Scènes de la vie future*. I caught myself rejoicing when he attacked America and I am much upset about it. I notice that I have extremely bitter feelings. Why should I? I certainly had some very discouraging experiences, when the Civil Service Commission declared me unfit for government service after all I had done for them, or when I was attacked and smeared in Detroit, but such occurrences must be expected when you are in public life. I think I was disappointed in America because I expected too much. I must remember the bright side of my American years, the kindness I experienced from so many parts, the good friends I have, the former students who are devoted to me. Right now I live on money that comes from America, and every line I write is addressed to America. It is difficult to live between two continents because you do not belong to any of them. In America I was a foreigner in spite of citizenship and in Switzerland where I am at home I look to America all the time. But I have my house in Pura, and my study in the house, and here I'll stay and work. FRIDAY, OCTOBER 3

G. wrote and wants me to revive the International Society of the History of Medicine. I am a vice-president and apparently am supposed to be the next president, an office I would never accept. Here again I feel that it is too early for official international cooperation. Unofficially a lot can be done, of course, but there is too much hard feeling for a successful convention. I think, moreover, that we, the old generation, should abdicate and that the young people should build up a new organization along new lines and when they feel that the time is ripe for it. The old society achieved very little. The conventions were pleasant social affairs with good food and good drinks. They provided an excuse for visiting a country, but that was about all. Committees were appointed which never did anything and the official publication of the society, *Aesculepe*, an advertising sheet, was a scandal. SATURDAY, OCTOBER 4

I acted like a coward today. I was to begin working on the book at

212

9:00 a.m. sharp. I had been looking forward to this moment for a long time and today's work would not have been difficult at all. All I had planned to do was to read what I had written on Egypt so far and get my notes on the current chapter in shape. But I escaped, ran away from the task, had all excuses ready-made. I slept badly, woke up at 6 after only five hours of sleep, did not feel well; my heart, you know. My sister wrote that my mother was worse. I kept myself busy all the time, began writing my New York address, unpacked books, dusted them, found that my wine was spoiling because the cellar is not good, has no ventilation, cooked a superlative risotto Milanese, a real work of art, spanked the cats because they were eating lizards. Yet I know, I am sure that I am able to do the work, and here better than anywhere else. I know that whatever I may write will be better than what other medical historians could write on the subject because I know more and have a novel approach. There is nothing to be afraid of and I know well enough that once I am started I will experience the great joy that only creative work can give. And so I will make a new start tomorrow and I am confident that it will be a better one.   TUESDAY, OCTOBER 7

Yes, I made it. At 9 sharp I was at work on the book and made good progress until 5. I read the Egyptian chapters with much pleasure, made notes about gaps and illustrations.   WEDNESDAY, OCTOBER 8

I have a new bookcase made by Eugenio Sciolli, our local *falegname*. It is squeezed between my couch and the wall. And in this case I will keep those books that I like best. There will be one shelf each for Oriental, Greek, German, Russian, French books, for art, music, philosophy. The room is greatly improved, looks much larger. I also have a nice carpet on the wall. All I need now are curtains and a rug.

TUESDAY, OCTOBER 14

To die in beauty. Nature certainly does it, veiling her face with a cloak of rich colors, not the pastel colors of spring, the virginal white, the pink and tender green, but the whole scale from the darkest red to the lightest gold. In Baltimore, in front of my dressing room, was a gingko which at this time of year was my delight every morning. And here again I have a gingko in front of me, smaller, of course, as becomes a European tree, but with the same golden leaves.

Today for the first time in Pura I did not talk about the book, did not prepare it but actually wrote it, or at least 8 pages of it. I hope I am started now. At least I have more self-confidence.   TUESDAY, NOVEMBER 4

I was in Japan today, the whole day; I had simply dropped my work and went to Japan, not the Japan of McArthur, of military books, but the old Japan. I had a beautiful day, read poetry, passages from the Genji Monogatari, looked at woodcuts, read about making tea and putting flowers into a vase, read Lafcadio Hearn. How much is lost when an Asiatic country becomes Westernized! So much ugliness is brought in immediately and with capitalism a much more brutal exploitation sets in and imperialism develops as a matter of course. Asia must take over Western science to overcome poverty and disease but should do it without sacrificing its own rich traditions.

The bookcase along my couch has one shelf reserved for science and I hesitated a long time which books I should select. I feel so bitter against science since the atom bomb, and so many scientists I knew in America were like business men or were cold, inhuman and very conceited laboratory men.

My bookshelf! Today I put in the chief works of Alexander von Humboldt and the works of Charles Darwin. They represent the best type of scientist and it still is a joy to read their books. The *Ansichten der Natur* are great literature. There are few scientists of that type today. I knew some in Zurich in the old days but they are dead now. I also knew some at Cornell like Needham, but they were very old.

WEDNESDAY, NOVEMBER 12

Strange things do happen. When the mail came I saw that there was a letter from the "Rektor der Universität Berlin." I did not open it for some time because I assumed that it was a lecture invitation. I receive such invitations all the time and always turn them down. But it was not. The Rektor offered me the chair of the history of medicine and science, Diepgen's chair! The laconic epistle read:

> Im Einvernehmen mit der Deutschen Verwaltung für Volksbildung in der sowjetischen Besatzungszone berufe ich Sie hiermit auf den Lehrstuhl für Geschichte der Medizin und der Naturwissenschaften der Universität Berlin.
> DER REKTOR

The style is strange and not very encouraging but it may well be the Nazi heritage, Führerprinzip, "ich berufe Sie" *punktum*. I wish I knew the background history. Does the faculty want me or not? Have they been pressed by the government or by the Russians? Has Sauerbruch played a part in it? Are they sure that I will not accept and is the call a mere gesture to show how liberal they are?

If I were younger and in better health I might consider the matter. It would be interesting to lead young people to socialism, to pave the way for the complete socialization of medicine with all doctors on salaries, to work closely with the Soviet authorities. But as things are I need not waste one minute on the matter. And, after all, what a relief it is to be removed from the academic circus, to be without ambitions of that kind, to be able to live and work in this enchanting region.

Still, the letter upset the day and I decided that we should have a good bottle of Orvieto secco for dinner. I warned the family that there would be such a bottle whenever I was offered a chair. THURSDAY, NOVEMBER 20

There are so many reasons for being grateful to nature and the inventiveness of man, and one and not the least is that there is good tea in the world. I like a good wine, but nothing equals a cup of good tea, prepared in the right way and steaming hot. I found a Keemun in Lugano the other day which is really good. What I have not found yet is green tea. I just made an inventory and found that at the moment I have nine different teas, most of them very good ones.

FRIDAY, NOVEMBER 21

Arminio Sciolli came and we tasted my wine. It tastes very promising indeed. I learned that from San Martino on you must keep your kegs or demijohns closed with a cork, while before you close them with a handful of vine leaves—as I did. After Christmas I may bottle the wine. The whole rhythm is connected with the saints, experience of the centuries.

SUNDAY, NOVEMBER 23

Damn it! Instead of working on the book I worked on the plague, wrote five pages. I have an idea for a superb piece on the plague, a review of several books beginning with the local touch, the chapel of San Rocco, then *peste di San Carlo* (Ripamonti as contemporary source and La Cava as critical study), then Manzoni, the novelist who takes up the subject, and finally Camus' book to show that even today novelists are tempted by the subject. It is most restful to write such articles between chapters of the book.

THURSDAY, DECEMBER 11

Monthly shopping day in Lugano. The food stores and the wine stores are tremendous with all kinds of birds, chicken, guinea hen, ducks, geese, and game, pheasant, partridge, hare, venison. But there is no shopping hysteria as there used to be in America at this time of year. People seem to eat and drink well during the holy days but there is no high-pressure salesmanship that forces them to buy.

SATURDAY, DECEMBER 20

1948-57

THE LAST YEARS IN SWITZERLAND

The ten last years in southern Switzerland were indeed a great change from Sigerist's previous meticulously-scheduled pattern of living. But "retirement," a word frequently used in connection with his move, was very far from his mind. These were to be working years.

Sigerist's decision to return to his native country after spending fifteen productive years in an American university was indicative of a larger symptom. The demands made on him in Baltimore as teacher, scholar, administrator, public speaker, counselor to American and foreign students, librarian, committee member, writer, organizer, initiator, government and international consultant, traveler, tea drinker, and hand-shaker became so strenuous that his main love—creative research and the writing of his own books—had to be relegated more and more to the background. But he had always felt that all these myriad activities were but a preparation for his life's work, an aid to a better understanding of medicine as a contributor to civilization at large. When this "preparation" became not the means but the end itself, he felt that only a complete change could salvage his goals from the dust bin.

His magnum opus *was to be an eight-volume History of Medicine which he described in these words:*

A good many histories of medicine have been written during our century. Most of them were short one-volume books and most of them followed the same pattern. They were primarily histories of medical science, of the great doctors and their discoveries and writings.

What is needed, in my opinion, is a detailed comprehensive presentation of the subject and one that sets a new pattern for medical historiography.

For over twenty years I have prepared for the writing of a History of Medicine that will have eight volumes and will be fully documented. It will be a synthesis and at the same time the starting point for further research.

My approach is sociological, that is, I am studying the various civilizations of the world in their socio-economic structures, discussing their health problems, what they did to promote health, to prevent illness, to restore health once it had broken down, and possibly to rehabilitate the sick. Then I discuss who the chief actors were in this drama, their training, their contributions, and the ideals that guided their actions.

The book is meant to be both a contribution to history and one to medicine. It should give us a more complete picture of the development of civilization and, on the other hand, should make us aware where we came from in medicine, at what point we are standing today, and in what direction we are marching.

The plan of writing "one volume a year" of this monumental work was optimistic. Ill health which set in after 1954 slowed his progress; the absence of the stimulating give-and-take between colleagues and students to which he had been accustomed all his life contributed also to a slower rate of speed. During his lifetime Sigerist was able to complete volume I of his History; volume II was only partially finished but was published after his death. What a pity that chronology dictated the need for writing ancient medical history first, for how much knowledge and insight Sigerist could have brought to the history of the Middle Ages, and to the nineteenth and twentieth centuries.

The format of his diaries changed in Switzerland. He was no longer restricted to the usual 8 x 10 printed Standard Daily Journal with a page a day, but used large books of plain white paper. As a result the entries varied greatly in length and were kept at irregular intervals.

1948

Pura

A spring day, glorious sunshine, 10°, what a blessed climate! I am nervous about the lectures I have to give in Zurich next week, particularly since I have to give them in German. And as usual I am unable to prepare them in advance so that I will have to work on them up to the last minute. THURSDAY, JANUARY 8

Back at Pura—I felt like kissing the earth, and the walls of my study— after a very hard week in Zurich. It was most unsatisfactory. First the

217

weather was absolutely beastly, with a horrendous Föhn wind during the first few days, then rain and slush, then cold and not one ray of sun during the whole week. As a result of this ghastly weather I caught cold the second day.

The lectures were most unsatisfactory also. Oh, the surface was brilliant. I had an enormous crowd in the largest lecture hall and it kept growing with every lecture. And yet I felt quite clearly that there was no response to the lectures. They were much too progressive for a conservative and even reactionary faculty and student body. Whenever I spoke I felt a certain hostility and resistance that I never had in America.

Another disappointment was a very trivial one. I had been told that the University wanted to honor me and naively I had assumed that they planned to give me a degree which would have pleased me very much coming from my home university. You get degrees from the periphery but usually not at home. In the beginning of one of my lectures the Rector Magnificus announced very solemnly that the Senate of the University had decided to make me an honorary guest (Ehrengast). I heard later that this is a distinction bestowed upon bankers, industrialists, and other business men from whom the University expects money. Your name is entered in a book and you are invited to the various exercises. It was disappointing to find myself placed into this category but after all what difference does it make?

One evening I spent with the American students. They were very nice, very grateful for what I told them. But on the whole they were a rather sad lot, mostly Jewish students who had been refused everywhere at home and now felt self-conscious, handicapped by the language.

All in all it was a week grey in grey, with hard work and little sleep. I learned from it that I should not accept such invitations. They wear me out and cost too much time. Besides I am between two continents now, in Switzerland but writing for America. I have no contacts whatever with the young Swiss generation. They are as foreign to me as young Zulus or Tibetans. SUNDAY, JANUARY 18

The news just came that Gandhi had been murdered—yesterday afternoon in Delhi while he went to the place where he used to pray and address the people. His death is a great loss to the whole civilized world because it means the loss not only of a great statesman, but of a great man, of a saint. I remember the day when Tolstoy died and I feel the same sadness today. How small is a Lord Mountbatten, a Churchill, a Truman compared to a Gandhi. I did not like all his policies but I venerated him. From the day of Amritsar on he was with us, with all of us who were of good will, who wanted peace on earth and who had the welfare of the people at heart. How few truly great people are in the world today? Nehru, Mao Tse Tung, the leader of Viet Nam, almost all Asiatics, men of great culture who had been persecuted, had suffered for their ideals, had grown through suffering. Without Gandhi the world is much poorer

218

today but I hope that his death will unite the people of India as never before. It is fortunate that the murderer was a Hindu and not a Moslem.

SATURDAY, JANUARY 31

A week has gone by. I spent a day in bed with a cold. I like my room so much that being in bed is a joy. I planned the room to that end. I would like to die here and not in a hospital. I thought that some day I may have to spend weeks or months in bed and this is why I had a library built in with the books I like best.

SUNDAY, FEBRUARY 8

There are strange happenings, coincidences which are hard to explain. I felt so sad about Gandhi's death and wrote what I felt to a number of American and Indian friends. Now today I receive an airmail letter from Mrs. Langford Rae. She was attending the funeral of Gandhi when she suddenly heard a young man mentioning my name. She turned around and asked him if he had my present address. And he gave her my address. I do not know who he was. But is it not strange? I know so few of the 400 million Indians and yet two met and recalled me at the funeral of Gandhi.

I am not becoming superstitious and remain the old materialist that I have always been but there are strange coincidences.

WED., FEBRUARY 11

News that moved me deeply came from Belgium. A doctor sent me a mimeographed condensation of my Soviet book which was made by a group of Belgian doctors in 1942 and published underground, over 4,000 copies. Five hundred of them were seized by the Gestapo and two workers were killed in the fight that ensued. There is no edition of any of my books that I will treasure more.

SUNDAY, MARCH 17

The November-December number of the *Bulletin* came and I felt very sad because it is the last number to come out under my name. How much labor, imagination, time, how many efforts have I put into this journal! I launched it at the bottom of the depression, had to run after money to keep it alive, built it up from small beginnings and published 21 volumes. During the war I made a superhuman effort not only to get it out without interruption but to raise its standard, and I actually find that the volumes of 1943 were the best of the whole series when we had very good special numbers on English literature, public health, American medicine, physiology, Vesalius. I contributed my best editorials to these volumes and had a substantial article in every number. It was my way of protesting against the savagery of the time.

Now it is time for somebody else to take over and to make the *Bulletin* anew, his journal. It is never good to "hang on." Children grow up and leave you, this is in the plan of nature.

FRIDAY, MARCH 19

The greatest historical process of our time is the awakening of Asia.

This is infinitely more important than anything that has happened in the West. The fact that a billion people who lived in great poverty, in ill health, and many in ignorance are now demanding schools, medical facilities, a decent standard of living, and security is extraordinarily significant, backed as they are by a great cultural tradition with enormous spiritual reserves. The defeat of Japan was very good because it demonstrated that they took the wrong way, adopting Western capitalism. It is too late for that now and only a communist Asia can develop fully. The fact that the USSR is not only a European but also an Asiatic power gives it a position that the U.S. will never be able to hold, even if it keeps Japan and parts of China occupied, because this would merely be an imperialist measure while Soviet Asia is an integral part of the Union.   SATURDAY, APRIL 10

Met Štampar at the station in Lugano and brought him to the house. He is on excellent terms with his government, knows Tito well and holds him in high esteem. Tito listens to him in all health and scientific matters and he seems to have a very independent position. The progress made in the country is tremendous but he is afraid that some is done too quickly, also that in some cases the Russian pattern is followed too closely instead of being adapted to local conditions. He also fears that the members of the government live too well, in large villas with servants and automobiles. They have small salaries but many privileges. The present group is good but what will the next set be like? Will they resist corruption? Following the Russian pattern, professors, scientists, members of the Academy of Science are the highest paid workers.

He said jokingly that the Gestapo saved his life. He was arrested as soon as the Germans came and spent four years in jail, mostly in the police jail in Graz. If he had been left free, the Ustadi would have killed him. The Gestapo chiefs in Graz were Austrians, hence not as ferocious as if they had been Prussians. They had respect for the Professor even if he was an enemy. He shared a cell with eleven other prisoners and kept his morale up because he believed in his philosophy. Their food was of course bad—only 1,300 calories. He was in jail until the Russians liberated him. Now he is President of the Academy of Science, Director of the School of Hygiene, and President of the Interim Commission of the World Health Organization.   SUNDAY, APRIL 25

I wish I could record all that Štampar said because it is history which is not in the papers and will become known only very much later, if at all.

The Germans in Yugoslavia settled by Maria Theresa were completely assimilated but when Hitler came they went along with him. They were the best farmers of the country but now had to be driven out. Štampar wished the Hungarian minority could have been deported also because they acted like brutes, drowning thousands of people in the Danube, but it could not be done because Hungary now belongs to the Russian bloc.

Following the Russian pattern, authors are extremely well paid for their books and receive the money when they deliver the manuscript. This is very good but has one disadvantage, namely that professors write big textbooks, mere compilations, in order to make money.

Mestrović is teaching out at the University of Syracuse, at $5,000 a year, students who do not care, at a moment when his country is being rebuilt, when he could build cities and decorate the whole country with his statues.

Unfortunately Štampar had to leave today at noon.   MONDAY, APRIL 26

I love dahlias, the old fashioned ones that you find in every peasant garden and that the wine farmers stick in the kegs of must. They always remind me of my student days when in October we used to go on a *Sauserbummel* to taste the new wine which was so sweet and could give you such belly aches. But I also love the large dahlias which try to emulate chrysanthemums and have such a rich variety of colors. The whole winter I dreamt of having dahlias in the garden and for the last few weeks I developed a programme, selected the spots, decided on the kind of earth to be used, read up in books, studied catalogues of various firms, ordered sticks. There were to be two groups, one of large dahlias of different colors, well protected near the house, and another group of gay little pompoms at the further end of the garden. Finally the great day came, the roots arrived, beauties sent by a Zurich firm.   SUNDAY, MAY 9

A letter from China. A doctor read *The University at the Crossroads* and wants to translate my essay on medical education into Chinese. Of course I am delighted, and very interested to see that this particular essay had wide repercussions all over the world. It formulated what many people vaguely felt.   FRIDAY, MAY 14

There is no denying that I made very little progress with the book. This entire week I did not write one line and I do not know why. The chapter is easy; the end of the section on Egypt is in sight. I did not feel too well but I never do. Maybe I am undernourished, have a very low caloric diet and a rather monotonous one, perhaps I should revise it and make sure that I have 1,200 calories. Maybe I am drinking too much wine (perhaps to add calories because the wine I am having just now is pretty bad). During the whole week I did nothing but write a book review and sixteen letters, and read a couple of books. At any rate things must change and I must make a great effort to overcome this deadlock: strict but sufficient diet, strict discipline of labor, and some exercise so that I may sleep without drugs.   SATURDAY, MAY 22

In a review of Gide's *Diaries,* which are widely discussed in the States at the moment, I read: "What is it that drives a man to keep a journal so long? Each writer starts with his own need, but surely the reasons are always the same—the struggle against death and for time, the need to use one's life to the uttermost." This is probably correct. All my life I have tried not to waste time feeling that every day was precious and when I did waste a day—and I wasted many—at least I wanted to know how it happened and why.

J. and N. brought me from Zurich records of Britten's *Serenade, Opus 31*, for tenor, horn, and strings, a fine piece of work not only in craftsmanship but also in imagination. How well one can sing an English text when the music has been written for it! The British Empire may be disintegrating but the country has produced Auden, Isherwood, Spender, Britten and that compensates for it—not to forget that great woman, Virginia Woolf, whose *The Moment and Other Essays* I just began reading with immense pleasure.

Britain, moreover, is launching today its Social Security Plan, including free medical services for all, without a means-test. The plan in my opinion is not ideal but it is a great step in the right direction and the fact that a conservative country, with a conservative Labor party, took the step will have great repercussions abroad.   MONDAY, JULY 5

Rudolf Hagelstange is probably the most forceful poet of the younger German generation. He was born in 1912, in other words was just 21 when Hitler came into power and 27 when the war broke out. Friends just sent me his *Venezianisches Credo,* a series of sonnets written at Venice in 1944 while he was a soldier in the German army. He was disgusted with the Nazis and all they stood for and turned to the world of the spirit, of beauty and love:

> Wie soll der Ärmste ferner arm sich wähnen
> da ihm die Lust der Götter doch geblieben:
> ein Geist, zu sinnen, und ein Herz, zu lieben.

He firmly believes in the future:

> Der Feige weihe sich dem Untergange,
> der Narr dem Taumel und der Knecht dem Raube.
> Mir aber, unzerstörbar, brennt der Glaube
> an neuen Tag . . .

The language of the poems is beautiful and they reflect the strong emotions of a man who kept quiet for a long time ("Ich habe lange, lange wie ein Stein geschwiegen"), and now may express himself again because the twilight of the Nazis holds the promise of a new day.

                                        TUESDAY, AUGUST 24

Hagelstange wants freedom:

> Denn Freiheit ist der Odem unseres Lebens,
> das Salz der Speise und der Wind im Segel,
> der Stolz des Löwen und das Glück der Vögel,
> das Recht des Mannes.

222

We all want freedom but what do we mean by it, what do I mean by it? What freedoms do I cherish? Let me see:

1. *The freedom to engage in creative work.* This is very difficult to obtain because in our society work at large is a privilege and creative work is frowned upon. I have it now but for how long?

2. *Freedom of thought.* This exists in very few countries today. In the U.S. it is now only on paper and "thought control" is as real as in Kuomintang China. Switzerland is in that respect probably one of the freest countries.

3. *Freedom from material needs.* The fewer material needs I have the more freedom I possess. I will not have to waste time earning money but may devote my efforts to creative work.

I think I will resume my study of Chinese after an interruption of almost 40 years. I am not sure that I will succeed, but I think it is worth trying. China is the only country that I would like to see before I die. If I memorize three characters a day—while shaving—it would be 1,000 a year. Of course I don't know if my memory is still good enough.

I just finished reading Robert Payne's *China Awake,* a splendid book, his diary of crucial years in both Chinas. Like every individual outside the American State Department he is disgusted with the corruption of the Kuomintang. Now I am reading *The Dream of the Red Chamber* in the German translation of Kuhn.   SUNDAY, SEPTEMBER 26

A terrific thunderstorm with blazing lightning. I tremble for my flowers and leaves. So much depends on the weather this month. If it is good the leaves will stay on the trees for some time and the chrysanthemums will bloom for many more weeks. But everything is fragile at this time of the year, and wind and frost can destroy so much. Yet the winter flowers are coming forth, the pink ones whose name I don't know, black hellebore, and the callicanthus is full of buds.

A good working day with a programme fulfilled 100 per cent.

MONDAY, NOVEMBER 8

Lugano has a new art gallery. It had it for a long time but until yesterday it was not open to the public. It was collected by a Hungarian baron who died last year and the family, in order to obtain tax exemption, had to open it to the public three days a week. It is a superb collection of old masters beautifully displayed. We went today for a general survey and I plan to go and study it every month. A striking Last Supper of El Greco, some very good Hans Baldung Grien, a beautiful Carpaccio. It gives an excellent cross section through the various classic and baroque schools and is undoubtedly the best such Swiss collection after Basle.

1949

Pura

Reading the American journals is most depressing. They talk about television, new radio sets, new automobiles, and other such rubbish. And, of course, there is a lot of talk about democracy, freedom, and America's world leadership. Who wants democracy? Where is there democracy? In Switzerland women have no franchise and apparently don't want it, and many men don't care to vote. In America, Indians and many Negroes have no franchise, and many white people don't vote either. What is freedom? To many Americans it is the right to call the President a son-of-a-bitch. Yet free is he who is free from passions and has a minimum of material needs.

I do not see what America could give to the Ticino. Most people have sufficient food and shelter. What is needed is better craftsmanship. This has deteriorated considerably in the last few hundred years. Needed are better poets and painters. Could America give this?   SUNDAY, JANUARY 16

This morning I read the presidential address of an Indian colleague who with a group of other doctors is trying to reconcile Ayurveda and modern scientific medicine. It is a beautiful address, enthusiastic but sober. The author is fully aware that India has a message to the world which is true. While I read I was always thinking of my second volume. It was to be on Greco-Roman medicine but now I find that this is a very one-sided Western point of view. Hindu civilization was as high as the Greek and at the same time. Indian medicine was certainly equal to Hippocratic medicine. The task therefore would be to picture the parallel development of Greek and Indian medicine. Why one developed later along scientific lines while the other remained static is a problem that I will not have to tackle before volume IV.   MONDAY, JANUARY 17

I have been thinking about India most of the night. The West had its Renaissance 500 years ago. It led to a development of science and technology which may well destroy Western civilization. India has its Renaissance now and from it a new culture and a new medicine will blossom forth.

Russia is in its infantile period, imitating America—probably has to in order to produce some basic commodities for its people. But it will not stop there.   TUESDAY, JANUARY 18

224

Long letter to Nora in which I made the following point: the richer a country becomes, the more its civilization becomes one of *ersatz*—television instead of real shows, radio instead of concerts, movies for theatre, plastics instead of beautiful woods and metals, in addition frozen meat, fish, fruit, vegetables, and salted butter instead of the fresh foods that a French working woman has. I thought for a long time what I would care to see in a television machine. Finally I thought that it might be nice to see the Acropolis, but then I felt that you must not only see, but be able to touch the velvety marble of the Parthenon. Or I thought I would love to see the Taj Mahal again, but you must be able to sit in front of it for hours and watch the changing light.   TUESDAY, FEBRUARY 1

Russia, the Ukraine, and Byelorussia have withdrawn from the World Health Organization and the satellites will probably follow. It is most regrettable because the protection of health seemed to be the one field in which all nations could cooperate. Practically, it will make no difference because the Russians hardly ever came and never paid their dues, but it is a bad move nevertheless.

A bad wind seems to be blowing at Moscow at the moment. I heard that Lina Stern[65] is in disgrace. Proud and independent as she is, she refused to accept a censure from the CP. They disliked one of her scientific theories and she bluntly declared—so I hear—that they did not know what they were talking about. Prokofiev is censored and many others.

I have only one explanation for this unfortunate condition, namely that the men at the top have been in power for too many years. This is never good and they are bound to lose touch with reality. They are too much removed from life. Lenin went to factories to address the workers every few days at the risk of his life, but the present leaders live in an ivory tower.   WEDNESDAY, FEBRUARY 16

A very nice invitation to give the Bryce lecture at Somerville College in Oxford. It is tempting. I have not been at Oxford for very many years and I have many friends there. But I am afraid to take to the road again. I should not interrupt my work and I am afraid to become restless once I see the sea again and an airplane. I would like to see India once more and would love to go to China. These are the only journeys I really care to make.   FRIDAY, FEBRUARY 18

Just had a letter from the Oxford Press. My manuscript mailed January 4 arrived in New York February 17, in 44 days. Considering that this is supposed to be the atomic age, the time seems rather long and in the eighteenth century it was probably possible to have a manuscript in America in 44 days also. It is a strange world which wants

[65]Lina S. Stern, a physiologist, was a member of the Academy of Medical Sciences, Moscow, and Director of the Institute of Physiology Laboratory.

more and more science and yet is unable to solve the most elementary problems that could be solved with eighteenth-century knowledge.

TUESDAY, FEBRUARY 22

One of the chief tasks of UNESCO, as I just read, is to finance international conventions. Scholars should meet and discuss their problems; this is the generally accepted view. I have attended many national and international conventions from 1920 to 1947 and when I look back I think that the chief gain was that I made some very nice trips at reduced rates and had many excellent dinners. The contacts were frequently mere displays of nationalism with much oratory, the papers were rushed through and could as well be read at home, pompous resolutions were passed and no action was ever taken, people like Sudhoff were offended all the time because they thought that they were not paid enough attention. The national conventions in America like those of the A.A.A.S. or Historical Association were horrible mass meetings. I think what scholars can gain from a convention is extremely little and it would be better to spend money to keep them working at home.

FRIDAY, FEBRUARY 25

There is, thank God, some heartening news from America. A foundation, the Bollingen Fund, awarded a prize of $1,000 to Ezra Pound for his *Pisan Cantos* in spite of the fact that he is in a mental hospital and under indictment for treason. Ezra Pound in my opinion is the greatest American poet since Walt Whitman, and his *Pisan Cantos*, written while he was arrested by the U.S. Army, are a masterpiece. Of course you must know a lot to appreciate him, even some Chinese, but when you do, you enjoy his poetry more than anything else.

MONDAY, FEBRUARY 28

Spent a day in bed not feeling well and reading Kinsey's *Sexual Behavior of the Human Male*. It is an honest book but naive in many ways. The chief mistake, in my opinion, is his concept of outlet. Every ejaculation of sperm is an outlet no matter whether it is intercourse with a beloved woman, or a boy masturbating in a corner, or a shepherd fornicating with a calf, and yet—by Jove—there are differences in value and the outlet is totally different. The results of the survey are in no way surprising at least not to the European reader, but it is of course important to have the facts in figures. The book lends itself to gross misunderstandings. It is obvious that almost everybody at some time or other had some homosexual experience, but this does not mean anything. The book may have some good effect in America in that it will blast some conventional views and explode the idea that people are "virtuous." But I doubt that it will lead to any action since the country is so conservative and reactionary that it will cling to its old prejudices.

WEDNESDAY, MARCH 23

I read or rather re-read every day a chapter of the *Dhammapada*. There is no better book to teach you *aequanimitas* and I need it, irritable as I have become.

Buddhism appeals to me much more than Christianity—always did. It is logical, just, and compassionate. I like its attitude toward animals and plants. And who knows, if matter and energy are never lost, there may be a spirit which is not lost either. How true it is that your actions and nothing else determine your happiness or unhappiness.

TUESDAY, APRIL 12

I am now determined that when I begin to write volume II (I hope very soon) I shall stop drinking any alcoholic beverages—not for moral and not even for health reasons but as part of the programme to simplify my life. It also should increase my working capacity. With volume III I will become a complete vegetarian and with volume IV I will stop drinking tea. Thus I will gradually detach myself from earthly bonds and will become freer than before. Of course this all makes you unsociable and isolates you from your fellow men but I am alone anyway—in spite of the many visitors, for the last week was very lively.

SATURDAY, APRIL 30

Today I finished writing the narrative of volume I, but I do not feel like being "through" because such a book is never finished. Now I have to read the Mesopotamian section critically, then I must complete the illustrations and appendices, then I will have to correct galley proofs and page proofs, and once the book is out I will immediately start preparing the second edition or at least collect materials for it. Still it is good to know that this is finished at last and I am looking forward to the writing of volume II.

THURSDAY, MAY 26

It is interesting that I am not gaining weight but rather losing some although I eat everything. I suppose this is because I stopped drinking wine. Several *boccalini* of *vino rosso* and a few glasses of vermouth every day added a good many calories to my diet. I still have premature contractions of the heart almost every day, very few, but still. I wonder if the constant use of privine has something to do with it. I tried to get neo-synephrine for a change, but it seems not available here, and without some nosedrops I cannot breathe.

SUNDAY, JUNE 19

Summer solstice. The longest day of the year. Now they will become shorter, but my second volume is launched.

I had incredible difficulties in writing my quota today, yet the subject was easy, the geography of Greece for which I had plenty of material, yet I could hardly formulate my sentences—I succeeded finally.

MONDAY, JUNE 20

I have at least three incurable diseases: 1. arteriosclerosis and all that goes with it; 2. a chronic rhinitis and; 3. a parapsoriasis en plaque. Yet I work from 9:00 a.m. to midnight with short intermissions. Illness need not necessarily be disabling although it always is a handicap.

WEDNESDAY, JUNE 22

A long interruption, Zurich, Basel, Geneva, finding my way back to the book, much research in order to prove my point that Greek medicine began like that of other civilizations with religion, magic and, of course, empiricism—but I can prove it, I have now all the materials in hand and tomorrow I shall start writing. A nuisance that all the Swiss libraries are closed at the moment—vacations. These European libraries! After the comfort and efficiency of those in America. No soap to wash your hands and in Basel neatly cut newspapers for toilet paper. They must have an employee doing nothing else but cutting up newspapers. It looks puritanical—we use our funds for books, not for toilet paper. Sounds good. It is very hot, real summer, but Basel was still hotter. Only 76 degrees at my desk here, and in Baltimore—how far it all seems—sweating and a Cuban cola, now water or at best cider. But Pura is real; my room, my studio is my world. Baltimore, New York, Leipzig, Berlin, Zurich, Paris— these are all dreams, very realistic, but dreams about which you have scrapbooks and photo albums with Clotilde von Derp, the Hofgarten, Colonial exhibits, Chinese characters, the cry of peacocks. Beautiful dreams with the smell of the London subway, but also dreams with ghosts. Here in Pura, in my studio, is peace, a home, and the history of the world. Why are people constantly inviting me, luring me away, to Denmark, Sweden, Finland? I just accepted three lectures in Copenhagen. I did it because it is far away still, September 1950. Much can happen until then. Why should I go away? The grapes will be ripe, the chrysanthemums will begin to bloom and there will be mist on the mountains.

WEDNESDAY, JULY 29

The drought begins to be serious. There is a shortage of water and my poor garden will suffer. I kept it green all these weeks. The sky is eternally blue, cloudless. We need a storm, a whole night's rain.

To live slowly and consciously, not to be buried in work, with time to read, to look around, taking days off from time to time. Not to let work degenerate into routine, but to give it a festive character every day.

In Zurich I saw Bruno Hauff, my former Leipzig publisher, a very efficient man who thrives under any regime. He is in Stuttgart, has built a house for the firm, is very active. He was the most pleasant publisher to deal with I ever had. Whenever we had a project we discussed it at Aeckerlein's Keller with a good meal and a bottle of champagne. Hauff did all our Institute publications for the sake of prestige and must have lost heavily on them.

SATURDAY, JULY 30

All these days I prepared for the spring, planted hundreds of bulbs, azaleas, peonies, anemones, and many other shrubs. The three camellias are full of buds. Will I live to see such splendor once more?

The first half hour in the morning when I get up and shave is a time when I worry a great deal, without any particular reason, just the transition from sleep to being awake, perhaps the result of subconscious dreams. Well, to overcome this unpleasant moment and to begin the day in style I learn poems by heart while I shave. Today I began learning Mallarmé's *L'Après-midi d'un faune. Ces nymphes, je les veux perpétuer.* It is a difficult poem and it will take me some time to learn it, but it is a great joy not simply to read a poem but to penetrate it, to analyze it until every shade of every word becomes clear.

I had a medical check-up with Professor Löffler in Zurich and the interview was just the contrary to what I had expected. I was afraid he would make much fuss, but he minimized my illness. To him hypertension is not a disease but a condition. My diastolic pressure was lower than a few weeks ago, less than 120. So it is not quite rigid. Löffler said that he advised all his hypertension patients to stick to their jobs, even high officers in very responsible positions. The Swiss insurance companies accept such patients at a slightly higher premium. There is no doubt that American medicine is overdoing things. Hypertension has become a major source of income for the general practitioner and he is not going to give it up. Of course it may kill you or rather the underlying condition may, but then you may also die from other causes. At any rate I am very glad that the consultation with Professor Löffler will not change my mode of living. He gave me a very good advice, namely to take some nitroglycerine. I should have thought of it myself.

"You are eating much bitterness." The Chinese words of sympathy. Is it not a splendid way of putting it? We are all eating much bitterness indeed.

I finished reading *The Dream of the Red Chamber* which really is one of the great novels of world literature, a great picture of the old China.

The year had many failures but was not so bad after all. Two books went to the press:
1. Volume I of the History
2. The letters of Jean de Carro (a small item but an independent publication nevertheless).
Two books were published:
1. *Los grandes medicos*
2. The Chinese edition of *The University at the Crossroads.*
In addition I wrote two papers and five book reviews. Something

was achieved but it could have been more and I will try to increase and improve my production next year.

On the positive side I can register furthermore:

That both children are doing very well.

That my health was relatively good and that I stopped drinking and eating meat (with few exceptions), but enjoyed very good teas.

That I got ever closer to nature, improved my garden, and enjoyed my flowers and my cats.

That I became ever more equanimous probably due to my study of Hindu philosophy, particularly Buddhism.

That my American friends did not forget me but wrote warm letters giving me the feeling that I am remembered and missed.

THURSDAY, DECEMBER 29

1950

Pura

Old as I am, I am trying to improve my handwriting. There is no excuse for writing badly an ugly scrawl. Writing should be clear, easy to read, and in good style.

Read what I had written on Homeric medicine in order to get the "join" with the next chapter. It reads quite fluently. Now I want to make the point that religious medicine is always archaic in character, and then of course emphasize the cult of Aesculapius.

Three good scented teas, jasmine, rose, and orange blossom but now I shall need some phenobarbital on top of it all.   MONDAY, JANUARY 16

Wrote eight letters, nothing else. Read Mayakovsky—fascinating his autobiography and his *ars poetica*. The Soviets had so many brilliant writers in the beginning. They had the revolutionary fervor and had lived through the great experience of revolution and civil war. They were not under state control as they are today. They could experiment. Lunacharsky was a brilliant commissar of education who translated Goethe and attracted progressive artists from all over Europe. I would not even know the name of the present minister of education—probably a bureaucrat. Mayakovsky would be inconceivable in today's Russia and yet he was a revolutionary writer and artist if there ever was one. And what is Sholokhov doing today? Ehrenburg wrote his best novels long ago. Where is the good humor of Kataev and Zoshchenko? There will be a change of policy some day, must be, but how is it to come about?

MONDAY, JANUARY 23

There are two situations in life that are close to happiness. One is when the immediate future looks very bright. I experienced this several times in my life. In 1911 I was twenty in Paris, finding the city of my childhood again on my way to London, a student of oriental languages. The whole world seemed open, ready to be conquered. In the summer of 1914, in Munich, I was away from home, on my own for the first time, enjoying every single day, with theatres, concerts, art exhibits, books, friends, deciding to become a student of medical history—the last few months of the pre-war world. 1932 when I began my activities at Hopkins detached from all European ties, making a new start in a new environment, respected, with a great task ahead. And finally in the summer of 1947, back in Europe with the expectation of finding a home, a last home, rediscovering nature, again with a great task ahead, with three secure years to come, quiet years of meditation and work.

The other situation is when you have that warm feeling of having accomplished a job well. I have rarely had it because I am always very critical of my work. Whenever I finished a book I decided that next time I would try to do better. But I had that warm feeling several times: in 1924 (or was it 1923?) after I had given a series of lectures at the University of Munich. In the spring of 1932 after my lecture tour in the States and after I had been offered the Hopkins chair. Again in 1944 when I came back from Saskatchewan.

Now there is nothing to look forward to—but the serenity of old age. The future is uncertain. I hope that my present work is good but I am sure it could be better. What I must strive for is equanimity.

THURSDAY, FEBRUARY 9

Next year I shall be 60 years old. If I am still alive I will spend the day somewhere on the Mediterranean—the mother of us all—perhaps in Sicily or on Capri. I would like to escape all fuss. I know from experience what a plague such decimal birthdays are to the colleagues. Sudhoff used to give orders on what he wished to have done to honor him—Festschrifts, portraits, a medal, a bust, etc. When I had the—very large—Sudhoff medal made he looked at it, threw it away and thundered: "Die Virchow Medaille ist grösser!" Every five years we had to find something new to satisfy him, yet it was never enough.

FRIDAY, FEBRUARY 17

I am in a turmoil, feel frightfully confused and do not know why. I have not written a line in weeks and kept busy day and night without achieving anything. Of course my health is bad and this has something to do with it. I sleep only with drugs and then not more than five hours. In the morning I am tired and feel sick in the stomach. The heart beats irregularly with extra systoles. This is no excuse for not writing. Marcel Proust wrote his great book in bed, his room filled with vapors so that he could breathe more freely. There must be psychological reasons for my condition and I must try to be aware of them.

Question number one: Was Pura a success or a failure? Would I have achieved more in the atmosphere of a university? Judging from the number of pages written it cannot be called a success and I might have written just as much with a full academic schedule. On the other hand I do not know how I would have fared in a university with my reduced physical capacity.

I cannot go back to a university because I am not orthodox. In all countries today orthodoxy is required of the teachers. In many American states teachers are under oath to teach only the accepted philosophy. I do not fit into any organization any more—and this is another great source of confusion. In Leipzig and Baltimore I knew where I was going. I had deep convictions and taught what I considered true, unafraid. Now I feel torn between Marxist materialism and Indian spiritualism, between ideals of my youth of a life in beauty, and my career as a fighter for social progress.   SATURDAY, MAY 7

A week of readjustments. I went to England to give lectures and I left Pura with nothing but raw material. Hence I had to work very hard on the spot. But all six lectures went off very well. The first was an address on "Medicine in 1850" with which I opened an exhibition at the Wellcome Museum. The following day I addressed the Society of the History of Medicine at Oxford, an organization of undergraduates, and there my task was not difficult. I spoke about "The Study of Medical History" and we had a good discussion. Then on the first of June I gave my principal Oxford address, the James Bryce Memorial Lecture on the early Middle Ages, a highly technical, philological, scholarly lecture. For a moment I was afraid that the subject might be too dry and too special, but the lecture was received very well and in the following days I met and consulted with many medievalists. Back in London I spoke to the Historical Section of the Royal Society of Medicine, and I think the lecture was a full success. The hall was packed full. Colleagues had come from Oxford, Cambridge, Swansea, and Edinburgh. London was having a heat wave with 87° that day. In my lecture I summarized the first chapter of my book. It was Credo and Apologia. The next lecture was to the Medical Branch of the British Library Association and this was perhaps the one that succeeded best because everything was just right. It was not too hot, the hall had much atmosphere (London Medical Society, Lettson's foundation), the desk was not too high and not too low, and the audience was very responsive. The lecture had been announced as "The Medical Library as a Centre of Historical Research" but what I did was reminisce about my personal experiences in libraries with librarians and historians. And everybody including myself seemed to have a good time.

Finally I addressed the Sigerist Society on "Developments and Trends in the Provision of Health Services," an easy task because I was among friends and spoke on a very familiar subject.

These six lectures gave me a lot of work and forced me to interrupt the book for several weeks, but the result was worth the effort. I found that I am still able to captivate an audience, that I have a well-established reputation (someone introduced me as having become a legend), that I can talk with the same ease to philologians as to specialists in social medicine. I came home with more self-confidence than I had before.

SATURDAY, JUNE 17

I had a very good impression of England; it probably is the most democratic country in the world at the moment. Communists are on the faculty of every university and in Oxford I saw a fascist parade. There is no hysteria of any kind, no talk about a cold war and the country feels that it can afford to be very tolerant. I attended a meeting of the Oxford Regional Hospital Board where the Regius Professor sat next to a union man and following which all members had lunch together.

Everybody I talked to was critical of some aspect of the National Health Service but all agreed that it was a great step forward and nobody would dream of giving it up. It is a democratic, orderly, well behaved country and London still is the center of a great empire, and not only a commercial, but a great cultural center.

SUNDAY, JUNE 18

The bankruptcy of political democracy is illustrated in a terrifying way by last Sunday's voting in Switzerland. The issue was not unimportant, a new statute for federal finances and an amendment to the Constitution, a minor one, but still an amendment. In the whole of Switzerland only 53 per cent of the electorate went to the polls and in the Ticino only 26 per cent. In other words the people don't care what happens to them. How can one expect nations to fight wars, people to die in order to force political democracy on other nations if they do not believe in it, if they are too indifferent, too lazy mentally to take advantage of their democratic rights and to fulfill their duties as citizens? This creates a very serious situation and paves the way for the dictatorship of an individual or of a group. Switzerland is not a single case. Other so-called democratic countries behave exactly the same way.

SATURDAY, DECEMBER 9

A Dr. Miller of the Massachusetts General Hospital wants me to contribute an essay on my own cardio-vascular disease for a collection of similar physicians' case histories. My first impulse was to refuse because the task is very difficult. However an hour later I found myself making notes and so I think I shall have a try and shall see what I can write during the Christmas week. It is a very interesting idea which must be developed philosophically and the more I think about it the more tempted I feel to write such an essay. Having three incurable diseases I certainly have enough to tell.[66]

TUESDAY, DECEMBER 12

[66]*Living Under the Shadow* was the title Sigerist gave to the article in which he described his own adjustment to illness. The essay was published at various times, and was included in a collection of articles by eminent physicians who were likewise handicapped by an illness of some kind.

I had hoped to have a quiet Christmas week but I just received a very exciting letter from the Dean of the Medical Faculty of the University of Berne. They intend to establish a chair of medical history provided they can find the right man and would like me to take the chair. Of course I am pleased and feel honored that they ask me in spite of my advanced age and impaired health, about which they must be informed.

SATURDAY, DECEMBER 16

Touching the naiveté of some aspects of American life! In the *Saturday Review of Literature* somebody writes about the Great Books of the University of Chicago and of the study groups they are conducting in St. Louis. They are attended by people from all walks of life—including Negroes (think of it!)—who meet once every two weeks and discuss what they have read. This is certainly very praiseworthy and it is better to read Homer or Plato than to play canasta. What I would like to know is: have these people sufficient preparation to understand what they read? Does their reading affect their life, do they change their mode of living, or is it merely some kind of parlor game they are indulging in? Great books, not 100 of them but many hundreds, are friends with whom you live all your life, constantly. You read and reread them and assimilate many of them so that they become part of your own substance. When they mean something to you you feel disinclined to read trashy best-sellers (most best-sellers are trash) and you will rather read than play cards. One golden rule should always be observed: never read the newspapers and journals before you have read at least fifty pages of a worthwhile book—every day.

WEDNESDAY, DECEMBER 20

1951

Pura

A new year has begun and with it the second half of the century. The future is as uncertain as could be, politically, culturally, and also as far as my personal future is concerned, physically and also economically. Never mind! I still believe in the values that I always cherished; I can still hold a pen and I have money for nine months. Much can happen during that time. I must hold to my work, must work hard and efficiently, and must carry on relentlessly irrespective of external events. I spent the day putting the finishing touch to the *plan rabot* [work plan], getting my study in good sailing condition, and tomorrow morning at 9:00 a.m. sharp I'll make a new start. May it be under good auspices.

MONDAY, JANUARY 1

Sze writes that he began translating *Civilization and Disease* into Chinese. "I find it very interesting work," he says, "and moreover it gives me practice in Chinese writing which I was forced to relinquish for two years." This shows that even a Chinese, born and educated in China, has difficulties with writing.   THURSDAY, JANUARY 4

A great pleasure today: the mail brought a nice edition of Horace that I had ordered (the Tusculum edition). So far I had only a school edition which was good and complete but looked like a school edition, while this new one is attractive in print, binding, and particularly format. You can put it in your pocket and this I will certainly do when I go to Italy. I will also take along Goethe's *Italienische Reise* and his *Römische Elegien*. I am looking forward to this trip, seeing Rome again and particularly the Mediterranean, our great mother who gave birth to our entire Western civilization.   WEDNESDAY, MARCH 7

Intolerance and hypocrisy are perhaps the chief characteristics of our time. The modern state demands complete orthodoxy of its members and it does it in the name of freedom and democracy. In some states the heretics are jailed and killed, in others they are merely ostracized, but they are persecuted in all as the modern state does not tolerate any opposition. The latest European racket is that the parties in power simply change the electoral system in such a way that it will freeze out the opposition. This is a very short-sighted policy because it will by necessity create a revolutionary situation. In Italy under the new system the communists lost control of many cities although they increased their vote by 7 per cent. In France the communists lost almost one half of their parliamentary representation but only 2 per cent of the votes, a very small loss considering the tremendous rise of the fascist-Gaullist vote.   FRIDAY, JULY 6

The beautiful project of an American university in Lugano has been brutally destroyed. Everything was ready, the money had been raised, seven American universities were backing the plan, the building was ready, the canton and city were most cooperative—when the State Department stepped in and declared categorically that it did not wish this university established. Of course—the government would not be able to control it, the university might become a focus of liberalism, without teachers' oath, possibly even an American university in exile. Intolerance, hypocrisy and civil cowardice here as everywhere. What a sad world!
                    FRIDAY, JULY 20

In the most creative period of the world's history, in the sixth and fifth centuries B.C., countries were very small—Greece, India, and China. This had the great advantage that poets, artists, scholars, philosophers deserted the countries in which their work could not thrive and flocked to the courts where their work was appreciated. There was always a ruler somewhere who attracted creative men. Such a condition no longer prevails today in an age of intolerance and nationalism. Countries deny passports to citizens who are unorthodox so that they cannot found universities in exile. And most countries do not accept refugees if they are politically or intellectually active in any way.   FRIDAY, AUGUST 17

During the entire past year I lived as in a fog. I worked, of course, read many books, gave lectures, saw the sun rise and saw it set; I made decisions, travelled, but somehow it all happened behind a curtain, a thin curtain of gauze. I did not feel elated when Eos came from behind the mountains, did not feel like crying when the first rose blossomed. I registered the Korean war but it did not make my heart bleed. This is why I neglected my diary—I had little to tell. And yet—I have not many years to live and hence I should make the best of every single day, should live consciously, should endow every one with some special attraction. Every day should mark a step forward toward something better, purer, and brighter. I must resume this diary, must give myself a daily account of experiences, achievements, and failures.   DECEMBER

The last week of the year is one during which you look back and forward. I kept a record of all the books read during the year, not in connection with my work but for recreation, mostly in bed, after midnight. There were 107, or an average of 2 a week. I was astonished to find that only 34 were books written before 1900, while 35 were written between 1901 and 1940, and 38 from 1941 to 1951. I should have thought one half of all the books I read had been older books. Why read so many new books when you have 4,000 years of tested good literature easily available? In the course of my work I obviously read long passages from Homer, Pindar, the Pre-Socratics, *Rigveda* and *Atharva Vedal,* but I listed only books read from cover to cover.   WEDNESDAY, DECEMBER 26

It is time to make the balance of the year. There is much on the positive side, first of all that volume I came out and had an unusually good reception. The Soviet book had a third Chinese edition, and I had news of a Japanese translation which they hope to publish soon. The German translation of *Medicine and Human Welfare* is in the making, and so is a third German edition of *Grosse Aerzte.* German and Italian editions of the History are being prepared.

I wrote eight papers one of which, *Living Under the Shadow,* just came out in the *Atlantic* and seems to get a good deal of attention. Moreover, I wrote seven book reviews, some of which were not bad.

I gave seven lectures in various Swiss cities in English, German and French, and all of them were very successful, were received with warm applause. What I said was not new to me but was new to the audience. To me the lectures were important as they showed me that I still can captivate an audience.

On the positive side I would also register that I attended a meeting of the panel of experts on social medicine of W.H.O. (World Health Organization) in Geneva. I had not done this kind of work for a number of years and felt somewhat apprehensive when I entered the Palais des Nations, but soon I felt in my true element and greatly enjoyed the work. It keeps me in touch with the problems of world medicine.

A highlight of the year was the trip to Italy in April, particularly the days in Rome and Florence when I renewed acquaintance with works of art that had meant so much in my life. The two weeks in Amalfi with Salerno and Paestum were very pleasant also, and I particularly enjoyed being on the shores of the Mediterranean.

On the occasion of my sixtieth birthday I experienced a great deal of heart-warming sympathy, was presented with a Festschrift and made an honorary member of several learned societies.

I was able to buy new bookcases so that my library is in much better condition than ever before. Since the middle of November I have a good secretary which is a tremendous help and last but not least, my appointment at Yale was renewed.

And so the year was a good one in many ways and I have good reason to be grateful for all it gave me. Unfortunately there is also a strongly negative side of the ledger. The greatest failure was that I made practically no progress with volume II of the History. I must try to analyze why this happened. It is not that I lost interest in the book. I was fascinated by the subject of the few chapters I wrote, the pre-Socratic philosophers and beginnings in India. But somehow I felt paralyzed, frozen. I was at my desk every day, made careful plans, but when it came to writing I just could not do it, had inhibitions, escaped by doing something else. One cause of this failure may be the insecurity in which I lived. For an entire year I had no income. The lack of a secretary was a serious factor also. I wrote over 1,000 letters myself. The offer of a chair by the University of Berne was another factor of insecurity. The faculty had offered me the chair and was negotiating with me, but not yet the government. When would this come? And should we consider acceptance, would I have to take the chair under all circumstances? Consciously or not this problem was with me and worried me all the time. There is no doubt that I also lost ground as far as my health is concerned, but I was in a vicious circle: if the work had proceeded well, I would have felt better as I always do when I have written five pages in the morning. But since the work was stalled I felt badly, and feeling rotten in the morning seemed a valid excuse for not writing the book.

Well, conditions have changed. I am in much better circumstances than a year ago and will make a great effort to finish volume II as soon as possible.

It is midnight. The family sleeps. I have a bottle of old Scotch and am drinking to the health and happiness of all those who are dear to me.

MONDAY, DECEMBER 31

1952

Pura

The sun is rising gloriously. And every time I see it rise from behind the mountain I feel like raising my arms and reciting the hymn of Ikhnaton:

> Thou shinest beautiful on the horizon of heaven,
> O Living Disk, who didst live from the beginning.
> When thou risest in the Eastern Horizon
> Thou fillest every land with thy beauty.
> Thy rays embrace the lands even to the limit
> Of all thou hast created. Thou art Re,
> Thou reachest unto every land, uniting all
> For thy beloved son, Ikhnaton.

Indeed, I am not *"living under the shadow,"* but in bright sunshine, in an enchanting region. The little snow we had melted long ago under the rays of the sun. The first primroses are in bloom, promise of spring. Snowdrops, crocuses, even tulips have pierced the dark cover of mother-earth and are striving to behold the sun.

> Thy rays nurse all fields, which grow when thou shinest.
> And thou hast created the seasons to nourish them.
> For thyself thou hast made a heaven to shine in
> Where standing alone thou beholdest thy works.

Nineteen fifty-two! May it be a good year, productive, lived consciously, a year of peace and sunshine.   TUESDAY, JANUARY 1

Hannes Meyer here, a truly great man. The Bauhaus, center of Germany's progressive architecture, hence faculty and students progressive also politically. Gropius, now at Harvard, then Meyer director. Trouble with the authorities as early as 1930. Goes to Moscow, makes a plan with his brigade for the reconstruction of the city. Then Mexico, Cardenas government, 600 schools in three years. Now aged, beginning Parkinson, lives at Crocefisso, still full of ideas and plans, brings a pile of literature on the new China. How refreshing to talk to such a man, so few of them here—a truly great man.   FRIDAY, MAY 9

In front of me is a photo of Perugino's Mary Magdalene from the Pitti Gallery, a sweet face, beautiful hands, but the golden tone of the original is lost on a hard black and white photograph. Strange that the Church made her the sinful woman, an assumption for which there is no evidence in the Gospel. But I suppose that the sinful woman of Luke 7:37 had to have a name attached to her, and it was a beautiful thought to identify her with the woman who later was so close to Christ. At least a saint who was not butchered but died a natural death, according to the *legenda aurea.*

Martin Gumpert came. I like him very much. He is a man who has made a great success in the States without becoming pompous. His books are best-sellers and he took up a very profitable specialty, namely geriatrics, but he is as modest as in the past. I knew him in Berlin and he impressed me because he was practicing social medicine before there was much talk about it. He was in charge of a free cosmetic clinic which rehabilitated socially very many people.

He lives here in the best hotels but has a charming way of saying how much he enjoyed eating *Rehrücken mit Morcheln und Rahmsauce*, all delicacies unknown in the States. He interviewed old writers, statesmen, philosophers, and other prominent people and wants to show that old men are not necessarily gaga. Of America he said that when he came over in the thirties he found a country where there was no fear, while today there is fear.   FRIDAY, SEPTEMBER 5

When my grandson Christopher left last month I wanted to say to him: "My dear little boy! I shall probably never see you again, but I am very happy that I had a chance to know you. Short as the summer has been, you brought happiness to an otherwise not very happy house. I am sorry that you are leaving but, of course, it had to be; everything has an end, and you belong to America. You are an intelligent and sensitive boy, and I wish you not necessarily happiness, but a rich and creative life. As long as I live I shall remember you with deep affection and I am happy that you carry my name, dear boy."

Of course I said nothing of the sort as I could not talk at the moment; the tears were too close.   TUESDAY, OCTOBER 7

The world is grey in grey, rain and fog, hunters are shooting little birds, one of our cats disappeared, probably ended in the frying pan of some brute. Yet it could be luminous, the gingko is pure gold and the persimmon a rich red velvet. A few roses are blooming and seem sad that they came so late. Three more weeks before I go to England. Well, it has to be. And so much work ahead. I wish I could read and sleep. I am so tired.

MONDAY, OCTOBER 20

Again back in Pura, for in the meantime I was in France, in Nancy, attending a meeting of W.H.O. on the teaching of preventive and social medicine. I came home completely exhausted and frozen to the marrow of my bones. First I froze in England where the heating of homes has not passed the palaeolithic stage. Nancy was not better. The hotel had central heating but the radiators had steam only for one hour in the morning and one hour in the evening and the only way to keep warm was to stay in bed or in a hot bath. We had Indian, Persian, and Peruvian members who suffered even more than I. Formerly when you went to India the government gave you a special allowance for the purchase of tropical clothes. I think W.H.O. should give you an allowance for the purchase of Arctic clothing when you meet in the winter in countries that have no heating facilities. All of us kept complaining that we were not meeting in Geneva where we would have had all comfort and facilities. But we met in Nancy in honor of Parisot, a pioneer of social medicine who is seventy and will retire soon. The meeting was his swan song and we were his freezing fellow swans.   SATURDAY, DECEMBER 13

My Heath Clark Lectures in London were successful. The audience kept growing to the end, the applause was very warm. At the end I was presented with a piece of jewelry, a laurel wreath in enamel on gold. It was given to Mr. Heath Clark when he retired from business by his friends in the city, and was now passed on to me. Heath Clark was a business man who was interested in public health and not only in its technical but also in its cultural aspects and problems, a rather unusual combination.

Still I did not feel satisfied because what I said, most of it, was probably new to others but not to me, and I hate repeating myself all the time. When you are at the end of a career and have published hundreds of books and papers it is probably difficult not to repeat yourself. Still, I shall have to do more research before I publish the lectures.
                    WEDNESDAY, DECEMBER 17

Sartre has brilliant ideas. In the last number of *Les Temps Modernes* (vol. 8, October-November 1952, p. 701) he makes a most pertinent statement, one which I wish I had found myself. He says that anti-communism as a means of propaganda could develop only in a country which like the U.S. has no communists. In Italy, in France, and other countries where you meet communists every day, where you know that the postman, your maid, your taxi driver, the milkman are communists it would be very difficult to make you believe that these honest hard-working people eat little children for breakfast and have only one idea—to overthrow the government at any moment. In America, however, where you don't know communists, how can you prove that they do not eat little children? Where there are no Stalinists everybody may be suspected of being one, and the average man plays a dual part: he denounces others when he is with the crowd, and is denounced when he is alone. The victim, of course, can never prove his innocence since he does not know what the charge is. How very true this is.   SUNDAY, DECEMBER 28

1953

Pura

From tomorrow on I shall be on a very strict schedule for the next four months. May I have enough health and strength to carry out my programme. If I fail I shall have no other alternative than to abandon everything, Yale and Pura, and to finish my life as a beggar in Benares or somewhere else in India. SUNDAY, JANUARY 4

The best we can do is to begin preparing for death. I began reading old diaries, just read 1933. How I could work at that time! The whole day at the Institute, writing at night, *Amerika und die Medizin,* many pages, working every day until 2:00 a.m. in a very small room full of cigar smoke. Now I am old and sick but the stars were beautiful last night when we walked up from Caslano. These stars will continue to shine when we are gone. Life goes on and young people will look to the heavens seeking the Great Bear and the Lock of Berenice.

SUNDAY, JANUARY 18

Delhi plans to create an institute of the history of medicine. B. just wrote me about it. If they want me I shall go there permanently at a low salary, just enough to live. I would love to end my life there and when the day comes, to have my ashes thrown into the Holy Ganges. Romanticism? Maybe, but after a life of hard realism one must be allowed a few romantic moves. At any rate I immediately began preparing myself, learning Hindustani. It does not seem too difficult as the language has many Arabic and Persian words with which I am familiar. But I have a miserable book that I once bought in Delhi, a manual for the master race to talk with servants. It will do for the beginning. TUESDAY, FEBRUARY 3

Full moon rising at 9:00 p.m. I addressed it:

> The moon in May
> Came all the way
> To look and see
> The misery
> Of human, beast, and flower
> In diesem Tal der Trauer.

Then I noticed that I had addressed the moon in May instead of the April moon. Thank God we are not yet at the end of May.

WEDNESDAY, APRIL 29

Typed a paper on the desirability of creating a museum of the history of science in Geneva, dictated letters, planted five geraniums, read *Les Temps Modernes.* I like the journal. It is outspoken and courageous. It requires guts to speak up at a time when no state tolerates any opposition or criticism. In Switzerland a communist national councilor and journalist was just sentenced to jail for having made statements that the government did not like, and Professor Bonnard, one of our finest humanists and a real poet, is facing trial for treason for believing that the board of the International Red Cross cannot be considered neutral. It is the same as in America or Russia. We live in a savage age. The West is in full decadence and disintegrating, worshiping the machine, relying on brute force for its protection as it has no spiritual reserves. The only hope is Asia. THURSDAY, APRIL 30

> Der Mai ist gekommen
> Die Bäume schlagen aus
> Da bleibe wer Lust hat
> Mit Sorgen zu Haus.[67]

Of course you have to stay at home and worry. What else can you do when three publishers are waiting for manuscripts. Wrote seven letters, attended to current affairs, planted zucchini, cucumbers, paprika, sunflowers, and marigolds.

I have been thinking of writing my autobiography as I have lived during an interesting period of history, but I have kept the project in reserve. Should I ever be disabled so that I could not write my other books, I always could dictate the story of my life. Moreover I really do not know how to write such a book. Most autobiographies I read were frightfully boring. They were interesting for the writer and his family but for nobody else. One should write an autobiography only if: 1. one had very unusual experiences, or; 2. one can present the subject in a different way. So far I really do not know what I could do in my own case. FRIDAY, MAY 1

I just had a most exciting week in Basel. After my two lectures the Dean of the Medical School asked me to come to his office and there he told me point blank that the government and the faculty wished to create a chair of social medicine but would do it only if I accepted it. Bang!!! I was entirely unprepared for such an offer. They also think that medical history needs a boost. They would do anything to make it easy for me. I could maintain my residence in Pura, come every fortnight, give a lecture and a seminar. Jung, the psychiatrist, lives near Zurich and is *Ordinarius* in Basel. Jaspers was appointed professor of philosophy at the age of 65, is over 70 now and may carry on as long as he wishes. In other words, the very sound policy of Basle is to have the best available men on the faculty no matter what the external circumstances may be. MONDAY, MAY 25

Excursion on the Lake of Como because the weather is very beautiful and because it is the fourteenth of July. The beautiful road to Gandria, then Menaggio and the lake, a little fog which lifts toward evening. Como, its cathedral with the statues of the two Plinys. It is extraordinary to have the statues of two heathens in the midst of the façade of a Christian monument, but one was very liberal at that time, that is in the fourteenth century. This is no longer the case today. TUESDAY, JULY 14

A harassing month has come to an end. I wrote or dictated 107 pages and 61 letters. Many visitors came. I cooked quite often. And now the end stretch. Before Christmas all the manuscripts must be at the printer.

[67]German folk song.

242

Absolute discipline. No drinks except on Sunday or when we have visitors. Each day must be prepared carefully, and every evening I will write a few lines about the results achieved during that day. I hope my health will be good enough. The first of January I would like to be able to begin volume III of my History—the Middle Ages, but it will still be the Orient, the Arabs, the Persians, India, and China. SUNDAY, AUGUST 30

A completely sterile week—fear of the book, poor health, many visitors, torrential rains. Next week I must make a great effort.

I found an excellent sentence in a letter by Pliny the Younger: "Satius est enim otiosum esse quam nihil agere."

Until the end of the year I will read only the Greek, Latin, and Indian classics aside from the few medical books I have to read. Most modern books are a complete waste of time, and the newspapers are infected. All of them—the Swiss even more than the others—are propaganda sheets in the cold war. I am less and less interested in politics and take refuge in the world of books. Why poison the little time that is left to me?

SATURDAY, SEPTEMBER 26

I am rereading *Lost Horizon* by James Hilton. It is H's favorite book and how well I can understand him. All of us who are harassed and hounded by publishers would like to escape, live in a Shangri-La. What irony that an American warship has been named Shangri-La!

FRIDAY, OCTOBER 2

1954
Pura

I received an invitation to spend two weeks in Yugoslavia for a series of lectures and to study the country's health services. I will accept with great pleasure. It will be a beautiful trip; I have excellent recollections of my trip in 1938, and the lectures will not be difficult. I hope I can arrange it for May or June, in the good season. This invitation gives me much pleasure. MONDAY, JANUARY 4

To Berne. The cultural attaché of the USSR, Smolin, had asked me to come. The Soviet Minister of Public Health invites me to spend six weeks in his country in February and March. It's a great honor and I would love to accept the invitation for I am anxious to see the Soviet Union again from where I have such good memories. But I cannot travel before having finished my books. Well, that's a question I must treat diplomatically.

MONDAY, JANUARY 18

I am on a reducing diet. I really weighed too much—81 kilos. In one week I lost 3 kilos. My system is very simple: I don't eat. Today's menu:

Breakfast: a cup of tea at 7:30.
Lunch: cornflakes and tomato juice.
Supper: a boiled egg and a tangerine.

Between meals, a glass of vodka and some dry crackers. That's all, and the result is very good. I follow the American saying: "Six days of fasting and one day of feasting," that is to say I eat only when it is worth my while. One must make a difference between nourishing oneself and eating. To nourish oneself is a necessity, while eating is an art.
                                                           MONDAY, FEBRUARY 8

A telegram announcing that yesterday I had been elected a Fellow of the Royal College of Physicians of London, which pleases me immensely. The British have been so good to me and I am extremely touched. It's a great honor to be a member of their Royal College. The new members will be received on May 13. Of course I am invited but I have so much work that I don't know what to do.   FRIDAY, APRIL 30

It took me seven years to find out what the best restaurant of the neighborhood was, but I did find out. It is the Grotto del Renzo in Sorengo. The owner and *chef de cuisine* is a German-Swiss. We had lunch there today and it was simply delicious. I first had *canneloni farciti,* better than I could possibly make them myself, swimming in butter, drenched with rich herbs. Then an *osso bucco* such as I had never tasted before, melting in your mouth, and finally strawberries and cream. This is the place to go whenever there is a chance. I am on a strict reducing diet, but once a week I do not nourish myself but eat, and eating is a great art.

I wrote twelve pages of my Memoirs today, reminiscences of Zurich, of Büchner and Lenin, and of the now defunct liberalism of Switzerland. So the day was not lost in spite of much eating and visitors. SUNDAY, JUNE 20

After two days of tomatoes and cucumbers I am weak again and needed two capsules of nitroglycerine. The trouble with these reducing diets is that they completely upset your stomach. You lose whatever appetite you had, have diarrhea, and even the sight of raw carrots becomes abhorrent.   WEDNESDAY, JUNE 23

I was quite sick last night, vomited. I don't know why. So today I decided to stay in bed, to have my monthly day of rest and fast. But I got up at 4:00 p.m., ate a little something as I felt weak. Maybe my kidneys are rotten and I have early symptoms of uremia. The doctor, of course, does not tell you what he sees in the eye and you have to guess from inadvertent remarks.

A rather disturbing symptom: the ring finger and small finger of my right hand are sometimes colorless, but I restore the circulation easily by rubbing them or dipping them in hot or cold water. A few days ago, however, the two fingers were completely lame. I had no control over them, could not possibly stretch them. I kept them under running cold water, and the circulation or whatever it was came back after a while, but it was a strange feeling.

Today's mail was just splendid. I had sent six bound volumes of my collected reprints to the Royal College of Physicians to show them my appreciation of having been elected a Fellow. I had intended to present these copies to the Swiss National Library, but Switzerland never took any notice of me, while England and the British Empire at large showered me with honors, more than I deserved—three honorary degrees and the F.R.C.P.   TUESDAY, JUNE 29

Yesterday I cooked a very good Sunday dinner with W. as guest. I always wondered where his money came from. Today, after a planter's punch and a few glasses of wine, he disclosed the source of his wealth. You cannot beat these Germans! When King Ibn Saud of Saudi Arabia was sick, he went to Düsseldorf for treatment with a large retinue. A member of his court tried to find out if somebody in Düsseldorf could make the kind of robes they wear with gold embroidery but, of course, handmade. W., who must have had some connection with the textile industry, took a hammer, as he said, hit a machine which from then on embroidered with little faults that looked as if the work were handmade. Now, he says, he ships 18,000 such robes a day—or a week—to all countries of the Arab League at a tremendous profit and also makes the golden strings they wear on their head. He makes designs for these robes. This just shows how German industry is again conquering the world markets. Once they have rebuilt their army and their general staff with American aid, they will be ready to start trouble again.   MONDAY, JULY 5

Had two very good days, wrote seventeen pages, thirteen letters, twelve pages of my biography, and five of a paper on *The Beginnings of American Medicine,* a short paper that I must write because it pays $200, and I just need some extra money for the many visitors in autumn, and my trip to Rome. A paper that brings in money need not be bad. The one on *The Physician's Writing and Reading* I consider one of my best.

The weather is warmer and for the first time in weeks we could have lunch in the garden.

I had a row with the maid last Saturday because her husband had about taken over our house and was here day and night. But this is settled now. When the females are crazy, the best you can do is retire and work.

A most interesting letter from Japan. All left-wing doctors are refused hospital appointments. So they join forces, organize small hospitals of their own, and found their own medical association. They have the confidence of the people and get along well.   THURSDAY, JULY 15

Soon it will be time for me to leave. My ashes will rest next to those of my mother. We left space for my name on her tombstone. Life could have been different, but one has to accept life as it comes and make the best of it. I am not afraid of death. I had a long life which gave me much—good children, good friends of both sexes, honest work. I shall leave something behind, not much because my field of work is not so important. I do not know whether I would have created more in Oriental studies. Probably not, because our gifts are limited. I should make a will, but it is such a nuisance to have to organize one's own departure. Yet it should be done.

THURSDAY, OCTOBER 7

I am very sick. Friday I had a chill, 38.3°, went to bed. The next day I had an atrocious pain in the left part of the abdomen, a spasm of the colon which lasted over three hours. I took atropin and whatever else I could find. Sunday the spasm lasted six hours and the pain was excruciating, so much so that I called a doctor who could not help much. Yesterday the pain was over. Today it started again, but I got rid of it with spasmo-cibalgin before it could fully develop. Yet this is not important. Much more disturbing is the fact that I have a partial paralysis of the right leg. I still can walk but with difficulty, and I have not full control over the leg. Last year, and even before, I had pains in this leg, but last summer they disappeared completely. Now this paralysis began a few days ago. I had other cerebral symptoms recently. My right hand suddenly became lame, but only for a short moment. I used to take a tablet of coramine and all was well, whether *post* or *propter* I do not know, maybe *propter* because I just took twenty drops and the leg feels better. Then twice I had disturbances of speech. Nobody noticed it but me because I avoided the words that I could not pronounce. There is something wrong in the left part of the brain, probably spasms of the arteries.

Last night toward morning I was dreaming. The more invalid I become, the more I live in day and night dreams. TUESDAY, OCTOBER 12

Last night's—very primitive—dream: I was at the banquet of an international congress seated at the end of the table. Everybody was served but me. The first course was a cheese course, the second pineapple and whipped cream. I asked my neighbor: "Are you the son of Castellani?"

Explanation: 1. Feeling of inferiority as I have not done any work in the last few days; 2. At the Congress in Geneva they forgot to give me a membership card so that I felt left out and, of course, was too shy to ask for one. Castellani is one of the few foreign fellows of the Royal College of Physicians.

I am still very sick. THURSDAY, OCTOBER 14

With the October 14, 1954 entry the diaries end abruptly. A few days later Sigerist suffered a rather severe stroke, and was hospitalized for many weeks in a nearby hospital. In January, 1955 he returned to his beloved Casa Serena and was installed in a downstairs room to avoid climbing stairs. Very gradually he regained his impaired speech and the use of his paralyzed limbs. His recovery was good enough to enable him to enjoy another two years of life.

In March, 1957 he had a second stroke from which he never regained consciousness. He died at home on March 17, 1957.